THE DE MAGNETE OF WILLIAM GILBERT

Harding del.

Clamp sc.

D.ʳ WILL.ᵐ GILBERT,

Physician to Q.ⁿ Elizabeth.

From an Original Picture in the Bodleian Library Oxford.

Pub.ᵗ May 1.ᵗ 1796 by S.ʳ R. Harding Pall Mall

THE

DE MAGNETE

OF

WILLIAM GILBERT

BY

DUANE H. D. ROLLER

MENNO HERTZBERGER

AMSTERDAM 1959

X764483748

PREFACE

This volume is a modified version of material written some five years ago and presented as a doctoral dissertation at Harvard University. The original suggestion that Gilbert's *De magnete* was worthy of study came from I. Bernard Cohen. I received aid in locating sources from many persons, notably the staff of the Harvard College Library, David Wheatland, and Bern Dibner.

In the quotations from Gilbert's *De magnete* herein, accent marks have been omitted, as well as contractive symbols (other than "q;" for que). The vast majority of such omitted symbols are those for a letter "s" following an "e" and a letter "m" following a vowel. In revising and correcting the manuscript for publication I have been fortunate in having available the resources of the DeGolyer Collection of the University of Oklahoma Library. Bern Dibner has continued to extend his characteristic helpful hand, specifically in providing Figures 1, 14, and 28. The aid of Menno Hertzberger throughout the process of publication, beginning with his suggestion that this volume be printed, is gratefully acknowledged.

For all of my interest in the history of science I am forever indebted to two men: Frederick Barry and my father.

DUANE H. D. ROLLER

The University of Oklahoma
March 1, 1959.

TABLE OF CONTENTS

CHAPTER ONE

ELECTRICITY AND MAGNETISM BEFORE GILBERT

The concepts which lie at the base of electricity and magnetism in the 16th Century began to develop some two millennia before. Consequently prior to examining Gilbert's work it is important to establish the technical background of those sciences, as it existed in the 16th Century: in the present chapter the history of the major concepts provided to Gilbert by the past will be examined, in terms of some specific historical examples.[1] One often tends to think of a science as consisting of a set of phenomena or facts and a theoretical structure. It is not, however, possible to cleanly divide fact from theory. The phenomena of a science can have no independent existence and cannot be described independently of a theoretical structure: the act of observing a phenomenon consists of the perception of stimuli and hence the observation cannot be separated from the education and beliefs of the individual concerned. One is perhaps tempted to try to eliminate the individual and his background by going beyond observation, eliminating perception, and considering the stimuli themselves as the phenomena. To choose the simplest sort of phenomenon, consider a large sheet of black paper upon which there is a very white line. We may say that at a particular point in front of the paper stimuli exist: we believe that light arrives at this point whether or not an observer is present there, and the presence of this light presumably might be detected, without perception, by some mechanical device.

Ignoring for the moment the question of the complex theoretical structure that leads us to believe in the existence of the stimuli at the point, we may say that we have reduced the situation to the cold, hard facts: the stimuli. But to this we must add that these facts are meaningless, insofar as the white line is concerned. For, in our example, the stimuli

[1] Several books and papers have dealt with the early history of electricity and magnetism, many with much more volume, thoroughness and detail than this chapter will display. See, for example: Park Benjamin, *The intellectual rise in electricity: a history*, London, Longmans, Green and Co., 1895; Edmund Hoppe, *Geschichte der Elektrizität*, Leipzig, Johann Ambrosius Barth, 1884; A. Crichton Mitchell, "Chapters in the history of terrestrial magnetism," *Terrestrial Magnetism and Atmospheric Electricity*, vols. 37(1932), 42(1937), 44(1939), 51(1946); Alfred Ritter von Urbanitzky, *Elektricität und Magnetismus im Alterthume*, Wien, Pest, Leipzig, A. Hartleben's Verlag, 1887; see also George Sarton, *A guide to the history of science*, Waltham, Mass., Chronica Botanica Co., 1952, pp. 162–163; Jean Daujat, *Origines et formation de la théorie des phénomènes électriques et magnétiques*, Paris, Hermann et Cie, 1945.
The history of electricity and magnetism is, like any thread of a culture, related to every other thread:

are merely light arriving at the point from certain directions, and there are possible an infinite number of different white lines, straight and curved, of an infinite number of different lengths and of an infinite number of different orientations, that will produce these same identical stimuli.

Any attempt to resolve the ambiguity and get at one particular white line as the source of the stimuli involves either a theoretical structure or human perception. Thus for certain physiological reasons, an experienced human may resolve this ambiguity because he has binocular vision and because he can apply knowledge from his previous experience. Or, he may somehow detect the stimuli at two points in front of our sheet of paper and interpret them in the light of our theoretical structure of geometry—which, incidentally, we have been tacitly using throughout discussion of this example.[2]

The history of science is filled with examples of scientists who are known to have been exposed to certain stimuli but failed to interpret those stimuli as meaning the occurrence of certain phenomena which were "observed" by later workers. The difference stems from a difference in background rather than from a difference in ability.[3] Consequently, it does not seem profitable to ask: what were the phenomena available to this scientist, how did he interpret them, which of the available facts did he discover and which did he fail to discover?[4] Since the facts have no existence independently of the theoretical structure, we shall focus our attention upon that structure. We shall ask what the scientist believed, without regard to whether he was right or wrong as judged by comparing his views to our modern theories. For if an individual held a certain belief, if he transmitted this belief to others, and if they in turn were influenced by the belief, the question of how the belief agrees or disagrees with our modern beliefs is not particularly relevant in the history of science.

Finally, as a corollary to the point of view just expressed, the "phenomena" or "facts" will be considered as inventions rather than as discoveries. For they are not only inter-

in particular, the philosophical background is of great importance, a point to which we shall return in discussing early Chinese knowledge of the lodestone. Every portion of the history of magnetism and electricity from Thales to Gilbert lacks a detailed modern study in the setting of then current philosophies. Neither this chapter nor this volume is devoted to an attempt to fill these lacunae.

[2] This question of perception has been treated at length by Ernst Mach, in various places. See, for example, his *Beiträge zur Analyse der Empfindungen*, Jena, Verlag von Gustav Fischer, 1886.

[3] As an illustrative example, William Gilbert completely failed to observe electrostatic repulsion, a phenomenon not in accord with his conceptual scheme for electricity. This repulsion was discovered by Cabeo, who began with the knowledge that Gilbert's scientific work was necessarily in error, since it bolstered the Copernican theory. Yet Cabeo had at best no more exposure to the "facts" of repulsion than had Gilbert.

[4] Of course certain stimuli may not have been available, so that an upper limit, so to speak, is placed upon the scientist by his environment.

pretations of stimuli, but also generalizations of a great deal of experience, and are thus better thought of as theories than as isolated elements of a real natural world that has existence independently of man.

I. Antiquity

Terminology

The natural magnet or *lodestone* is found fairly commonly throughout the world, and is usually the mineral magnetite, Fe_3O_4. In antiquity it was given a variety of names,[5] of which λίθος ἡράκλεια [lithos Herakleia] is the most definite and least ambigious. This term, the Heraclean stone, was never used to mean anything other than the lodestone. It probably stems either from the name of the town of Heraclea near Mt. Latmus in Caria, on the boundaries of Lydia, or perhaps directly from the name of the mythological figure, Heracles. A second widely used term is λίθος μαγνῆτις [lithos magnetis], which may have come from the name of one of the two towns named Magnesia in Lydia, one of which is near Heraclea. There is considerable opinion[6] that this term, Magnesian stone, came into use through a misunderstanding,[7] but whatever its source it became eventually the most important, and yields our English word *magnet*. λίθος λυδια [lithos Lydia] or λίθος λυδική [lithos Lydike] sometimes appear, probably because of the location of Heraclea and the two Magnesias. λίθος σιδηρῖτις [lithos sideritis] was also used, probably stemming both from the fact that magnetite is an iron ore, to which σιδηρῖτις was applied, and from the effect on iron of the lodestone: for example σιδηραγωγούση λίθος [sideragogouse lithos], or "iron-attracting stone."[8]

In Latin antiquity, the Greek term ἀδάμας [adamas], meaning "unconquerable" and applied by the Greeks to the hardest objects such as hard iron and the diamond, led to a confusion between diamond and the lodestone that persisted until at least the 16th century, in a variety of forms. This is the source of the French word *aimant*.

---

[5] Th. Henri Martin, "De l'aimant de ses noms divers et de ses variétés suivant les Anciens," *Mémoires présentés par divers savants à l'Académie des inscriptions et belle-lettres*, series 1, vol. vi, 1st part (1861). Reprinted in Martin's *La foudre l'électricité et le magnétisime chez les Anciens*, Paris, Didier et Cie., 1866, which is the source used here.

[6] Martin, *op. cit.* (fn. 5); Mitchell, *op. cit.* (fn. 1), I, p. 113; Philipp Buttmann, "Bemerkungen über die Bennennungen einiger Mineralien beiden Alten, vorzüglich des Magnetes und des Basaltes," *Museuum der Alterthumswissenschaft*, vol. 2, pp. 5–8, 102–104.

[7] See *infra*, quotation above fn. 11.

[8] See *infra*, quotation above fn. 56.

In English, the term *magnet* has survived from classical antiquity, but is no longer used simply for the natural magnet or lodestone. Since "magnet" alone is an ambigious term in any discussion in which both natural and artificial magnets appear, "lodestone"[9] will be consistently used for the natural magnet.

The First Mention of Lodestone Phenomena

An obvious prerequisite to an interest in a lodestone is having one. In retrospect we might expect early attention to be directed at interactions between either lodestone and iron or between pairs of lodestones. Such however is not the case: early remarks are directed solely at the behavior of iron in the presence of lodestone. Hence the existence of iron is a second prerequisite. Since magnetite is a common form of iron ore, the physical stage for the beginnings of magnetism is set with the advent of the iron age. This occurred in the Mediterranean Basin sometime after the 14th Century B. C. In Homer iron is mentioned, but as a luxury, so that 1000 B. C. may be roughly set as a *terminus a quo.*

There is, however, a third prerequisite, namely, the existence of a conceptual scheme concerning a uniformity and a regularity in nature. For there must be some method of sorting the myriad daily experiences into those of interest and those not of interest; initial interest in the lodestone stems from apparent violations of natural law on the part of pieces of iron near the stone. These violations are only apparent, however, because natural law cannot be violated. Faced with an apparent violation that cannot be, the scientist has two choices: he "discovers" that the natural law was not a law at all, that it has been incorrectly formulated and that he must reformulate it so that it is no longer violated; or, he demonstrates that the violation was only apparent, and explains why it does not exist. If we support a lodestone in the air and place a small piece of iron alongside of or underneath it, the iron will often remain there, apparently without support. To both us and to the Hellenic philosopher the lack of support is only apparent, since objects having weight fall unless supported. This was the principal and fundamental magnetic phenomenon of antiquity. The "law" that heavy objects fall unless supported is so well established that its modification is unthinkable. The very earliest mentions of magnetism are thus not concerned with whether such a support exists: from the very beginnings of recorded statements on magnetism the question is: "Why does the lodestone attract the iron?"

[9] Or "loadstone." From the Anglo-Saxon, *lād,* journey. Like the German Leiderstein, "lodestone" originates from the compass property of the natural magnet.

14

The earliest dated mention of the lodestone is attributed to Thales of Miletus (c. 624–548 or later) by Aristotle (384–322/1).

> Thales, too, to judge from what is recorded about him, seems to have held soul to be a motive force, since he said that the stone has a soul in it because it moves the iron.[10]

From this brief remark, it may be surmised that Thales' reference to the lodestone was incidental: the topic of discussion is soul, not the lodestone, and there is no indication whatsoever of a claim of discovery of any sort of phenomenon. The lodestone apparently is being used in an illustrative manner in a discussion of a broader topic. Finally, the nature of the action of the lodestone is not under discussion but is known: here a cause is being assigned to that action.

Plato, the Samothracian Rings, and the Denial of Attraction

> In the *Ion,* Plato (c. 428–348/7) wrote of
>
> …the stone which Euripides named a magnet [*Μαγνῆτιν*], but most people call "Heraclea stone". For this stone not only attracts iron rings, but also imparts to them a power whereby they in turn are able to do the very same thing as the stone, and attract other rings; so that sometimes there is formed a quite long chain of bits of iron and rings, suspended one from another; and they all depend for this power on that one stone.[11]

As was the case with Thales, these remarks of Plato's about the lodestone are definitely incidental to a discussion of a quite different matter, namely, the manner in which the Muse transmits inspiration to men through other men.

Plato wrote that the lodestone "attracts" and *magnetic attraction* has remained with us

[10] *De anima,* I, 2, p. 405a, lines 19–21. *The works of Aristotle translated into English,* ed. W. D. Ross, vol. 3, Oxford, Clarendon Press, 1931. The word "magnet", in the extract, has been changed to "stone", since the original is λίθος. *Aristotelis opera omnia Graece et Latine cum indice nominum et rerum absolutissimo,* vol. 3, Paris, Ambrosio Firmin Didot, 1854, p. 435. Diogenes Laertius (3rd Century B. C.) wrote: "Aristotle and Hippias affirm that, arguing from the magnet [λίθος της μαγνπιδος] and from amber, he attributed a soul or life even to inanimate objects." Loeb Classical Library, Diogenes Laertius, *Lives of eminent philosophers, with an English translation* by R. D. Hicks, vol. I, London, William Heinemann; New York, G. P. Putnam's Sons, 1925, p. 24. None of the writings of Hippias of Elis (fl. c. 420 B. C.) are extant; nowhere in the Aristotelian corpus is there any reference to such a property of amber, much less a reference to Thales having knowledge of it.

[11] *Ion,* ch. v, 533D. Loeb Classical Library, *Plato with an English translation,* vol. 3, London, William Heineman; New York, G. P. Putnam's Sons, 1925; *Ion,* tr. by W. R. M. Lamb, p. 421.
The reference to Euripides is possibly to a remark in an extant fragment of a lost play, the *OEneus:* "Hominum judicia offuscans, velut lapis Magneticus, opinionem ad se trahit, iterumque avertit." (*Euripidis opera omnia;…,* Glasgow, Academic Press, 1821, vol. 7, p. 640, fragment v of the *Oeneus.*)

to the present day as a phrase representing the fundamental magnetic phenomenon. To say that object A is attracted by object B is to mean that there is a force upon A directed toward B and presumably due to the presence of B, but that there exists no detectable connection between A and B. It is likely that the concept of attraction stems from the muscular tensions that are produced in an individual when subjected to stimuli that inform him of the presence of nourishment, a member of the opposite sex, or some other object capable of satisfying some fundamental human need. Under such circumstances a primitive man may well feel that he is being pushed, pulled, urged, toward the "attracting" object. When a force is found to be urging an inanimate object toward another, and when the source of that force is similarly occult, the concept of "attraction" may be transferred from the animate case.[12]

Yet conceptually the idea of "attraction" has generally been highly unsatisfactory: when one object affects another, scientists have sought the material connection between them, particulary when the effect is a force. Plato himself wrote in the *Timaeus:*

> Furthermore, as regards all flowings of waters, and fallings of thunderbolts, and the marvels concerning the attraction of amber [ἠλέκτρων] and of the Heraclean stone – not one of all these ever possesses any real power of attraction; but the fact that there is no void, and that these bodies propel themselves round one into another, and that according as they separate or unite they all exchange places and proceed severally each to its own region, – it is by means of these complex and reciprocal processes that such marvels are wrought, as will be evident to him who investigates them properly.[13]

This passage certainly does not make clear the mechanism that Plato envisages. Yet the idea that there is "no drawing power" but that physical effects must mean physical contact – in short, that *magnetic attraction* is not an "attraction", was one of the most powerful motivations in the important work in theory of magnetism from before Plato to long past the time of Gilbert.

This is the place where the possible confusion previously referred to (p. 13) may have occurred. The argument is, briefly, this: Euripides is writing of a form of talc that looks like silver and which causes the observer to believe he has found silver, with consequent later disappointment. Some weight is lent to this argument by a passage by Theophrastus of Eresus, Lesbos (c. 372–288) in which he describes such a talc-like stone under the name of "Μαγνῆτις λίθος" (*Theophrastus's History of stones,* Greek and English ed. by "Sir" John Hill, London, 1746, pp. 104–107.) It is of interest, however, that Plato does not specify his sources in Euripides and that he uses the term "magnet" rather than "Magnesian stone."

[12] Sec Hélène Metzger, *Attraction universelle et religion naturelle chez quelques commentateurs anglais de Newton,* Paris, Herman et Cie., 1938, part 2, pp. 66–69.

[13] *Timaeus,* 80c. Loeb Classical Library edition of Plato's works, cited in fn. 11, vol. 7, 1929, tr. R. G. Bury, pp. 214–215.

Empedocles, the Atomists, and the Beginnings of Mechanistic Explanations

According to Alexander of Aphrodisias (fl. 193–217 in Athens),[14] Empedocles of Acragas (c. 490–435) proposed that an emanation from the lodestone entered the pores of nearby iron and expelled the air therefrom. A similar penetration of the lodestone by emanations from the iron caused the iron to be drawn toward the lodestone. We are not given sufficient information to permit us to understand the detail of this process. However, Empedocles developed a general theory of change and mutation in terms of the flow of four elements in and out of pores which, he postulated, exist in every object, and his views on magnetism are in accord with this conceptual scheme.[15] The effect of the lodestone on iron is, as with Thales and Plato, neither a novelty nor itself under investigation: the causes of the effect are the question at hand.

This mechanistic view is an understandable development of ideas set forth concerning the nature of matter by the Ionian schools of philosophy.[16] It came to fruition in the atomistic theory of matter, perhaps first set forth by a contemporary of Empedocles', Leucippus of Miletus (5th Century B. C.),[17] but known to us through Democritus of Abdera (c. 460–c. 370). Democritus held that the influence of one body on another takes place through mechanical pressure or contact, one form of which included atomic emanations.[18] Since iron is denser than lodestone, he concluded that there is more space between the latter's atoms. Atomic emanations from the lodestone enter the iron pores and expel iron atoms therefrom, which move toward the lodestone entering its pores and in doing so draw the iron in the same direction. The symmetry of this atomistic explanation seems to have raised the question as to why the iron is affected by the lodestone but the lodestone is not affected by the iron; Democritus apparently explained this lack of symmetry in terms of a lack of symmetry in the mechanism. Due to the larger

---

[14] *Questiones naturales*, II, 23. The relevant passage is quoted as item A89, in the Empedokles section of Hermann Diels, *Die Fragments der Vorsokratiker*, 5th ed., 3 vol., Berlin, Weidmannsche Buchhandlung, 1934–1938, vol. 1, p. 306. See also, Kathleen Freeman, *The pre-Socratic philosophers: a companion to Diels, Fragmente der Vorsokratiker*, Oxford, Basil Blackwell, 1949, pp. 172–204, esp. 181, 190.

[15] Leon Robin, *La pensée grecque et les origines de l'esprit scientifique*, Paris, La Renaissance du Livre, 1928, pp. 119–134, esp. 124.

[16] See John Burnet, *Early Greek philosophy*, London and Edinburgh, Adam and Charles Black, 1892, pp. 30–82; Theodor Gomperz, *Greek thinkers*, vol. 1, tr. by Laurie Magnus, London, John Murray, 1906, pp. 323ff; Robin, *op. cit.* (fn. 15), pp. 41–56.

[17] According to Aristotle, e.g., *De generatione et corruptione*, I, 8, 325a. *The works of Aristotle translated into English*, ed. W. D. Ross, tr. H. H. Joachim, vol. 2, Oxford, Clarendon Press, 1930, 325a.

[18] See Diogenes Laertius, *op. cit.* (fn. 10), vol. 2, pp. 453–455. Among Democritus' works listed by Diogenes, pp. 454–461, is περὶ τῆς λίθου. See also Robin, *op. cit.* (fn. 15), pp. 135–146.

17

interatomic spaces in the lodestone, there is greater activity on the side of the lode-stone and hence greater effect on the iron.

The atomic theory of classical antiquity reached its most famous expression in the *De rerum natura* of Titus Lucretius Carus (c. 95, 98 – c. 55), where the mechanism is described thus:

> principio fluere e lapide hoc permulta necessest
> semina sive aestum qui discutit aera plagis,
> inter qui lapidem ferrumque est cumque locatus.
> hoc ubi inanitur spatium multusque vacefit
> in medio locus, extemplo primordia ferri
> in vacuum prolapsa cadunt coiuncta, fit utque
> anulus ipse sequatur eatque ita corpore toto.
> nec res ulla magis primoribus *ex* elementis
> indupedita suis arte conexa cohaeret
> quam validi ferri natura et frigidus horror.
> quo minus est mirum, quod dico, ibus ex elementis
> corpora si nequeunt e ferro plura coorta
> in vacuum ferri, quin anulus ipse sequatur;
> quod facit, et sequitur, donec pervenit ad ipsum
> iam lapidem caecisque in eo compagibus haesit.[19]

The ambient air has been introduced here as an element of the mechanism. Plutarch (c. 48 – c. 123) gave an explanation much like Lucretius' in a commentary on Plato's denial of attraction (p. 13).[20]

Lucretius also reported

> Fit quoque ut a lapide hoc ferri natura recedat
> interdum, fugere atque sequi consueta vicissim.
> exultare etiam Samothracia ferrea vidi
> et ramenta simul ferri furere intus ahenis
> in scaphiis, lapis hic Magnes cum subditus esset:
> usque adeo fugere ab saxo gestire videtur.[21]

A modern observer of the phenomena described by Lucretius would not identify it as repulsion. Yet Lucretius did, and in the modern sense of the term, writing

---

[19] *De rerum natura*, Bk. 6, Verse 40, lines 1002–1016. H. A. J. Munro, *T. Lucreti Cari de rerum natura libri sex*, 4th ed., Cambridge, Deighton Bell and Co., London, G. Bell and Sons, 1886.

[20] Plutarch, *Platonic questions*, Q.VII, 7. *Plutarch's Morals*, tr. by several hands, corrected and revised by W. W. Goodwin, Vol. 5, Boston, Little, Brown, and Ca., 1870, pp. 425–449. See *infra* above fn. 38.

[21] Lucretius, *op. cit., ed. cit.* (fn. 19), VI, 41, lines 1042–1047.

> aere interposito discordia tanta creatur
> propterea quia nimirum prius aestus ubi aeris
> praecepit ferrique vias possedit apertas,
> posterior lapidis venit aestus et omnia plena
> invenit in ferro neque habet qua tranet ut ante.[22]

The concept of repulsion thus is clearly introduced at this time.

Medicinal Use of the Lodestone in Antiquity

Following the references to the lodestone attributed to Thales and Empedocles, the next known is by Hippocrates of Cos (b. c. 460 B. C.–died at a very old age), who not only mentioned magnetic attraction but also referred to medicinal properties of the lodestone,[23] the earliest of a long line of references to medicinal use of the lodestone, extending into modern times. The earliest known account of the surgical use of the lodestone is said to be in the writings of Susruta, a Hindu surgeon who lived before 450 B. C.[24]

Although we shall see medical uses of the lodestone serve to establish knowledge of it and often of the phenomenon of attraction, they seem to have had negligible effect upon the development of the science in antiquity, and hence are not of interest to us here.

Explanations of Magnetic Attraction in Terms of Sympathies

Pliny (23–79), in his compilation of ancient knowledge, sets forth the idea of "sympathies and antipathies" as a cause of various phenomena:

> pax secum in his aut bellum naturae dicetur, odia amicitiaque rerum surdarum ac sensu carentium et, quo magis miremur, omnia ea hominum causa, quod Graeci sympathiam et antipathiam appellavere, quibus cuncta constant, ignes aquis restinguentibus, aquas sole devorante, luna pariente, altero alterius iniuria deficiente sidere, atque, ut a sublimioribus recedamus, ferrum ad se trahente magnete lapide et alio rursus abigente a sese,...[25]

---

[22] *Ibid.,* lines 1048–1052.

[23] *De mulieribus,* I, 5. Mitchell, *op. cit.* (fn. 1), IV, pp. 326 and 347; Martin, *op cit.* (fn. 5), p. 11, where Martin notes: "Les anciens connaissaient les propriétés styptiques des oxydes de fer; les medecins grecs vantaient surtout pour cet effect l'aimant et l'hématite [Fe2O3]..."

[24] George Sarton, *Introduction to the history of science,* 3 vol., Baltimore, Williams and Wilkins, 1927– 1948, vol. 1, pp. 76–77. Hereafter this work is referred to as "Sarton, *Introduction.*"

[25] *Historia naturalis,* bk. 20, chap. 1. Loeb Classical Library edition, *Pliny's Natural History with an English translation,* in ten volumes [9, plus one to be published], Cambridge, Harvard University Press; London, William Heinemann, Ltd., 1949–. Vol. 6, tr. W. H. S. Jones, p. 2.

Galen of Pergamum (129–c. 199) held a similar doctrine, and strongly attacked the atomistic explanations of Epicurus. Galen compared the lodestone to: (1) cathartic drugs which attract certain qualities (e.g. bile and phlegm); (2) drugs which remove thorns and arrowpoints and drugs which draw out animal poisons or arrow-tip poisons; (3) "corn," which has a greater ability to draw water [into itself] than has extreme solar heat [to draw it out of the "corn"].[26]

The concepts of sympathy and antipathy were of great influence upon medieval thought concerning magnetic phenomena, as we shall see in Parts II and III of this chapter.

Chinese Knowledge of the Lodestone

It is not at all unlikely that the magnetic compass originated in the Orient, or that it was an Arabic application of Oriental knowledge of magnetism. The history of magnetism in China has been considerably confused by frequent mentions in Chinese literature of a "south-pointing chariot."[27] This device was a horse-drawn wagon containing a complex arrangement of gears and upon which was mounted a figurine that allegedly always pointed south. It may have been that the gear system responded to changes in direction of motion of the wagon and turned the figurine; it may have been that the wagon was simply a distance recorder. One thing is clear: the south-pointing chariot was not a compass nor was its mechanism actuated by a compass.

The historical difficulties, both of language and philosophy, seem to make any study of early Chinese writings on the lodestone ineffective at the present time. There is general agreement in secondary sources that in the 4th Century A. D. Kuo Puo wrote:

> The magnet draws the iron, and the amber attracts mustard seeds. There is a breath which penetrates secretly and with velocity, and which communicates itself imperceptibly to that which corresponds to it in the other object. It is an inexplicable thing.[28]

Perhaps the most striking thing about Kuo Puo's statement is the great similarity of ideas to those developed in the Mediterranean basin. The "magnet" "draws the iron"; there is "a breath" from the magnet; this breath "penetrates"; there is a correspondence

---

[26] *On the natural faculties*, bk. I, chap. XIV. Loeb Classical Library edition, *Galen on the natural faculties*, with an English trans. by A. J. Brock, London, William Heinemann, New York, G. P. Putnam's Sons, 1916, pp. 82–87.

[27] Li-Shu-hua, "Origine de la boussole", *Isis*, vol. 45 (1954), pp. 78–94, 175–196.

[28] As quoted in Benjamin, *op. cit.* (fn. 1), p. 74, who calls attention to the similarity of ideas herein and in earlier Greek writings on the lodestone.

between the breath and something in the iron. The congruence to Greek magnetic theory is considerable. Yet there remains the possibility that there was an independent development in China.

Any decision on the independence of Chinese knowledge must await two additions to our knowledge. First, examination of the early Chinese passages by scholars having a thorough knowledge of both Chinese and Greek: thus, for example, do the words in those languages that are both translated "attracts" have the same concepts behind them (see fn. 12)? Second, are the concepts that appear in the Chinese texts amenable to contemporary Chinese philosophical ideas concerning the structure of matter and the nature of physical actions?

Under any circumstances, there seem to be no grounds whatsoever for believing that Greek knowledge was influenced by Chinese, in antiquity. The oldest reasonable claim for knowledge of the lodestone in China[29] dates from the epoch of the Warring States (403–221 B.C.), long after the earliest Greek remarks on the lodestone.

The Amber Effect

Amber is a generic name for fossil resins from long extinct coniferous, resiniferous trees. The best known of these fossil resins is succinite. Although found throughout the world, the vast majority of this fossil resin originates from the southern Baltic coast, where it occurs in early tertiary strata.[30] Amber was widely prized as an ornament in prehistoric times, and prehistoric amber trade routes have been traced in considerable detail.[31] Along these trade routes amber of Baltic origin is found, in settings that leave no doubt of its early date, and indeed amber is mentioned as an ornament in Greek literature from Homer on.[32]

[29] Excluding claims based upon the south-pointing chariot and mythology which have sometimes placed the compass as well as the lodestone in 2700 B.C., well back into the neolithic period in China. According to Li-Shu-hua, *op. cit.* (fn. 27), p. 175, in the Tcheou dynasty in the Liu-che-tch'ouen-ts'ieou, there appeared the statement: "The lodestone makes iron come or it attracts it." Again the similarity to Greek expressions is extraordinary.

[30] Frank Dawson Adams, *The birth and development of the geological sciences*, Baltimore, Williams and Wilkins Company, 1938, p. 470; Ellen C. Semple, *The geography of the Mediterranean region: its relation to ancient history*, London, Constable and Co., Ltd., 1932, p. 684; George C. Williamson, *The book of amber*, London, Ernest Benn Ltd., 1932, pp. 184–194.

[31] J. M. de Navarro, "Prehistoric routes between Northern Europe and Italy defined by the amber trade," *The Geographical Journal*, vol. 66 (1925), pp. 481–507; Semple, *op. cit.* (fn. 30), p. 224: "The ancient amber route from the Baltic, one of the earliest trade routes of Europe,..."; p. 684: "Everywhere in the Mediterranean Basin amber was in demand from the earliest time. Amber beads were found in the ruins of Troy and Cnossos..." Large amounts of amber were found in excavations at Mycenae: Arthur Evans, *The Palace of Minos, a comparative account of the successive stages of the early Cretan civilization*

Knowledge of amber was widespread in Greece by the 9th Century B. C. The common Greek name for it was ἤλεκτρον [elektron], and in the earlier uses of the term there is some doubt as to whether it meant amber or a golden alloy.

> Il est certain que, dans les auteurs postérieurs à Hérodote, ce mot grec ἤλεκτρον, de même que le mot latin *electrum*, désigne habituellement l'ambre jaune ou succin. Il n'est pas moins certain que pourtant, dans beaucoup d'auteurs postérieurs à Hérodote, ces mêmes mots, en grec et en latin, désignent un métal qui avait à peu près la même couleur, savoir, un alliage d'or avec un cinquième ou un quart d'argent.[33]

Herodotus (c. 484–c. 425) mentions ἤλεκτρον as said to come from "the northern sea," which seems quite unambiguous.[34]

Plato coupled the lodestone and amber together, attributing attraction to both of them and then proceeded to deny attraction to either (p. 16). This is the first known mention of any such property associated with amber. But again, as with the lodestone, this *amber effect* is mentioned incidentally, in an illustrative manner, as something apparently familiar to his readers.

Theophrastus wrote of the *Lapis Lyncurius,* which has

> an attractive power, like that of Amber, and is said to attract not only Straws and small pieces of Sticks, but even Copper and Iron, if they are beaten into thin Pieces. This *Diocles* affirms...
>
> Amber also is a Stone: It is dug out of the earth in *Ligurgia*, and has, as the before mentioned, a Power of Attraction. But the greatest and most evident attractive Quality is in that Stone [the Heraclean stone) which attracts Iron.

as illustrated by the discoveries at Knossos, London, MacMillan and Co., vol. 2, part 1, 1928, p. 174. K. G. Jakob, "Neue Beiträge zum Studium des kaspisch-baltischen Handels im Mittelalter; I. Neue Studien, den Bernstein im Orient betreffend," *Zeitschrift der Deutschen Morgenländischen Gesellschaft,* vol. 43 (1889), pp. 353–387.

[32] Homer, *Odyssey,* bk. xv, line 460; bk. xviii, line 296. But in bk. iv, line 73, amber is probably not meant as sometimes noted, for there the reference is to the metal electrum. Loeb Classical Library edition, *Homer: The Odyssey, with an English translation* by A. T. Murray, 2 vol., Cambridge, Harvard University Press; London, William Heinemann Ltd., 1946.

[33] Th. Henri Martin, "Du succin, de ses noms divers et de ses variétés suivant les anciens," *Mémoires présentés par divers savants à l'Académie des inscriptions et belles-lettres,* 1st series, vol. 6, 1st part. Reprinted, Martin, *op. cit.* (fn. 5), pp. 95–138, which is the source used here. The quotation above is from p. 96. See also: *Handbuch der klassischen Altertums-Wissenschaft in systematischer Darstellung,* V, part 1, *Geschichte der antiken Naturwissenschaft und Philosophie,* Nördlingen, Verlag der C. H. Beck'schen Buchhandlung, 1888, A (*Naturwissschaft*), Sigmund Gunther, p. 60; Ferdinand de Lasteyrie, *L'electrum des anciens etait-il l'email?* Paris, Didot Freres, Fils et Cie., 1857.

[34] Herodotus, History, III, 115. Loeb Classical Library edition, *Herodotus, with an English translation*

But this is a scarce stone, and found in but a few Places; It ought, however, to be ranked with these Stones, as it possesses a like Quality.[35]

It is not certain just what lyncurium meant. From other remarks about it, by Theophrastus, it may have been topaz, tourmaline, or zircon.[36] But here is the genesis of the concept of a class of substances displaying a common property. Yet implicit in Theophrastus' remarks there is a difference between the lodestone and the others: the lodestone attracts only iron, while amber and lyncurium attract all sorts of things, including iron.

The nature of the amber effect is described in more detail by Pliny

> ceterum attritu digitorum accepta caloris anima trahunt in se paleas et folia arida et philyras, ut magnes lapis ferrum.[37]

This work, be it remembered, was always available in Europe and emphasized two points that turned out to be of great importance: the amber must be heated *by being rubbed;* rubbed amber attracts all sorts of things while the lodestone only attracts iron.

Plutarch, in his discussion of Plato's denial of attraction (fn. 20), extended the atomistic-mechanistic explanation of magnetic attraction to include the amber effect:

> And neither amber nor the lodestone draws anything to it which is near, nor does any thing spontaneously approach them. But this stone emits strong exhalations, by which the adjoining air being impelled forceth that which is before it; and this being carried round in the circle, and returning into the vacuated place, forcibly draws the iron in the same direction. In amber there is a flammeous and spirituous nature, and this by rubbing on the surface is emitted by recluse passages, and does the same that the loadstone does. It also draws the lightest and driest of adjacent bodies, by reason of their

by A. D. Godley, London, William Heinemann, New York, G. P. Putnam's Sons, 1921–1930, 4 vol., vol. 2, pp. 140–141. "...I do not believe that there is a river called by foreigners Eridanus issuing into the northern sea, whence our amber is said to come,..."

[35] Theophrastus, *op. cit.* (fn. 11), pp. 125–137. Diocles of Carystus, the "second Hippocrates" has been studied in detail by Werner Jaeger, *Diokles von Karystos. Die griechische Medizin und die Schule des Aristoteles,* Berlin, W. de Gruyter & Co., 1938.

[36] Sydney H. Ball, *A Roman book on precious stones; including an English modernization of the 37th booke of the historie of the world, by C. Plinius secundus,* Los Angeles, Gemological Institute of America 1950, p. 136.

[37] Pliny, *op. cit.* (fn. 25). *C. Plini Secundi naturalis historiae libri xxxvii. Post Ludovici iani obitum recognovit et scripturae discrepantia adiecta,* ed. Charles Mayhoff, vol 5, Leipzig, B. G. Teubner, 1897, p. 402.

tenuity and weakness; for it is not so strong nor so endued with weight and strength as to force much air and to act with violence and to have power over great bodies, as the magnet has. But what is the reason the air never draws a stone, nor wood, but iron only, to the loadstone? This is a common question both by them who think the coition of these bodies is made by the attraction of the loadstone, and by such as think it done by the incitement of the iron. Iron is neither so rare as wood, nor altogether so solid as gold or a stone; but has certain pores and asperities, which in regard of the inequality are proportionable to the air; and the air being received in certain seats, and having (as it were) certain stays to cling to, does not slip away; but when it is carried up to the stone and strikes against it, it draws the iron by force along with it to the stone. Such then may be the reason of this.[38]

Here again, both the essential similarity and the striking difference in the two phenomena are stressed. The similarity was the effective factor until at least the 16th Century.

Pliny

The works of Greek and Latin authors assured continuous knowledge in the West of the phenomenon of magnetic attraction.[39] One of the most important modes of transmission of information was through Pliny's *Natural history* (p. 19). Compiled from "voluminum circiter duorum milium,"[40] it is quite uncritical, largely leaving discrimination to the reader. Never lost to the West, Pliny's compendium was of great importance in shaping European thought in the realm of natural history.[41]

Pliny discusses the lodestone four times.[42] In addition to his attribution of magnetic attraction to sympathies (p. 19), he sets forth a great deal more information about magnetism which we may summarize thus:

1. Near the river Indus there are two mountains, one of which attracts iron and one repels it. A man with iron nails in his shoes cannot raise his feet from the one or put them down on the other.

---

[38] Plutarch, *op. cit., loc. cit.* (fn. 20), pp. 436–437.

[39] It will be convenient to think of this phenomenon as the movement of iron to the lodestone: in Gilbert's terms, the first of five "magnetic movements."

[40] *Historia naturalis*, Preface, 17. See *ed. cit.* (fn. 25), vol. 1, p. 12.

[41] Sarton, *Introduction*, vol. 1, p. 249.

[42] Pliny, *op. cit.* (*eds. cit.* fns. 25 and 37), bk. 2, chap. 98; bk. 20, chap. 1; bk. 34, chap. 42; bk. 36, chap. 25.

2. Ptolemy II planned to roof a temple with lodestone so that his sister's iron statue might be suspended in the air. The project was not completed.
3. The lodestone was discovered by a shepherd who found that the iron tip of his staff and his shoe nails adhered to the ground in a certain locality.
4. There are five different kinds of magnets, from five different regions, differing in color and sex, the feminine ones lacking attractive power. One of these attracts other magnets.
5. A stone named "theamedes," from Ethiopia, repels and rejects all kind of iron.
6. Iron can acquire the properties of the magnet and chains of iron rings hanging from a magnet may be formed. This so-called "live-iron" inflicts more severe wounds than does ordinary iron.
7. Iron near a magnet springs toward it, clasps it, and is held in its embrace.

The lack of reference in Piny to the mechanistic explanations of the Greeks is striking and important to the later history of magnetism.

II. The Interim Period

With the decay of the Graeco-Roman culture in the first few centuries of our era, perhaps best characterized by and certainly strongly influenced by the displacement of Europeans from the sea trade of the Mediterranean basin, influential work in magnetism seems to have come to a near standstill in Europe. Yet awareness of the lodestone and some of its properties was continuous.

Diamond and Lodestone

The confusion between diamond and lodestone has already been mentioned (p. 13), a confusion that persisted and was strengthened by the belief that a diamond near a lodestone disables the latter. This confusion was implicit in Pliny's classification of the lodestone (siderites) as one kind of adamas.[43] Caius Julius Solinus (late 3rd Century) wrote

> Inter adamantem & magnetem est quaedam naturae occulta dissensio, adeo ut juxta positus non sinat magnetem capere ferrum: vel, si admotus magnes ferrum traxerit, quasi praedam quandam adamas magneti rapiat, atque auferat.[44]

[43] Pliny, op. cit., ed. cit. (fn. 37), bk. 37, chap. 14.
[44] C. Iulii Solini Polyhistor ad optimas editiones collatus praemittur notitia literaria accedit index. Editio accurata, Zweibrücken, Typographical Society, 1794, chap. 52, para. 60, p. 171.

25

Solinius' work, a geographical compilation, exerted great influence.[45] The disabling of the lodestone by the diamond is repeated by Aurelius Augustine (354–430),[46] who was affected by both Pliny and Solinius.[47] The connection between diamond and lodestone persists in the *Etymologiarum sive originum* of Isidore of Seville (c. 560–636), who wrote

> Hic autem dissidet cum magnete lapide in tantum ut iuxta positus ferrum non patiatur abstrahi magnetem, aut si admotus magnes conprehenderit, rapiat atque auferrat.[48]

This work was an influential protoype encyclopaedia,[49] and in the discussion on the lodestone[50] Isidore clearly shows the influence of Pliny and Augustine.[51]

William Gilbert repeatedly refers both to the belief that diamond disables lodestone and to the alleged magnetic properties of the diamond,[52] and even ultimately feels it necessary to write that an alleged case of display of magnetism by a diamond "Hoc quidem contrarium esset regulis nostris magneticis. Ob eamque causam periculum nos fecimus septuaginta adamantibus praestantibus, coram multis testibus..."[53] with entirely negative results. Nevertheless both forms of the confusion persisted long after Gilbert.[54]

Magic

It is understandable that interests in magic should be drawn to the occult nature of magnetic attraction, and that the magnet should enter into magical practices.[55] Hippolytus, Bishop of Portus Romanus (3rd Century) in his *Philosophumena* wrote

---

[45] Sarton, *Introduction*, vol. 1, p. 341.

[46] *De civitate Dei contra paganus*, bk. 21, chap. 4. *Sancti Aurelii Augustini Episcopi De civitate Dei libri xxii*, ed. B. Dombart, Leipzig, B. G. Teubner, 1877, p. 494.

[47] Lynn Thorndike, *A history of magic and experimental science*, vols. 1 and 2, New York, Macmillan, 1923; vols. 3–6, New York, Columbia University Press, 1934–1941; vol. 1, p. 510.

[48] *Originum seu etymologiarum*, bk. 16, chap. 13. *Isidori Hispalensis Episcopi etymologiarvm sive originvm libri xx*, ed. W. M. Lindsay, 2 vol., Oxford, Clarendon Press, 1911.

[49] Sarton, *Introduction*, vol. 1, pp. 471–472.

[50] Isidore of Seville, *op. cit.* (fn. 48), bk. 16, chap. 4.

[51] Sarton, *Introduction*, vol. 1, p. 341, states that he was influenced by Solinus as well. Ernest Brehaut writes: "It seems probable that his working library contained works of the following authors: Lactantius, Tertullian, Jerome, Ambrose, Augustine, Orosius, Cassidorus, Suetonius, Pliny, Solinus, Hyginus, Sallust, Hegesippus, the abridger of Vitruvius, Servius, the scholia on Lucan, Justinus." Ernest Brehaut, *An encyclopedist of the dark ages: Isidore of Seville; Studies in History, Economics and Public Law* edited by the Faculty of political science of Columbia University, no. 1, New York, Columbia University, vol. 48, 1912, pp. 46–47.

[52] *Gvilielmi Gilberti Colcestrensis, medici Londinensis, de magnete, magneticisqve corporibvs, et de magno magnete tellure; Physiologia nova, plurimis & argumentis, & experimentis demonstrata*, London,

Terrae motus imitantur ita ut omnia moveri videantur, per stercus ichneumonis cum lapide magnetico [σιδηραγωγούση λίθω] in carbonibus accensum.[56]

The influential Lapidary falsely ascribed to Aristotle and which reached Europe from Islam by the 12th Century, describes an alchemical process using a lodestone. After the final step:

> so schlägt eine Feuerflamme daraus hervor, die gegen zehn Ellen Höhe erreicht und alles verbrennt, was in ihren Bereich kommt.[57]

Marbode (11th Century) devoted the first chapter of his *Liber lapidum* to adamas,[58] giving such examples as how a burglar could drive the occupants of a house away by sprinkling lodestone over hot coals, and describes a property of the lodestone that seems to have excited considerable interest, namely that an unchaste wife will fall out of bed if a lodestone is applied to her head. This story, in various forms, is often repeated, for example by Alexander Neckam (1157–1217) in his *De naturis rerum*.[59]

Medical Use of the Lodestone

The lodestone has long been a popular medical instrument (p. 19). Dioscorides of Anazarbos (1st Century A. D.), whose encyclopaedia of materia medica embodied the results of Greek research in pharmacy and applied botany,[60] recommended lodestone for "drawing out gross humors."[61] Oribasis of Pergamum (c. 325–c. 400), whose commendation of Galen helped the latter's popularity,[62] mentioned the lodestone's medicinal virtue in his *De facultate metallicorum*.[63] *Marcellus Empiricus* (late 4th, early 5th Century), a Gallo-Roman physician noted:

Peter Short, 1600. (Hereafter this work is referred to as "*De magnete*.") Bk. 1, chap. 1, pp. 2, 7; bk. 2, chap. 38, pp. 109, 112; bk. 3, chap. 13, p. 143.

[53] *Ibid.*, bk. 3, chap. 13, p. 143.

[54] [S. P. Thompson], *Notes on the de magnete of Dr. William Gilbert*, London, privately printed, 1901, pp. 4–5.

[55] Many examples appear in Thorndike, *op. cit.* (fn. 47), *passim*.

[56] *Philosophumena*, bk. 4, chap. 4, para. 12. *Philosophumena sive haeresium omnium confutatio opus origeni adscriptum e codice Parisino productum recensuit, latine vertit notis variorum suisque instruxit, prolegomenis et indicibus auxit*, ed. Patrice Cruice, Paris, 1860, p. 111.

[57] Julius Ruska, *Das Steinbuch des Aristoteles*, Heidelberg, Carl Winter's Universitätsbuchhandlung, 1912, pp. 154–155.

[58] Thompson, *op. cit.* (fn. 54), p. 18. Chapter 43 of Marabode's work is on *magnes*.

[59] *De naturis rerum*, chap. 88. See *Alexandri Neckam de naturis rerum libro duo...*, ed. Thomas Wright, London, Longman, Green, Longman, Roberts, and Green, 1863, chap. 88, p. 178.

[60] Sarton, *Introduction*, vol. 1, p. 258.

[61] See *The Greek herbal of Dioscorides*, englished by John Goodyer (1652–1655), ed. and published

Magnetis lapis, qui antiphyson dicitur, que ferrum trahit et abicit, et Magnetis lapis, qui sanguinem emittit et ferrum ad se trahit, collo alligati aut circa caput dolori capitis medentur.[64]

Aëtios of Amida (fl. 527–565), physician to the Byzantine court, discussed medical uses of lodestone in his medical encyclopaedia,[65] and Alexander of Trales (6th Century) recommended it for gout and epilepsy.[66] The usual practice seems to have been to bind the lodestone to the affected part. St. Hildegard of Bingen (1st half of 12th Century) recommended its use, together with an incantation, for curing insanity.[67]

Thus through the first eleven centuries of our era the lodestone is known, principally through medical uses, uses in magic, and as an example of occult powers, in the West. Mentions of it are widespread in both space and time: St. Aldhelm (2nd half of 7th Century), "'the first Englishman who cultivated classical learning with any success and the first of whom any literary remains are preserved'"[68] mentions the lodestone as did Kuo Puo (p. 20); there are known mentions of the lodestone in works originating in every century from the second to the twelfth. Yet there is little of this medieval European knowledge that seems either original or enduring in the later study of magnetism.

Islam

The lodestone was also well know in Arabic-speaking countries in this same period.[69] Having available the Greek corpus at a much earlier date than did Europeans, Muslim writers from the 7th Century on display a greater interest in the nature of the magnetic attraction. Jābir ibn Haiyān (Geber) (fl. c. 776), the most famous of the Arabic alchemists,[70] shows clear Greek influence in his discussion of the imponderability of the magnetic force:

by Robert T. Gunther, Oxford, University Press, 1934. Gunther notes that he has done little editing: this is evident and makes quite difficult any attempt to determine the source or validity of the work as a whole or of its parts.

[62] Sarton, *Introduction*, vol. 1, pp. 372–373.

[63] *De facultate metallicorum*, chap. 13. Cited by Gilbert, *De magnete*, bk. 1, chap. 1, p. 2.

[64] *De medicamentis*, chap. 1. See *Marcelli de medicamentis liber*, ed. Maximilianus Niedermann, Leipzig and Berlin, B. G. Teubner, 1916, p. 33.

[65] Sarton, *Introduction*, vol. 1, p. 434; Thompson, *op. cit.* (fn. 54), p. 6.

[66] Thorndike, *op. cit.* (fn. 47), vol. 1, p. 581.

[67] *Subtleties*, iv, 18. See Thorndike, *op. cit.* (fn. 47), vol. 2, p. 143.

[68] Thorndike, *op. cit.* (fn. 47), vol. 1, p. 636.

[69] Clement Muller, "Essai sur la mineralogie arabe," Part 2, *Journal Asiatique*, 6th series, vol. 11 (1868), chap. 14 (l'aimant), pp. 170–178.

[70] Sarton, *Introduction*, vol. 1, p. 532.

Es war ein Magnetstein der 100 Dirhem (etwa = 300g) Eisen aufhob. Er blieb einige Zeit bei uns, dann näherten wir ihn einem andern Eisenstück, und er hob es nicht auf. Wir glaubten, dass sein Gewicht grösser als 100 Dirhem (etwa = 300g), sei, und wogen es, und siehe da, es wog nur 80 Dirhem (etwa = 240g). Es hatte also seine Kraft abgenommen, sein Gewicht war aber dasselbe wie zuvor geblieben.[71]

Geber also shows this influence in his discussion of the nature of the magnetic attraction:

Und das stärkste, was in dieser Welt existiert, sind die feinen geistigen Dinge, die man nicht mit den Sinnen wahrnimmt; sie werden nur mit dem Verstande wahrgenommen; wie der Stein das Eisen durch eine geistige Kraft anzieht, die man nicht fühlt und nicht sieht. Sie dringt durch das Dichte des Messings (oder anderes gelbes Metall), während das Messing zwischen ihr und dem Eisen sich befindet, so weit sie will.[72]

Geber then goes on to speak of poisons as such spirits. Wiedemann also attributes to Geber a statement found in Qazwini which speaks of a sympathy between iron and lodestone and an emmanation from the latter that is "smelled" by the former.[73] Here too is found drawn the common analogy between lodestone and iron and lover and beloved.

Al-Kindi (d. c. 850 or 873), translator of Aristotle and other Greek writers, in his *Theory of the magic art [= On Stellar rays]* makes the interesting dichotomy that the science of physics considers contact actions between objects; he then gives as examples of more occult interactions between remote objects the lodestone and the reflection of an image in a mirror.[74] This work of al-Kindi was known in Europe at least by the 14th Century, since it was condemned at Paris in that century.[75]

Qustā ibn Lūqā (Costa ben Luca) (fl. c. 864) also spoke of the occult nature of the lodestone, citing it as an example of the sort of thing one would not believe without seeing it,[76] and uses this, as had Augustine and many others, as an argument for not adopting too skeptical an attitude toward strange phenomena reported by others.

Pliny's myth of the magnetic mountain seems to have a renascence in a somewhat

[71] Eilhard Wiedemann, "Beiträge zur Geschichte der Chemie bei den Arabern, I," *Sitzungsberichten der Physikalisch-Medizinischen Sozietät zu Erlangen,* vol. 36 (1934), p. 325.

[72] *Ibid.,* p. 324.

[73] *Ibid.,* p. 326.

[74] Thorndike, *op. cit.* (fn. 47), vol. 1, p. 643 ff.

[75] *Ibid.*

[76] *Ibid.,* p. 652 ff.

different form in the writings of Ibn al-Faqih (fl. c. 903), a Persian geographer whose *Book of countries* is lost but of which a compendium exists.[77] Wiedemann reports magnetization of iron described by Ibn al-Faqih in the following terms:

> …wenn man an diesem Berge ein Messer, Eisen oder Schwert reibt, jenes Schwert und Messer Eisen trägt und dünne und dicke Nadeln anzieht mit grösser Kraft als der Magnetstein. Ferner ist es wunderbar, dass jener Stein selbst kein Eisen anzieht, wenn aber an ihm ein Messer oder Schwert gerieben wird, zieht es Eisen an: Schliesslich ist es noch wunderbar, dass, wenn er auch hundert Jahre bliebe, jene Kraft in ihm konstant wäre.[78]

Wiedemann adds that the "iron" was clearly steel, in view of the results obtained, and that the rocks of the mountain were clearly lodestones but not strong enough to display the attractive property directly. These arguments seem unconvincing. It would be of great historical importance if this is a valid case of magnetization of iron, for it would not only be the earliest known (excepting the noneffective case of the Samothracian rings, p. 15), but would be the only such case prior to the earliest descriptions of the compass needle. Yet the evidence is not sufficient, to my mind.

Medical writers in Islam also wrote of the lodestone, such as Hali Abbas (d. 994), one of the three greatest physicians of the Eastern Caliphate,[79] who recommended the lodestone be held in the hand for the cure of gout and spasms.[80]

A fairly elaborate discussion of the operation of the lodestone appears in the *Tauq al Hama ma (Neckband of the dove)* of Ibn Hazm (994?–1064?). In a chapter on the art of love in a passage translated by Wiedemann, Ibn Hazm speaks of a soul streaming toward another, when set free,

> …wie der Magnet das Eisen. Die Kraft des Magneten, die mit der des Eisens nahe verbunden ist, ist nicht so beschaffen, dass sie nach ihrer Naturgesetzmässigkeit oder ihrem reinen Wesen auf das Eisen zustreben muss, als ob sie von derselben Form und von demselben Elemente wäre, wie etwa die Naturkraft des Eisens wegen ihrer Stärke die ihr zukommende Gestalt zu erlangen strebt und zu ihm gezogen wird. Die Bewegung wird ja stets von dem Stärkeren hervorgerufen. Die Kraft des Eisens sucht, von sich aus, wenn sie von keinem Hindernis beschränkt ist, das, was ihr ähnlich ist, gibt sich

---

[77] Sarton, *Introduction*, vol. 1, p. 635.

[78] Wiedemann, *loc. cit.* (fn. 71), pp. 329–330.

[79] Sarton, *Introduction*, vol. 1, p. 677.

[80] *Liber totius medicinae necessaria cõtinens… quem Haly filius Abbas… edidit… et a Stephano ex arabica lingua reductus*, Lugd. 1523, bk. 1, chap. 45, para. 466. Thompson, *op. cit.* (fn. 54), p. 17.

ihm ganz hin und erhebt sich zu ihm infolge der Naturnotwendigkeit und durch die selbstgewählte Absicht. Haltst Du das Eisen mit der Hand zürück, so wird es nur dann vom Magneten angezogen, wenn dessen Kraft die des Zurückhaltenden übertrifft und letztere sich nicht als stärker erweist.

Sind die Eisenteile zahlreicher, so werden sie untereinander in Anspruch genommen und durch ihre "Gestalten" abgehalten, dass das wenige ihrer Kräfte, die zum grössten Teil erschöpft sind zu süchen. Ist der Magnetstein sehr gross und entsprechen dessen Kräfte den Gesamtkräften des Eisens, so tritt die ihm eigentümliche Natur wieder zutage.[81]

Again the influence of Greek thought is unmistakable. And indeed the important influence of the Muslim world in the history of magnetic theory is the amplification and transmission of Greek philosophical thought concerning the nature of the magnetic force – the mechanics of magnetism within the general framework of the Aristotelian cosmology.

In his study of the critique of Aristotle written by Hadsi Crescas (1340 – 1410), Harry A. Wolfson notes that "Hebrew literature became... the repository of the whole Aristotelian heritage of Greek philosophy"[82] in the two centuries between Maimonides (1135 – 1204) and Crescas, when "the centre of Jewish philosophical activity had shifted to non-Arabic speaking countries – to Christian Spain, to Southern France and to Italy..."[83]

Like their Parisian contemporaries, these Jewish philosophers of the 14th Century and earlier were investigating the inconsistencies in the Aristotelian cosmology, and the lodestone provided one such inconsistency. For although a motor may produce motion either as an efficient cause or as a final cause, in the former case it must itself move: yet the lodestone acts as an efficient cause without itself moving, an exception that evoked discussion and explanation, of which Wolfson has found four types in the Jewish literature:

> First, the magnet does not act as a motive agent in its attraction of iron. It is the iron itself which is moved toward the magnet by reason of a certain disposition it acquires when it comes within the vicinity of the magnet. This explanation is quoted by Averroes in the name of Alexander.
>
> Second, the motion of the iron toward the magnet is brought about by means of certain corpuscles which issue forth from the magnet and come in contact

[81] Wiedemann, "Beiträge, XLII," loc. cit. (fn. 71), vol. 47 (1915), pp. 96 – 97.
[82] Harry A. Wolfson, Crescas' critique of Aristotle, Cambridge, Harvard University Press, 1929, pp. viii-ix.
[83] Ibid.

with the iron and draw it toward the magnet. This explanation is attributed to the Stoics. It is also described by Lucretius. It is quoted by Averroes in the name of Alexander and is found in Maimonides.

Third, the magnet possesses a certain force which attracts the iron. Thales calls this force a soul. Plato and, according to Gershon ben Solomon, also Galen deny that this force is a soul but designate it simply by the term power. It is similarly called peculiar power by Joseph Zabara and peculiar property by Altabrizi.

Fourth, magnetic attraction is explained by the same principle as the natural motion of the elements. There is a certain affinity between the iron and the magnet analogous to the affinity which exists between the elements and their respective proper places. The magnet therefore does not act as the efficient cause of the motion of the iron but rather as its final cause. This explanation is advanced by Averroes and is also discussed by Gershon ben Solomon and his son Gersonides.[84]

Summary

Our knowledge of the period under discussion is scanty, whether we are discussing Islam or Western Christendom. Nevertheless the knowledge that we do have points unequivocally to two main ideas: knowledge of the existence of lodestones and of their property of attraction was widespread and never lost; there is not the slightest indication in any of this material of any new developments in magnetical theory or of new properties to be associated with the lodestone. With the single exception of the alleged magnetizing mountain of al-Faqih, there is no indication beyond the Samothracian rings of the magnetization of iron by any means, nor is there any indication that the property of attraction was thought to be permanently transferred to or acquired by the Samothracian rings.

In short, all that we know of the history of magnetism through the first eleven centuries of our era indicates that it was a sterile field of study that was slowly dying out in Europe among a welter of occultism, magic, and alchemy, and that Arabic and Jewish writers had little to offer beyond the ancient works which they held, as it were, in trusteeship.

---

[84] *Ibid.*, p. 91. See also the notes in this work, pp. 563–566, for a more detailed discussion of the literary sources of these ideas.

III. The Renaissance of Magnetic Knowledge: Orientation, Artificial Magnets, Polarity and the Compass

In the 11th and 12th Centuries a completely new magnetic phenomenon appears, like Athena: the orientation of the magnet into a definite and reproducible position, when set free to turn. Like magnetic attraction, orientation is not simply a phenomenon, but is a sophisticated generalization of experiences. Furthermore, we know no more of its origins than of the origins of the phenomenon of attraction, and it seems unlikely that further exploration of medieval literature will appreciably increase our knowledge in this respect. In the first place, the generalization itself must come into existence, be invented, before there is anything to record. Second, there is no indication whatsoever that this new property of the lodestone has a continuous history with the history of the theory of magnetic attraction: nothing in the prior history of magnetism indicates that the theoretical work in magnetism would have or could have led to this new property of the lodestone.

Finally, since the orienting property may be used in the marine compass, and since it is in this connection that we first learn of the property, the most reasonable conjecture is that the presence of and familiarity with the lodestone somehow led to the instrument, independently of philosophical studies. Such an instrument is of great value to mariners, and was undoubtedly considered a valuable trade secret by its early users.[85] These users were rarely writers, and it is accordingly difficult to judge the origins even of the compass from written information about it.

The Earliest Mentions of Orientation of a Magnet

Whatever the reasons, the earliest generally accepted mention of the orientation of a magnet is by the Chinese Shen Kua (1030–1093), in his *Essays from the torrent of dreams*, written late in his life.[86]

> A geomancer rubs the point of a needle with the lodestone to make it point to the south, but it will always deviate a little to the east, and not show the south; that to use the needle, it may be put on water, but it would not be steady; and also it may be put on the nail of a finger or on the lip of a bowl, but it is too apt to drop, because its motion is very brisk; that the best method

[85] Sarton, *Introduction*, vol. 2(1), p. 24.
[86] Sarton, *Introduction*, vol. 1, pp. 755–756; Mitchell, *loc. cit.* (fn. 1), I; pp. 110–122; Benjamin, *op. cit.* (fn. 1), pp. 75; Li-Shu-Hua, *loc. cit.* (fn. 27), pp. 182–183.

is to hang it by a thread, and to prepare the contrivance, one has to single
out a fine thread from a new skein of floss silk and fix it with a piece of
beeswax on the middle of the needle, the latter to be hung up where there
is no wind; that the needle would then always point to the south; that, on
rubbing a needle with a lodestone, it may happen by chance to point to the
north, and he (the author) owned needles of both sorts, and that no one
could as yet find out the principle of it.[87]

This quotation contains a rather staggering number of new concepts. The technique of
manufacturing an artificial magnet is described;[88] the artificial magnet is needle-shaped,
so that its orientation is easily determined; three entirely different methods of suspension
are described and despite five centuries of subsequent instrumentation the last mode
of suspension described remains one of the best known methods of support of such
devices. Again both language and philosophy interpose major difficulties in attempting
any detailed evaluation of Shen Kua's statement.

At the beginning of the 12th Century, Chu Yu wrote

In clear weather the Captain ascertains the ship's position, at night by looking
at the stars, in the daytime by looking at the sun; in dark weather he looks at
the south-pointing needle.[89]

The data and authenticity of this statement are generally accepted,[90] and it is the earliest
known account of the use of a compass. There is considerable difference of opinion,
however, concerning the nationality of the ship involved. This controversy, built around
the question of credit for the invention of the compass, is of no interest here. The
earliest known mention of the directive property is Chinese, but no one has proposed

[87] This particular translation of the passage is taken from Mitchell, *op. cit.* (fn. 1), II, pp. 242–243.
The translations given by Benjamin, *op cit.* (fn. 1), and Li-Shu-Hua, *loc. cit.* (fn. 27), differ markedly,
an indication of the present difficulty of making any detailed study of the history of magnetism in the
Orient. However, the variations in translation are unimportant in so far as the aim of this present
chapter is concerned.

[88] This is the earliest such description known, although we know that the Samothracian rings must
have been artificially magnetized, at least for the duration of a demonstration. Pliny (p. 25) seems to
imply that the rings retained the property of attraction after separation from the lodestone. Indeed, it is
tempting to reflect that the harder irons make both better tools and maintain magnetization better, but
this is certainly stretching Pliny's remarks far too much.

[89] In his Ping-chou-ko-than. According to Li-Shu-Hua, *loc. cit.* (fn. 27), this work is lost, but its texts
are largely retained in a 15th Century work. The translation here is taken from Friedrich Hirth, *The
ancient history of China,* New York, Columbia Univ. Press, 1908, p. 133, and agrees with Li-Shu Hua's
translation into French.

[90] Sarton, *Introduction,* vol. 1, p. 764; Hirth, *op. cit.* (fn. 89), p. 133; Mitchell, *loc. cit.* (fn. 1) 1, p. 111;
Li-Shu-Hua, *loc. cit.* (fn. 27), p. 188; E. Wiedemann wrote "Nach Dozy kannten die Araber den

an even reasonably satisfactorily supported theory of transmission of the knowledge to Europe.

The earliest known European mention of the orienting property appears in the writings of the Englishman Alexander Neckam (1157–1217). In his *De utensilibus,* Neckam wrote:

> Habeat etiam acum jaculo suppositam, rotabitur enim et circumvolvetur acus donec cuspis acus respiciat orientem, sicque comprehendunt quo tendere debeant naute cum cinossura latet in aeris turbacione, quamvis ad occasum nunquam tendat propter circuli brevitatem.[91]

In his other work, *De naturis rerum,* Neckam wrote:

> Nautae etiam mare legentes, cum beneficium claritatis solis in tempore nubilo non sentiunt, aut etiam cum caligine nocturnarum tenebrarum mundus obvolvitur, et ignorant in quem mundi cardinem prora tendat, acum super magnetem ponunt, quae circulariter circumvolvitur usque dum, ejus motu cessante, cuspis ipsius septentrionalem plagam respiciat.[92]

As with the Chinese, these earliest known European reports of the compass describe artificial magnetization of a needle. Suspension on a pivot is also described, and we are told that the point of the needle indicates "septentrionalem plagam."

Neckam's explanation of magnetic attraction is in terms of similitudes,[93] and he adds a new substance to the list of attractors: jet, noting "magnes trahit ferrum, lapis gagates paleam."[93]

An inevitable, although necessary, step in the development of magnetic knowledge is

Kompass schon im Jahre 854...," in *Ueber die Naturwissenschaften bei den Arabern,* Hamburg, 1890 (*Sammlung gemeinverständlicher wissenschaftlicher Vorträge,* N. F., S. 5, Heft 97), p. 20. Wiedemann also quotes an undated example of the use of the compass in the Indian Ocean. See also K. G. Jakob, *Östliche kulturelemente bei den Arabern,* Berlin, 1902, p. 2.

[91] Alexander Neckam, *De utensilibus.* In Thomas Wright's *A volume of vocabularies,* privately printed, 1857, p. 114. In the preface to his edition of Neckam's other work (*op. cit.,* fn. 59), pp. xxxviii-xxxix, Wright gives "ingenious conjectural emendations," to this passage, suggested by "Monsieur D'Avezac, of Paris." These emendations are minor except for the obvious one of replacing "orientem" by "septentrionem." The glaring–from the modern view–error in Neckam might be explained away by "corruptness of text" (although Wright indicates that this is very unlikely) or even perhaps by ingenious physical reasoning. Yet the idea that magnets are associated with all of the directions is an important–and not well explored–fact of late medieval writings, and we shall encounter it again in both Peter Peregrinus and Roger Bacon and, in a modified form, in Gilbert.

[92] *De naturis rerum,* chap. 98. See *ed. cit.* (fn. 59), p. 183.

[93] *Ibid.,* p. 182.

the association of the two magnetic motions, translation of the iron to the lodestone and orientation of the magnet. This step has been recorded by the early 13th Century, when we find James of Vitry writing of the lodestone drawing iron and then noting that an iron needle, after it has touched the lodestone always turns to the pole star.[94] From this time on a satisfactory theory of magnetism may be expected to have to account for the attraction of iron to the lodestone and orientation of the magnetic needle.

Thirteenth Century References to the Compass: the Source of Its Virtue

After Neckam's accounts, a flood of references to the compass appear in European literature.[95] Although he had spoken of the needle as indicating the "septentrionalem plagam," there is an immediate and obvious reason for associating the indicated direction with the pole star, as we have already seen in the remark of James of Vitry. In the early 13th Century Guyot de Provins,[96] an anonymous contemporary of Guyot's,[97] and Brunetto Latini[98] all describe, in markedly similar terms, the manner in which the magnetic needle points to the pole star. Michael Scot (d. c. 1235), the Scotch Averroist, astrologer and translator at the court of Frederick II,[99] specifically associated the lodestone-which-attracts iron with the lodestone-which-makes-a-compass:

> Item est lapis qui sua virtute trahit ferrum ad se ut calamita et ostendit locum tramontaine septentrionalis. Et est alius lapis generis calamite qui depellit ferrum a se et demonstrat partem tramontane austri.[100]

To explain the orienting as a pointing to the pole star does not, however, make any causal connection between the orienting and magnetic attraction. This connection was made by invoking the magnetic mountains (p. 24). Ptolemy had written:

---

[94] James of Vitry, *Historiae Hierosolimitane*, 91. *Iacobi de Vitriaco primum acconensis, deinde Tvsevlani espicopi, et. S. Eccl. R. cardinalis, se disque Apostolicae in Terra sancta, in Imperio, in Francia olim Legati, libri duo, quorum prior Orientalis, siue Hierosolumitanae: alter Occidentalis historiae nomine inscribitur*, Douai, Balthazaris Belleri, 1597, p. 194: "Acus ferrea postquam adamantem contigerit ad stellam septemtrionalem que, velut axis firmamenti, alijs vergentibus, non mouetur, semper conuertitur. vnde valde necessarius est nauigantibus in mari."

[95] Benjamin, *op cit.* (fn. 1), p. 146, wrote that after Neckam, "descriptions of it in the literature of other nations followed so rapidly as to leave their true chronological sequence in doubt, and under conditions which not only preclude the idea that the writers got their information from Neckam, but also that of the transmission of such knowledge *seriatim* from people to people. This suggests the radiation of the intelligence to the world from some central focal point." Benjamin offered Wisby as a possible focal point, but his evidence seems thin.

[96] *La bible,* lines 632–654. *Les Oeuvres de Guiot de Provins,* ed. John Orr, Manchester, University Press, 1915, pp. 29–30.

[97] Quoted by Francisque Michel, *Lais inédits, des XIIe et XIIIe siècles, publiés pour la première fois,*

36

There are said to be other islands here adjoining [India beyond the Ganges], ten in number, called Maniolae, from which they say that boats, in which there are nails, are kept away, lest at any time the magnetic stone which is found near these islands should draw them to destruction.[101]

Magnetic islands or rocks were well known in the Orient, Near East, and, by the 12th Century, in Northern Europe.[102] Thus, the compass needle is drawn to and points toward a mountain of lodestone in the north, just as it is drawn to a local lodestone. Guido Guinicelli, one of the earliest of the Italian poets to embody philosophical discussions in his writings,[103] pictured hills of lodestone beneath the pole star that imparted a virtue to the ambient air that attracted the iron, while the same virtue was transmitted afar to turn the compass needle toward the cynosura.[104]

Let us now briefly summarize the state of general magnetic theory. Iron is attracted to the lodestone, evidence of a sympathy between them. The magnetic needle turns to the north, evidence of a sympathy between it and the pole or pole star. We shall see that in the thirteenth century the magnetic needle was definitely known to turn to lodestone as well, and that a lodestone free to move also orientated. Thus the general theory establishes a sympathy between the lodestone, the north, and iron touched by lodestone. The first and last of this trio are tangible: the second is given materiality by specifying "the north" to be "the pole star" or, more plausibly if less supportable, the magnetic mountains of which lodestones were formerly a part. Attraction and orientation have not only been united in this general theory, by the reduction of orientation to attraction, but they have been brought into the general conceptual scheme of sympathies and antipathies.

d'après les manuscrits de France et d'Angleterre. Paris, Joseph Techner; London, W. Pichering, 1836, p. iii.

[98] Brunetto Latini, *Li livres dou tresor*, bk. 1, chap. 119, part 5. See édition critique, by Francis J. Carmody, Berkeley and Los Angeles, University of California Press, 1948, p. 107.

[99] Sarton, *Introduction*, vol. 2(2), p. 579.

[100] Quoted by Charles H. Haskins, *Studies in the history of mediaeval science*, Cambridge, Harvard University Press, 1924, pp. 294–295n.

[101] Ptolemy, *Geographia*, vii, 2. *Geography of Claudius Ptolemy... based upon Greek and Latin manuscripts and important late fifteenth and early sixteenth century printed editions, including reproductions of the maps from the Ebner manuscript, ca. 1460*, tr. and ed., E. L. Stevenson, New York, The New York Public Library, 1932, p. 157.

[102] Park Benjamin, *op. cit.* (fn. 1), pp. 98–99.

[103] H. W. Longfellow, *The poets and poetry of Europe*, Boston, James R. Osgood and Co., 1871, p. 511. „...to whom by acclamation is given the honor of being the first among the Italian poets who embodied in verse the subtilties of philosophy,..."

[104] P. L. Ginguene, Histoire littéraire d'Italie, I, Paris, Michaud Frères, 1811, p. 413, n. l. "In quelle parti sotto tramontana sono li monti della calamita, che dan virtute all' aere Di trarre il ferro;..."

However, this theory is not satisfactory, because orientation cannot successfully be reduced to attraction: the floating magnetic needle does not translate toward the north, it orientates into a particular angular position relative to the meridian. Yet the identical needle will translate toward a lodestone.

Another element of the dichotomy between attraction and orientation is the repulsing lodestone, Pliny's theamedes (p. 25): for where is the repulsion in orientation?

Both of these difficulties are resolved in the view recorded by Roger Bacon (c. 1214–1294) in 1266 or 1267:

> Et hoc est miraculum naturae in parte notum; scilicet, quod ferrum sequitur partem magnetis quae tetigit ipsum, et alteram partem fugit ejusdem magnetis. Et convertit se post motum ad partem coeli conformem parti magnetis, quae ferrum tetigit. Nam pro certo quatuor partes mundi distinguuntur in magnete, scilicet orient, occidens, septentrio, et meridies; et possunt per experientiam cognosci, secundum quod bene eprimitur ad quam partem coeli quaelibet pars tendit. Et tunc si a parte septentrionali magnetis tangatur ferrum sequetur illam partem qualitercumque meatur; scilicet sursum aut retrorsum, dextrosum, sinistrorum; et secundum omnem differentiam positionis. Et in tantum rapitur, quod si ferrum ponatur in vase pleno aquae, et manus ponatur sub vase, tacta pars demergit se in aqua in directum magnetis. Et si deferatur undique magnes extra nos, ferrum super partem tactam erectam currit in directum cujuslibet loci, ad quem defertur magnes. Et si ima pars magnetis objiciatur parti ferri tactae fugaret eam sicut inimicam; sicut agnus lupum. Et ablato magnete pars tacta dirigit se ad locum coeli similem parti magnetis.[105]

From this time on the concept of the repelling lodestone is on the wane, retreating into the mythology of magnetism along with the shepherd Magnes (p. 25), but still lingering on for centuries.

Bacon's remarks on the parts of the lodestone accentuate the validity of the reading of the Neckam manuscripts (see fn. 91) and the lack of justification for the "correcting" of those manuscripts. Bacon provides an explanation of orientation in terms of sympathy and hence consistent with the contemporary explanation of attraction. He specifically denies the importance of the pole star to the compass, on these grounds.

[105] J. S. Brewer, *Fr. Rogeri Bacon opera quaedam hactenus inedita*, I. London, Longman, Green, Longman, and Roberts, 1859, p. 383–384. Brewer assigned the name *Opus minus* (see his preface, pp. xxx-xxxviii) to the work from which this extract is taken. It was reproduced from the only known ms., which is incomplete and in extremely poor condition, having been written out by a copyist who was both ignorant and careless, and Brewer has made many corrections. Some other fragmentary ms. copies are now known: see pp. 389–390 of bibliography in A. G. Little's *Roger Bacon essays*, Oxford, Clarendon Press, 1914.

Vulgus philosophantium nescit causam experientiae vulgatae in hac parte, et credit quod stella *Nautica* facit ad hoc. Sed stella non facit ad hoc sed pars coeli. Et ita bene operantur tres aliae mundi partes; scilicet meridies, oriens, et occidens, sicut septentrio. Similiter non considerant quod quatuor imae partes mundi distinguantur in magnete. Sed tot attribuunt uni parti, quae cum stella convenit *Nautica* in naturali proprietate. Et aliae sunt hujusmodi experientiae et meliores non de ferro solum et magnete, sed de auro et omnibus metallis respectu diversarum specierum magnetis, sicut docetur in libro De Proprietatibus.[106]

Peter Peregrinus de Mahrincuria (fl. c. 1269) had a very intimate association with Bacon, who wrote:

...ad opera eorum, qquod est facile bonis mathematicis. Non sunt enim nisi duo perfecti, scilicet magister Jo. London. et magister Petrus de Maharn-curia [Mahariscuria] Picardus.[107]

Peter may have been Bacon's teacher:[108] it is certain that they communicated concerning magnetism. Although little is known of Peregrinus, his contemporaries seem to have had the highest regard for him.[108]

Peregrinus' Letter

A maturer and more highly developed form of the approach to the source of the magnetic virtue, indicated by Bacon, appears in the *Epistola de magnete*, written by Peter Peregrinus in 1269.[109] Peregrinus dismissed the pole star as an important element in the orientation because the lodestone pointed along the meridian, although the pole star is only on the meridian at two instants in each day.[110] He denied magnetic

[106] Bacon, *Opus minus.* See Brewer, *op. cit.* (fn. 105), p. 384.
[107] Bacon, *Opus tertium,* chap. 11. Brewer, *op cit.* (fn. 105), pp. 34–35.
[108] Sarton, *Introduction,* vol. 2(2), p. 1030.
[109] See S. P. Thompson, "Peter Peregrinus de Maricourt and his epistola de magnete," *Proceedings of the British Academy* (1905–06), pp. 377–408, for a detailed bibliography of mss. and printed versions. A critical version was prepared and published by Bertelli (1868) and republished, with corrections by Bertelli, by Gustav Hellmann, *Rara magnetica,* Berlin, 1898, No. 10 of Hellmann's *Neudrucke von Schriften und Karten über Meterologie und Erdmagnetismus.* Thompson published a translation in 1902, but only 240 copies were printed.
[110] This is by no means obvious. S. E. Morison, *Admiral of the ocean sea,* Boston, Little Brown and Co., 1942, 2 vol., vol. 1, p. 271, wrote that Columbus learned for himself of the diurnal revolution of Polaris, "a fact which many late medieval and renaissance astronomers had denied. Practical seamen had assumed for centuries that the North Star marked true north."

mountains as the source of lodestones (and hence of their virtue) on three grounds: lodestones are found everywhere; the polar regions are uninhabitable; the stone points south as well as north.

Peregrinus' letter is divided into two parts. Part I is a summary of technical information concerning magnetism, which we may in turn summarize thus:

> The lodestone has two exceptional points, just as the celestial sphere has two poles;
> The lodestone should be turned into a spherical shape;
> The poles of the lodestone may be found by: laying bits of iron wire on the stone, and drawing lines along the length of the wire, for the lines will converge to the poles; they may also be identified as the points of greatest force exerted on iron; they are also the points at which a bit of iron wire stands perpendicular to the surface of the stone;
> Of the two poles, the north pole is the one that points to the northern point of the heavens when the stone is floated on a piece of wood in water;
> The north pole of one lodestone attracts the south pole of a second, and the south pole of the first attracts the north pole of the first;
> Because of the attraction of unlike poles, if one pole is presented to the like pole of another magnet floating on a piece of wood, the floating lodestone will turn about;
> An oblong piece of iron that has been touched with the lodestone will turn toward the pole (when floated)—not the pole star;
> The end of the iron touched with the south pole of a lodestone turns to the north celestial pole, and the end touched by the north pole turns to the south celestial pole;
> Iron touched by lodestone is attracted by the lodestone, the northern part of the iron being attracted by the southern part of the stone and conversely;
> If iron touched by one pole of the lodestone is then touched by the other pole, the virtue in the iron is easily altered;
> If a lodestone is divided between the poles, new poles appear at the division, and the poles are unlike the original pole in that half;
> A divided lodestone tends to reunite, which is the reason unlike poles attract;
> A spherical lodestone carefully balanced on polar pivots with its axis parallel to the axis of the celestial sphere will undergo diurnal rotation.

It is quite certain that Peter did not invent these ideas, despite the fact that we know of no earlier work on magnetism containing them.[111] This first part of the letter has a

---

[111] H. D. Harradon, "Some early contributions to the history of geomagnetism: I," *Terr. Mag.* vol. 48 (1943), p. 5, wrote that "...many of these facts were already known... is indicated by the similarity of ideas on the magnet which are found among scientists who lived before or contemporaneously with de Marincourt, such as Vincent de Beauvais, Albertus Magnus, Roger Bacon, and Jean de S. Amand." We

curiously modern ring and could be taken as the summation of qualitative observation of basic magnetic phenomena, in a logical development of modern elementary magneto-statics, particularly since it gives the impression of defining the modern term *magnetic pole*. This impression is misleading: it would be better to emphasize that he is introducing the concept of *polarity* into magnetism, and avoid the modern term *pole*. Peter's explanation of orientation was this:

> Quidam autem debiles inquisitores opinati sunt quod virtus qua agit magnes in ferrum, fit in locis mineralibus, in quibus magnes invenitur, unde dicunt quod, licet ferrum ad polos mundi moveatur, hoc tamen non est, nisi quia minera lapidis in illis partibus situatur. Isti autem ignorant, quod, in diversis mundi partibus, lapis dicus invenitur, ex quo sequitur quod ad diversa mundi loca moveretur, quod falsum est. Et rursus ignorant quod locus sub polis sit inhabitabilis, eo quod medietas anni sit ibi dies, et medietas nox; quare ab illis locis ad nos posse portari magnetem, fatuum est estimare. Preterea cum ferrum, vel lapis, vertatur tam ad partem meridionalem quam ad partem septemtrionalem, ut patet per iam dicta, existimare cogimur, non solum a parte septemtrionali, verum etiam a meridonali virtutem influi in polos lapidis, magis quam a locis minere. Cuius signum evidens est, quod, ubicumque homo fuerit, videt, ad oculum, huius lapidis motum, secundum situm sui orbis meridiani. Omnes autem orbes meridiani in polis mundi concurrent; quare, a polis mundi, poli magnetis virtutem recipiunt. Et ex hoc apparet manifest quod non ad stellam nauticam movetur, cum ibi non concurrent orbes merid-iani, sed in polis; stella enim nautica, extra orbem meridianum cuiuslibet regionis semper invenitur, nisi bis, in completa firmamenti revolutione. Ex hiis ergo manifestum est quod a partibus celi, partes magnetis virtutem recipiunt.[112]

In Part II of his letter three instruments are described. The first is a lodestone enclosed in a light wooden container, for floating, with a subdivided circle on the container and north indicated thereon. An alidade is provided on the vessel in which the stone is floated, and the procedure for taking of azimuths of celestial objects with it is described. The second instrument contains a vertical axial wire, free to turn, enclosed in a container with a transparent top. A horizontal iron wire is mounted through a horizontal hole in

have already seen (pp. 38–39) that Bacon was familiar with many of the views recorded by Peregrinus. Also, he mentions the last item in our summary in at least two places. In the *Opus majus:* See John Henry Bridges, *The 'Opus majus' of Roger Bacon*, vol. 2, Oxford, Clarendon Press, 1897, pp. 202–203; In the *Epistola Frateris Rogerii Baconis de secretis operibus artis, et Naturae, et de nullitate magiae* chap. 6: See Brewer, *op cit.* (fn. 105), Appendix I, p. 537.
[112] *Epistola Petri Peregrini de Maricourt ad Sygerum de Foucaucourt militem de magnete*, bk. 1, chap. 10. See G. Hellmann, *op. cit.* (fn. 109).

the axle, the transparent cover is divided into 360 parts, and an alidade is provided. The iron wire is magnetized by bringing a lodestone near to the instrument.

The third instrument is a magnetic perpetual motion machine which we have reason to believe he never constructed.

This letter seems to have had considerable circulation[113] and may therefore be considered both representative of the state of knowledge in the 13th Century and influential upon thought concerning magnetism. It is known to have influenced several 16th Century investigators,[114] was the subject of a famous plagarism,[115] and in particular strongly influenced Gilbert.

A contemporary of Bacon and Peregrinus, John of St. Amand (fl. 1261–1298) expresses similar views in a very interesting passage in his medical commentary on the *Antidotarium Nicolai*.[116] The passage rejects repulsion of like poles, accounting for it as an attempt of unlike poles to join – a not at all unreasonable view. The attraction of unlikes is in turn explained as a complementing action. In particular, the theme that we see in Bacon and Peregrinus is repeated

> Unde dico quod in adamante est vestigium orbis, unde est in eo aliqua pars habens in se proprietatem occidentis, alia orientis, alia meridiei, alia septentrionis.[117]

That the thirteenth century should have explained magnetic phenomena in terms of sympathies is to be expected from the state of knowledge in the period. Yet while remaining within the sympathy-antipathy framework, magnetic theory has undergone significant changes. The magnetic mountains and the theamedes are unnecessary to those who will accept the spherical symmetry of this new sympathy. We will see Gilbert strongly denying any attraction of the compass to the pole and condemning his predecessors for their ignorance. Yet it is the thirteenth-century philosophers and not Gilbert who originate the spherically symmetric attractionless influence upon the magnet. Gilbert's contribution to magnetic theory is not the spherical symmetric influence but the source of that influence.

[113] S. P. Thompson, *op. cit.* (fn. 109), Appendix A, pp. 400–404, lists 28 mss. of the letter. One or two are 13th Century, and at least 14 are 13th or 14th Century.

[114] Harradon, *loc. cit.* (fn. 111).

[115] By John Taisner, Cologne, 1562. Sarton, *Introduction*, vol. 2(2), p. 1031; Thompson, *op. cit.* (fn. 109), pp. 404–405.

[116] The passage on the magnet is quoted, with English translation, by Lynn Thorndike, "John of St. Amand on the Magnet," *Isis*, vol. 36 (1946), pp. 156–157. Interesting as the passage is, it is of course a thirteenth-century passage; it is so typically thirteenth-century and congruent to the outlooks of Bacon and Peregrinus that it is difficult to comprehend what Thorndike meant when he commented "It also seems to approach the conception of positive and negative poles and of an electric current."

IV. The Deviation of the Magnetic Needle from the Meridian[118]

Unless there is an error in the Neckam manuscripts, which his editor believes is unlikely in view of the agreement between several different manuscripts,[119] Neckam wrote in one work (p. 35) that the compass pointed to the East, and in another wrote that it pointed to the North. Bacon (p. 38) clearly states that the compass will point in a direction that depends only upon the part of the lodestone that touches it. Peter Peregrinus wrote of using an oblong piece of iron (p. 40) as a compass, after it had been touched by the lodestone. Now if the poles of such a compass are located in the centers of their ends, the line connecting them, i.e., the magnetic axis, will coincide with the geometrical axis of the iron. But if the poles are on the sides of the piece of iron, the two axes may differ by any angle whatsoever.[120] These variations were slowly brought under control, in the practical art of navigation, and we find that, according to Fernando Columbus, compass makers covered the lodestone with cloth so that only the north end could be seen before magnetizing compass needles.[121]

By the beginning of the 15th century, a new generalization had been developed concerning a third magnetic motion. Difficulties in navigation by the compass, on land and at sea, were in part explained by this phenomenon: the (properly magnetized) magnetic needle does not point to the north but in some other definite direction, close to north. This generalization, like all generalizations in science, is only valid for an idealized, imaginary, nonexistent set of conditions. Today, knowing the conditions, we can approximately achieve them and then experimentally show that the generalization is approximately valid. We have already indicated one of the conditions: the magnetic axis and the geometrical axis must make a definite angle – preferably zero – for all time and for all needles. Yet in the absence of a better developed theory of magnetism, only by cut and try could this condition be met. That "Magellan is reputed to have had at least 35"

Since electric current is a concept invented centuries later and since it was invented to explain the whole complex of 18th Century electrical experiments, I find Thorndike's statement, at the very least, baffling.

[117] *Ibid.* "Adamas" is used throughout. Thorndike's translation of "vestigium orbis" as "a trace of the world" together with his interpretation that this "adumbrates Gilbert's contention that the earth is a magnet" seems hardly justified. That Gilbert's idea of the terrestrial sphere as having magnetic virtue was influenced by this thirteenth-century association of such virtue with the celestial sphere is not to be doubted. But "orbis" does not mean "terrae," and John does not write "orbis terrarum."

[118] In modern scientific terminology this phenomenon is named "the declination"; in modern nautical terminology, "the variation."

[119] Wright, *Volume of Vocabularies* (fn. 91), p. xvii.

[120] Thus if the length-to-breadth ratio of the compass is r, the angular separation of the axes due merely to locating the poles at the edges of the end faces may be as high as $1/r$ radians.

[121] According to Mitchell, *op. cit.* (fn. 1), II, p. 254, who states that this work is known only through an Italian translation published in 1571 by Alphonse Ulloa.

spare magnetized needles with him[122] is evidence that magnetization at sea was deemed untrustworthy at that time.

Again, today we know that one of the important conditions for regularity in a compass's behavior is that the region near to the compass be free of iron. This was known at least as early as 1538 when Joao de Castro found that conflicts in compass readings were due to the iron guns of the ship.[123] Yet in the 18th Century Captain Bligh, R. N., kept his pistols in his ships' binnacles, and Captain Cook, F. R. S.(!), kept his iron keys in the same place.[124] Any sort of regularity in the compass would be difficult to find under these circumstances.

There are three pieces of evidence that some writers have believed to be indicative of knowledge of the deviation prior to the fifteenth century.

The first of these is the passage attributed to Shen Kua (pp. 33–34) in the 11th Century. In addition to the lack of evidence that this statement had any effect upon later writers, my earlier remarks concerning the fragmentary state of our knowledge of Oriental science (p. 21) are applicable here.

Second, there is a line in the late 14th Century *Contra coniunctionistes* of Henry of Hesse (Langenstein) (d. 1397), "Item in partibus Norweie magnes in uno situ trahit ferrum et in alio propinquo (?) non." Thorndike[125] suggested that Henry "was acquainted with the variation of the magnetic needle near the north pole." The line does not seem to justify this statement.

Third, Geoffrey Chaucer wrote of the evening star, "As wisly as I saw the in the north-north-west."[126] Since the plane of Venus' orbit is inclined less than 4° to the plane of the ecliptic, Venus can never be far from the setting sun, and when furtherest north – at the time when the sun is about 45° east of the vernal equinox, it is still only slightly north of north-west and certainly not north-northwest. This peculiarity has attracted considerable attention: of interest here is the interpretation that this line indicates that Chaucer was giving a magnetic bearing. If one assumes that this is the case and also that the compass pointed some 20-odd degrees west of North at this time in London – an assumption without independent basis – then Chaucer's statement can be accounted for,

---

[122] H. L. Hitchins and W. E. May, *From lodestone to gyro-compass*, New York, Philosophical Library, 1953, p. 25.

[123] *Ibid.*, p. 52.

[124] *Ibid.*, p. 52.

[125] Thorndike, *op. cit.* (fn. 47), vol. 3, pp. 499–501.

[126] Line 117 of *The parliament of foules. The complete works of Geoffrey, Chaucer,* edited from numerous manuscripts by Walter W. Skeat, London, Oxford University Press, Humphrey Milford, 1929, p. 102.

after a fashion. But even with these not very reasonable assumptions there is still no reason to believe that Chaucer knew of the phenomenon of the deviation from the meridian.[127]

The first evidence that we have of deviation from the meridian is associated with land instruments. Portable sundials, probably constructed at Nuremberg, from the middle of the fifteenth century on indicate the deviation from the meridian by means of a mark on the compass dial.[128] Instructions printed on late 15th Century maps clearly indicate knowledge of the deviation, by directions printed on the maps concerning their use with a compass.[129] For example, more than one rose may be drawn on a single map, with legends to indicate which sort of a compass to use with each rose: a "bare needle," an "Italian compass," etc. And, Columbus' crew was familiar with the deviation.[130]

V. The Space Variation of the Deviation of the Magnetic Needle from the Meridian

Another source of information, similar to the portable pocket sundials mentioned above, concerning knowledge of the variation is the compass that is internally corrected for the variation. Thus the magnetic needle may be mounted upon the graduated compass card with its axis at an angle to the North-South line on the card, introducing a fixed angular error into the compass reading. This error is of course intended to off-set the error due to the deviation of the meridian, and is equal to it but in the opposite direction from the meridian. But by the end of the 15th Century it was becoming known that compasses constructed in different places did not agree. Examples of the differences were given a century later by Robert Norman, who warned that the observed variation depended upon whether a compass or a "bare needle" were used, and if the former, its origin was important.

> Of these common Sayling Compasses, I finde heere (in *Europa*) five sundry
> sortes or sets. The first is of *Levant,* made in Scicile, Genoüa, and Venice:

---

[127] A much more reasonable explanation would seem to be that given by John M. Manly, "Note on Astronomical Allusion," in "What Is the Parlement of Foules?" in *Festschrift für Lorenz Morsbach,* Halle a. S., Verlag von Max Niemeyer, 1913, namely that the phrase has the meaning of "in an unpropitious position," just as it does when used by Hamlet, Act ii, Scene 2, line 396: "I am but mad north-north-west."

[128] August Wolkenhauer, *Mitteilung Geographische Gesellschaft,* München, vol. 1, (1900–1906), pp. 161–260; G. Hellmann, "Die Anfänge der magnetischen Beobachtungen," *Zeitschrift der Gesellschaft für Erdkunde zu Berlin,* vol. 32 (1897), pp. 112–136.

[129] Wolkenhauer, *op. cit., loc. cit.* (fn. 128).

[130] Morison, *op. cit.* (fn. 110), vol. 1, p. 270.

And these are all (for the most parte) made Meridionally, with the Wyers directlye sette under the South, and North of the Compasse: And therefore, duely shewing the poynt *Respective,* in all places, as the bare Needle. And by this Compasse are the [Plats] charts made, for the most part of all the *Levants* Seas.

Secondly, there are made in *Danske,* in the Sound of *Denmarke,* and in *Flanders,* that have the Wyers set at 3 quarters of a point to the Eastwards of the North of the compasse, and also some at a whole point: and by these Compasses they make both the Plats and Rutters for the Sound. Thirdly,...[131]

Collectively this information affords a new phenomenon (already well known at the time the above passage was written), namely the variation of the deviation from the meridian with change of position on the earth's surface. Such comparisons do not seem to have been made, however, and one can imagine the explanations given by Mediterranean sailors of the failure of Flemish compasses to indicate North.

This new phenomenon came into being when Europeans moved westward from the region of eastward deviation of the compass into the region of westward deviations. And strangely enough, attention was called to the possibility of a shift in the direction indicated by the compass before the shift was sufficient to be observed, at least at sea. For west of the Azores Columbus' men were thrown into a near panic by apparent failure of the compasses to point to Polaris at sundown, September 13, 1492. We know today that the magnetic North and true North approximately coincided at the place where this event occurred, whereas in the Iberian pennisula magnetic North lay a little to the eastwards of geographic North. To this was added the coincidence that as Polaris first became visible that evening it lay nearly $3\frac{1}{2}°$ east of North, an event that would have been accentuated by any correcting, conscious or unconscious, mental or mechanical, for the former deviation to the eastward. Columbus explained the apparent westward deviation, to himself as well as to the crew, in terms of the motion of Polaris, and verified this hypothesis by an observation at dawn.[132] But 17 days later, he found the needles varying a full point to the westward.

> Eventually Columbus realized that he had observed a westerly variation of the compass and no doubt he was the first to report it.[133]

[131] Robert Norman, *The newe attractiue, containyng a short discourse of the magnes or lodestone, and amongst other his vertues, of a newe discouered secret and subtill propertie, concernyng the declinying of the needle, touched therewith under the plaine of the horizon.* London, 1581, chap. 10. In G. Hellmann, *op. cit.* (fn. 109).
[132] Morison, *op. cit.* (fn. 110), vol. 1, pp. 270–271.
[133] *Ibid.,* p. 271.

With the inauguration of trans-Atlantic voyages, involving considerable changes in longitude, this fourth "magnetic motion," the variation of the deviation with position, became a familiar phenomenon by the early 16th Century.

VI. The Deviation of the Magnetic Needle from the Horizontal

In 1544 Georg Hartmann wrote, in a letter to Count Albrecht of Prussia, that a magnetic needle

> nicht mehr wagrecht stehen, sondern fällt unter sich etwa um 9 Grad mehr oder minder. Ursach, warum das geschieht, habe ich Königl. Majestät nicht wissen anzuzeigen.[134]

There is no indication that the information contained in Hartmann's letter, which was first published in 1831, received any wide dissemination before that date. The effective discovery of the 'dip' of the magnetic needle was first published in 1581 by Robert Norman, although perhaps occurring some years earlier.[135]

The failure of the magnetic needle to remain in the horizontal plane is—like the other three movements of attraction, orientation, and variation—not a fact but an idea, not a discovery but an invention. In this particular case we have a quite clear record, written by Norman, of as much of the process of invention as one can perhaps ever hope to have. At the same time his remarks demonstrate sharply both the influence of instrument-making and curiosity upon physical theory, a particularly intriguing combination. "Hauing made many and diuers compasses," Norman writes, it was his custom to "finish and end them" before magnetizing the needle.

> I found continually, that after I had touched the yrons with the Stone, that presently the north point thereof would bend or *Decline* downwards under the Horizon in some quantitie:...[136]

Such experiences caused little difficulty or excited little interest, since Norman merely counterbalanced the compass with "some small peece of waxe in the South part

---

[134] Hartmann's letter is reproduced photographically, from the original in the Royal State Archives in Königsberg, together with a printed version, as the fifth item in G. Hellman's *Rara magnetica, op. cit.* (fn. 109).
[135] A. Crichton Mitchell, *op. cit.* (fn. 1), III, note 5, writes that he has searched for the origin of this dating, and believes that it originated with Henry Bond, *The longitude found*, London, 1676.
[136] Robert Norman, *op, cit.* (fn. 131), chap. 3.

thereof,..." It was not until he was commissioned to prepare a needle of a specified length that apparently required great care in construction that the problem became important to him, for having balanced the needle and magnetized it with the usual results, he cut a little off of the north end – and cut too much –

> ...and so spoyled the needle wherein I had taken so much paynes.
> Hereby beeing stroken in some choller, I applyed my self to seeke further into this effect, and making certayne learned and expert men (my friends) acquainted in this matter, they advised me to frame some Instrument, to make some exact tryal, how much the needle touched with the Stone would *Decline*,...[137]

Norman's book is of sufficient importance that we shall return to it later: here it is noteworthy that he both denied an increase in weight on magnetization of the needle, claiming that this could be shown by weighing, and that he argued strongly for a "point respective" which the needle honored, as it were, without attraction occurring, and whose location could be located by triangulation.

VII. The Five Magnetical Movements

It was noted (p. 40) that Peter Peregrinus knew that a spherical lodestone, carefully balanced, would undergo diurnal rotation. This view, so in accord with the concept of sympathy between the stone and the celestial sphere, was fortified by Peregrinus' warning that failure meant poor workmanship. Hartmann repeats it, writing

> Ich habe ein altes Pergamentbuch in dem Bauernkriege überkommen, in welchem ich auch finde die Kraft des Magneten; wie zu machen sei ein Instrument durch den Magneten, welches sich für und für bewege in gleicher Form, Zeit und Weil, wie sich der Himmel bewegt; also dass wie der Himmel sich in 24 Stunden einmal um das Erdreich sich bewegt, dass auch alles dies Instrument mit dem Magneten zugerichtet, auch gleicher Maass Zeit und in 24 Stunden sich herumbeweg, davon ich nicht viel wollte halten.[138]

The sympathy between heavens and the "micro-ge" and hence, by implication, the earth itself, had a predominant role in Gilbert's thinking.

[137] *Ibid.*
[138] Hartmann, *op. cit.* (fn. 134).

By the end of the 16th Century, any satisfactory theory of magnetism necessarily accounted for the magnetization of iron by the lodestone, the amber effect, and the five magnetical movements of attraction, orientation, variation from the meridian, variation from the horizontal, and diurnal rotation. This is precisely the organization of Gilbert's *De magnete:* after an introductory book, the remainder of the work is divided into five books, each corresponding to one of the magnetic movements. In the first of these, devoted to attraction, Gilbert devotes a chapter to forming a clear and distinct separation between the amber effect and magnetic attraction, placing the amber effect outside of the interest of the student of magnetism, and simultaneously creating a new field of study: electricity.

49

CHAPTER TWO

WILLIAM GILBERT

William Gilbert was born in 1544 at Colchester, Essex, the son of the well-to-do Recorder of that town. He attended Cambridge, receiving the M. D. degree in 1569, settled in practice in London about 1573, and became a well-known physician there. Near the end of the year 1600, after publishing his work on magnetism, the *De magnete,* he became one of the physicians to the Queen and died a few months after Elizabeth died, in 1603.

Gilbert's book, together with the opinions expressed about his scientific work by contemporaries and seventeenth-century successors, has assured him a place in practically all histories of electricity and magnetism, general histories of science, and biographical dictionaries and compilations. Yet little biographical information is available, principally because of two events: the destruction of portions of the town of Colchester during the Second Civil War siege of that town;[1] the destruction of the Royal College of Physician's building and of Gilbert's London home, Wingfield House, by the Great Fire of London. Biographers of Gilbert have therefore had to elaborate a few scanty items in attempting to provide him with a biography.

Considering these circumstances, a rather surprising amount is definitely known or may reasonably be inferred about Gilbert, but this knowledge has never been set down together in one place.[2] It is the intent of this chapter to present a coherent statement of what is known of Gilbert and what may safely be surmised about him. In the process of correcting errors that have crept into the literature we shall have opportunity to examine the manner in which biographical knowledge is modified and altered through questionable historical techniques.[3]

[1] The 1648 siege of Colchester was the principal military siege of the Second Civil War, and was accompanied by unusual hardship and damage. See G. F. Townsend, *The siege of Colchester,* London, Society for Promoting Christian Knowledge [*s.d.*].

[2] Our present knowledge is very largely due to the efforts of S. P. Thompson, whose extensive labors at the turn of the last century at once materially added to the facts about Gilbert and stimulated study of Gilbert by others.

[3] A surprisingly large number of biographical accounts of Gilbert exist, principally because the profession of this natural philosopher has brought him to the attention of historians of medicine. As George Sarton has pointed out, in "The History of Science versus the History of Medicine," *Isis,* vol. 23 (1935), pp. 313–320, medicine has evoked a great deal of history, much of which is poorly written. Two accounts

I. The Gilbert Family

The Gilbert family[4] was established by the marriage of John Gilbert to Joan Tricklove, the only daughter of a wealthy merchant of Clare in Suffolk, in the second half of the 15th Century. Their son, William Gilbert of Clare, was "Sewer of the Chamber" to Henry VIII; his son, Hierom, removed to Colchester in Essex, toward the end of the first third of the century, and became Recorder of that town. His first wife bore him four children, the eldest of which was William Gilbert of Colchester. By the end of the century William was physician to the Queen, and his arms had been "confirmed."

> The history of the family as shown in the records is a very typical one of the period. We have a rich merchant, who acquires his wealth at the close of the fifteenth century; he dies leaving an only daughter, who marries a man, probably of the yeoman class, and their son, by means of his grandfather's wealth, is enabled to engage in the great East Anglian industry of weaving, whereby he augments his wealth and becomes a person of prominence in the community in which he lives. By some means or other he obtains a minor position in the household of Henry VIII., whereby he *ipso facto* becomes a gentleman, and on his death his sons inherit his large fortune and become prominent merchants and professional men. By the time of Queen Elizabeth they are thoroughly established among the local gentry, and a coat of arms is "confirmed" to them by the complaisant Elizabethan Heralds, and we have a full-fledged family of gentlemen, whose origin is lost in the mists of antiquity. The story is that of hundreds of other families who rose during the

may be eliminated from further consideration at the outset. The first of these appeared in the first edition of the *Biographie universele, ancienne et moderne, ou, histoire, par ordre alphabétique, de la vie publique et privée de tous les hommes qui se sont fait remarquer par leurs écrits, leurs actions, leurs talents, leurs vertus ou leurs crimes ouvrage entièrement neuf, rédigé par une société de gens du lettres et de savants*, vol. 17, Paris, L. G. Michaud, 1816, and reads in its entirety thus: "GILBERT (GUILLAUME), médecin anglais du XVIᵉ. siècle, était né à Glocester. On ignore dans quelle universite il fit ses études: après avoir été reçu docteur hors de l'Angleterre, il alla se fixer a Londres, devint médecin de la reine Élisabeth, en fut comble de faveurs, et mourut le 30 novembre 1603, quelques mois après cette princesse. Il avait acquis pendant sa vie une certaine réputation en chimie et en cosmographie: toutefois il n'a rien écrit sur ces matières; et comme l'ignorance titrée et la simple qualité de favori conduisent aussi souvent à la renommée que le mérite réel, la reputation de Gilbert pourrait bien n'être pas mieux fondée que celle de beaucoup d'hommes grands à la cour, mais petit dans l'histoire. On a de lui *De magnete, magneticisque corporibus, et de magno magnete, tellure, physiologia nova, plurimis et argumentis et experimentis demonstrata*, Londres, 1600; Sedan, 1633, in-4°.; Amsterdam, 1651, in-4°. CH---T." It is not necessary to be convinced of Gilbert's importance to recognize that the author of this article is ignorant; the article is extremely inaccurate, incorporating not only the errors of others, but creating a number of brand new ones.

Second, an article by Frank H. Krusen, "William Gilbert, the father of electrotherapy," *Archives of Physical Therapy, X-rays, Radium, with International Abstract*, vol. 12 (1931), pp. 737–743, is so

Fig. 1. William Gilbert's arms, as they appear on the *verso* of the *De magnete* title page.

inept that it should not be considered a part of the literature: it has here been not overlooked but avoided.
[4] Three pedigrees have been published. The first of these is from the 1634 visitation of Essex by George Owen, York Herald, and Henry Lilly, and is here taken from *The visitations of Essex by Hawley, 1552; Hervey, 1558; Cooke, 1570; Raven, 1612; and Owen and Lilly, 1634. To which are added miscellaneous Essex pedigrees from various Harleian manuscripts: and an appendix containing Berry's Essex pedigrees,* ed. W. C. Metcalfe, London, Harleian Society Publications, vol. 13, 1878, p. 405, which in turn was taken from a supposed copy, namely Harleian MS. 1542, of the original.

The second pedigree was published by S. P. Thompson, "The Family and Arms of Gilbert of Colchester," *Transactions of the Essex Archaeological Society,* new series, vol. 9 (1906), pp. 197–211.

The third pedigree, the result of a study stimulated by the second, was published by C. A. Moriarty, "The Gilberts of Clare and Colchester," *Miscellanea Genenealogica et Heraldica,* vol. 5, 5th series (1924), pp. 216–234. Despite his motivation, Moriarty does not construct a composite pedigree, but publishes one based solely upon new information not contained in Thompson's article, and does not attempt to resolve the differences between them except where the new information shows Thompson to have been in error.

Tudor period, and who are noted for the shortness of their pedigrees and the magnificence of their claims.[5]

The effectiveness of the claim of distant ancestry is well illustrated by the 1662 remark of the influential Thomas Fuller:

> [Gilbert's father] first removed his family thither [Colchester] from Clare in Suffolk where they had resided in a genteel equippage some centuries of years.[6]

The family name was subjected to the usual vagaries of spelling of the time. In the documents published by Moriarty[7] one finds the following: Gylberd or Gilberd,[8] Gylberde or Gilberde,[9] Gylbard,[10] Gylbert or Gilbert.[11] Different forms are often used in the same document. At the same time, one form was clearly preferred: Jerome Gilbert, Recorder of Colchester, made some dozen entries in the Colchester Oathbook between 1543 and 1563, and always wrote "Gilberd";[12] his epitaph on a brass plate in Trinity Church, Colchester, now gone, gave the same form;[13] finally, the memorial monument erected in Trinity Church to William Gilbert by his brothers Ambrose and William the younger, reads "Gvlielmvs Gilberd."

[5] Moriarty, op. cit. (fn. 4), pp. 216–217.

[6] Thomas Fuller, The history of the worthies of England, London, 1662, p. 515.

[7] Moriarty, op. cit. (fn. 4).

[8] Star Chamber Proceedings, Henry VIII, John Gilbert of Clare. Chancery Proceedings, 1515–1518, John Gilbert of Clare; William Gilbert of Clare. Chancery Proceedings 1518–1519, William Gilbert of Clare. Court of Requests, 30 April 34 Henry VIII, William Gilbert of Clare. Will of Margery Gilbert of Clare uses "Gilberd" throughout. Will of Ann [Gilbert] Smith. Both forms used in Clare Court rolls throughout the fifteenth and sixteenth centuries.

[9] Court of Requests, 30 April 34 Henry VIII, William Gilbert of Clare.

[10] Court of Requests, 7 June 34 Henry VIII, William Gilbert of Clare. Court of Requests, 21 April 34 Henry VIII, William Gilbert of Clare.

[11] Court of Requests, 7 June 34 Henry VIII, William Gilbert of Clare. Court of Requests, 21 April 34 Henry VIII, William of Clare. Will of William Gilbert of Clare refers to him as "Gylbert," to his sons as "Gilbert." Will of Ann [Gilbert] Smith. A "Gilbert de Cavendish" appears in Clare Court Rolls for 14 Edward II.

[12] The oath book or red parchment book of Colchester, translated and transcribed by W. G. Benham, Colchester, "Essex Country Standard" Office, 1907, pp. 162, 165, 172, 174, 175, 176, 177, 179, 180, 182.

[13] A transcription of the epitaph, allegedly taken from the plate, is in R. Symond's collection in the Herald's Office, vol. I, folio 437, and is quoted by the following: Philip Morant, The history and antiquities of the most ancient town and borough of Colchester, in the county of Essex, 2nd ed., London, 1768, reissued, Chelmsford, 1815, appendix, p. 20; Biographia Britannica: or, the lives of the most eminent persons who have flourished in Great Britain and Ireland from the earliest ages, down to the present time:..., vol. 4, London, 1757, p. 2202; Thomas Wright, The history and topography of the county of Essex..., London, George Virtue, 1831, p. 310; Thompson, op cit. (fn. 4), p. 200, n. 1. See Infra, fn. 18

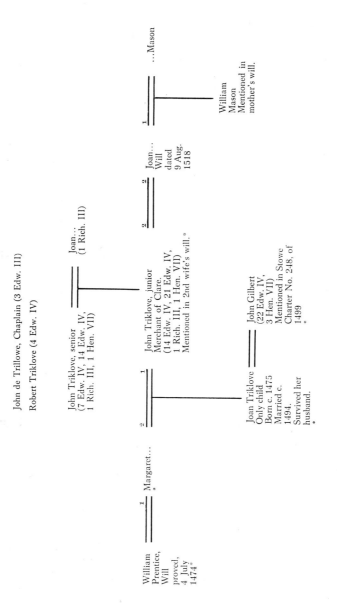

Fig. 2. The Trickloves of Clare. Derived from documents published by Moriarty, *op cit.* (fn. 4). The dates in parentheses are those of documents in which the person is mentioned.

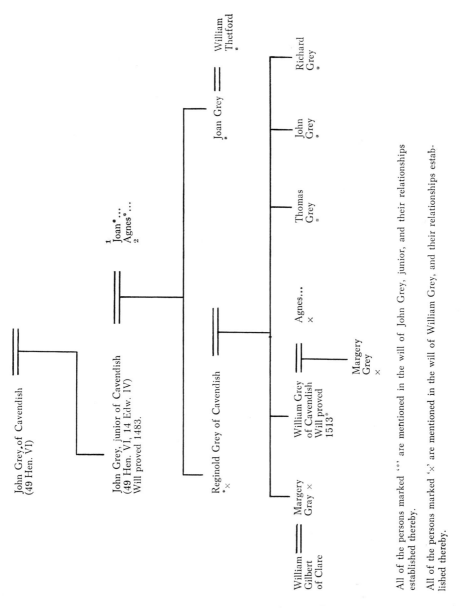

Fig. 3. The Greys of Cavendish. Derived from documents published by Moriarty, *op. cit.* (fn. 4).

55

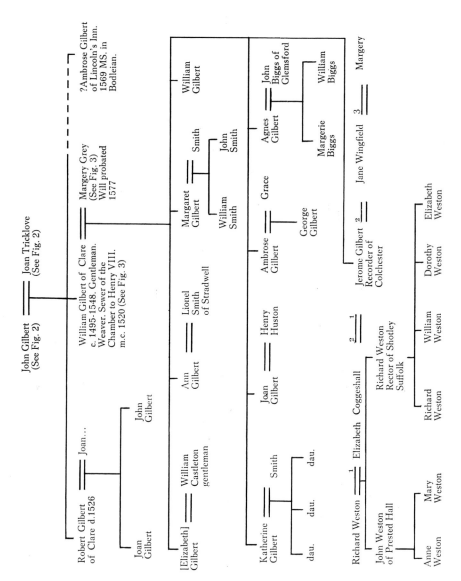

Fig. 4. The Gilberts of Clare. Derived from the pedigree given by Thompson, *op. cit.* (fn. 4), and the documents published by Moriarty, *op. cit.* (fn. 4), particularly the wills of William and Margery Gilbert of Clare.

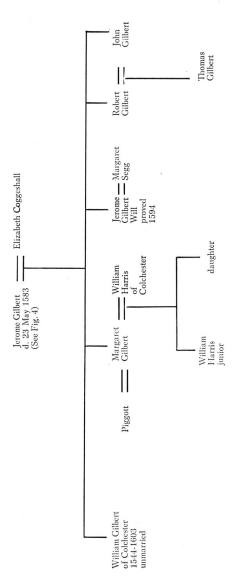

Fig. 5. The descendants of Jerome and Elizabeth Gilbert. Derived from the pedigree given by Thompson. *op. cit.* (fn. 4) and the documents published by Moriarty, *op. cit.* (fn. 4), particularly the wills of William and Margery Gilbert of Clare.

57

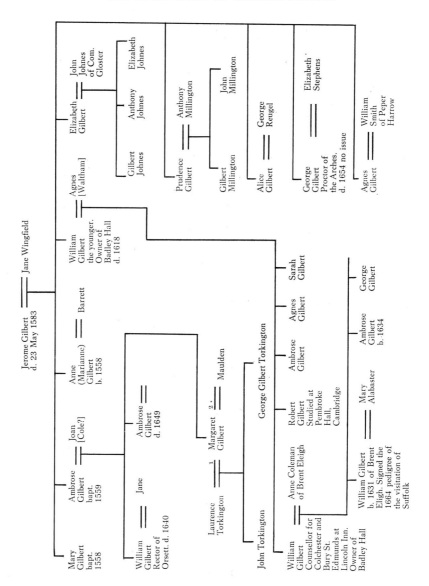

Fig. 6. The descendants of Jerome and Jane Gilbert. Derived from pedigree given by Thompson, *op. cit.* (fn. 4) and the documents published by Moriarty, *op. cit.* (fn. 4), particularly the wills of William and Margery Gilbert of Clare.

58

For these reasons, biographers of Gilbert have often tended to insist upon a return to the form "Gilberd." This seems unnecessary and, indeed, an undesirable antiquarianism. Two things are certain: whereas Gylberd and Gilbert might today reasonably claim to possess different names, there was no such differentiation in the sixteenth century and all of the forms of Gilbert discussed herein are no more than forms of the identical name;[14] custom has established usage of the form "Gilbert."

Gilbert's Immediate Family

Gilbert's father, Jerome Gilbert,[15] was the eldest son of William Gilbert of Clare.[16] He was brought up in the law and migrated to Colchester about the 1520's. There he became a free-burgess of the town in 1553,[17] and its Recorder, since his epitaph reads:

> Here lyeth the body of Jherome Gilberd sometime Recorder of this towne of Colchester, and Elizabeth his first wife and Margaret his daughter, he dyed 23 of May 1583.[18]

We know nothing more about him than that he made a generous, if not unusual, contribution to the local population (Figs. 5 and 6), executed quite a few deeds which are recorded in the *Oathbook* of Colchester, and left behind him a great deal of property when he died, which he had probably in turn inherited.

One Thomas Gilbert of Hintlesham, Suffolk, became a burgess of Colchester in 1429,[19] and Thompson believed him to be Gilbert's greatgreatgrandfather.[20] This seems most unlikely, but has crept into the literature.[21]

There is some indication of a more than usual close tie between William Gilbert and

---

[14] Indeed, William Gilbert's name appears in various forms. Thus in the Cambridge records both "Gylbert" and "Gilbard" appear. See John Venn and J. A. Venn, *The book of matriculations and degrees: a catalog of those who have been matriculated or been admitted to any degree in the University of Cambridge from 1544 to 1659*, Cambridge, at the University Press, 1913, p. 282. We shall encounter other forms.

[15] His first name is spelled variously as Hierome, Iherome, Hierom, Hieron, Jerom, in secondary sources.

[16] According to Thompson, *op. cit.* (fn. 4), p. 200.

[17] Colchester *Oathbook*, op. cit. (fn. 12), p. 172. B. W. Richardson, "The First Electrician—William Gilbert, M. D.," in Richardson's *Disciples of Aesculapius*, vol. 1 [vol. 2 published?], London, Hutchinson and Co., 1900, incorrectly gives this date as 1528, which is the date given by Thompson for the migration to Colchester.

[18] As given by Morant, *op. cit.* (fn. 13). The other versions (see fn. 13) differ in minor details.

[19] *Oathbook*, op cit. (fn. 12), p. 106.

[20] Thompson, *op cit.* (fn. 4).

[21] See the convincing argument of Moriarty, *op. cit.* (fn. 4), p. 216. Benham introduced this error, by an annotation, into the *Oathbook*, op. cit. (fn. 12). It is presumably the source of the error of Richardson, *op. cit.* (fn. 17), p. 3, in identifying Jerome Gilbert as a native of Hintlesham.

Fig. 7. Monument to Gilbert in Trinity Church, Colchester.

his brothers, particularly the two stepbrothers Ambrose and William the younger. Fuller reports that Gilbert was said to have "never married, purposely to have been more beneficial to his brethern."[22] Ambrose and William erected the monument to their older brother in Trinity Church, Colchester, and we shall see that they were quite generous in their description of his achievements in the inscription thereon.[23] It was William the younger who edited for publication – which, however, did not occur until half a century later – Gilbert's other and lesser known work, the *De mundo*.[24] All of this may simply mean that Ambrose and William the Younger were long-lived, surviving their brothers.

The Gilbert Colchester Home

Gilbert's will lists a house in Trinity Parish (Colchester). Morant wrote:

> His own house in this parish [St. Nicholas, adjoining Trinity], anciently called Lanseles, and Tymperley's, or Tympernell's (Old Taxation) is the same as Sergeant Price, the late Recorder of this borough, lived in; and now belongs to Thomas Clamtree, Esq. – George Horseman, and Frances his wife, daughter and heir of Roger Tymperley, sold it, in 1539, to Richard Weston, with a croft, of an acre and a half, gardens, and 3 rentaries thereto adjoining, lying in Trinity and St. Mary's. – Rot. Cur. 31 Henry VIII. rot. 14.[25]

A house that allegedly is this same "Tymperley's" exists today in Colchester,[26] and is one of the sights of that town. Richardson[27] reproduced a drawing of it, entitled "William Gilbert's residence at Colchester," and wrote (1900):

> ...the old church of the Holy Trinity; and hard by still stands Gilbert's house, once the Tymperley's. Friend Henry Laver, of Colchester, Surgeon there, and excellent antiquarian scholar, to whom I am much indebted, has taken a photographic view of the residence as it now is, which view Bertram Richardson has transferred to paper, as a fitting conclusion to this short history of the First Electrician.[28]

---

[22] Fuller, *op. cit.* (fn. 6), p. 515.

[23] See *infra*, pp. 84–85.

[24] *Gvilielmi Gilberti Colcestrensis, medici regii, de mundo nostro sublunari philosophia nova. Opus posthumum, ab authoris fratre collectum pridem & dispositum, nvnc ex duobus mss. codicibus editum. Ex museio viri perillustris Gvilielmi Boswelli equitis aurati &c. & oratoris apud Foederatos Belgas Angli,* Amsterdam, Ludovicum Elzavirium, 1661.

[25] Morant, *op. cit.* (fn. 13), p. 117n.

[26] W. G. Benham, *Guide to Colchester*, 16th ed., Colchester, 1925, pp. 102–103.

[27] Richardson, *op. cit.* (fn. 17), p. 43.

[28] Richardson, *op. cit.* (fn. 17), p. 44.

GVILIELMI GIL-
BERTI COLCESTREN-
SIS, MEDICI LONDI-
NENSIS,

DE MAGNETE, MAGNETI-
CISQVE CORPORIBVS, ET DE MAG-
no magnete tellure; Physiologia noua,
plurimis & argumentis, & expe-
rimentis demonstrata.

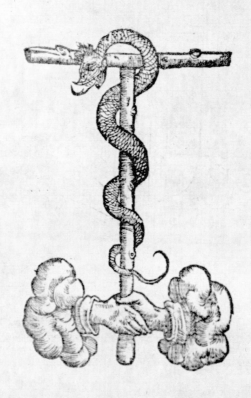

LONDINI

EXCVDEBAT PETRVS SHORT ANNO
MDC.

Fig. 8. Title page of the University of Oklahoma copy of the first edition of the *De magnete*.

A copy of this drawing found its way into the translator's preface of the first English translation of *De magnete*,[29] so that it is widely available to serve as a tie to the Elizabethan era and to stimulate interest in its former owner. Brother Potamian (M. F. O'Reilly), in 1901, described it as

> ...a house which, thanks to the appreciation of the authorities of that ancient town, the writer found in an excellent state of preservation on the occasion of his visit in quest of Gilbertiana.[30]

Thompson commented on the existence of the house, in 1904, quoting Morant's history of its acquisition by the Gilberts.[31] More recently, the author of a 1950 article on Gilbert is said to have "gathered the material for his article while on a trip to Colchester."[32]

There is, however, little reason to believe that this Tymperley's was Gilbert's Colchester residence. Morant definitely identifies the name as an *earlier* one, whereas the present house acquired its name later: Gilbert does not mention the name in his will, but calls it his "hed howse". A detailed study of the evidence, including an investigation of the deeds and the legally specified locations of the Gilbert properties, strongly indicates that the present non-Elizabethan Tymperley's was not the residence of Jerome and William Gilbert.[33]

II. William Gilbert of Colchester

Gilbert's Birth Date

The closing lines of the inscription on the monument erected to Gilbert by his brothers read

> Obiit anno redemptionis humanae, 1603 Novembris ultimo. Aetatis suae 63.[34]

---

[29] *William Gilbert of Colchester, physician of London, on the loadstone and magnetic bodies, and on the great magnet the Earth. A new physiology, demonstrated with many arguments and experiments*, tr. P. F. Mottelay, New York, John Wiley & Sons, 1893, p. xi.

[30] Brother Potamian, "Gilbert of Colchester," *The Popular Science Monthly*, vol. 49 (1901), p. 338.

[31] Thompson, *op. cit.* (fn. 4), p. 200.

[32] Rufus Suter, "Dr. William Gilbert of Colchester," *Scientific Monthly*, vol. 70 (1950), pp. 254–261.

[33] J. H. Round, "Dr. Gilberd's birthplace," *Transactions of the Essex Archaeological Society*, new series, vol. 10 (1909), pp. 307–311.

[34] See Fig. 7. George Sarton has used precisely such a monument erected at Darjeeling, Sikkim to Korosi Csoma Sandor as an example "of the constant need of vigilance" in the history of science; for although his death date is given as 1842 and his age then as 44, he was born in 1784! See Sarton's *The study of the history of science*, Cambridge, Harvard University Press, 1936, p. 15.

Writers on Gilbert have, not unreasonably, inferred from this inscription that: (a) Gilbert was born in 1540, according to his brothers, and (b) the source of this information is reliable.

There are, however, several difficulties about this birthdate. Gilbert, whose college record is well established,[35] entered St. John's in May 1558. On the hypothesis that he was born in 1540, he matriculated at the age of 18. This is extremely late, for the period – so late as to be unbelievable. Furthermore, a portrait of Gilbert painted in his lifetime apparently bore the inscription "1591: aetatis 48."[36] If this was the case, it is a better source of information than is the monument, since Gilbert himself would have undoubtedly scrutinized the inscription – indeed, he probably dictated it. The birthdate thus indicated is considerably more reasonable in terms of the date at which Gilbert entered college.

Finally, S. P. Thompson turned up a nativity of Gilbert that, together with the portrait, would seem to fix the birthdate with precision. Thompson wrote, in 1904:

> Until a few weeks ago the date of Dr. Gilbert's birth has always been given in his biographies as 1540, on the strength of the inscription on his monument, which states that at his death in 1603 he was in his 63rd year. This is certainly an error. On the portrait of him painted in his life-time, and by him presented to the University of Oxford, was the date 1591 and the inscription "aetatis xlviii." According to this he must have been born between March 26th 1543 and March 24th 1545/6, and not in 1540. But all doubt has been set at rest by the finding in the Bodleian Library amongst the Ashmolean manuscripts a nativity of Dominus Gilbertus Medicus, which specifically gives as the date of his birth the 24th of May 1544, at 2 hours 20 minutes p.m.[37]

One may perhaps view with question the precise minute of birth. Nevertheless, the converging evidence for a birthdate of 1544 is convincing.

Gilbert's Early Life

Information in the secondary sources concerning Gilbert's life before he went to the University is confined to such statements as the following:

[35] See *infra*, fn. 46.

[36] The portrait itself is now lost. See *infra*, above fn. 113.

[37] Thompson, *op. cit.* (fn. 4), p. 200. In a footnote Thompson added "As evidenced by a passage on p. 142 of *De Magnete*, Gilbert, in spite of his detachment from the fatuities of alchemy, and his scorn of metaphysics, gave credence to judicial astrology." Thompson's computation of the limits established by the portrait seems open to question, but in any case the portrait dates eliminate 1540 as a possible birthyear, placing Gilbert's birth in 1542 or later.

...after an education at the grammar school, was sent to Cambridge.[38]

Après avoir fait ses humanités au College de cette ville [Colchester], il fut envoyé par ses parens à Cambridge...[39]

...born and schooled in Colchester.[40]

No evidence whatsoever is available to support such remarks concerning Gilbert's schooling. The most cogent summary is thus that of Charles Singer:

Of William Gilbert's earliest years nothing is known,...[41]

Gilbert's University Education

In 1721 Anthony Wood wrote

WILLIAM GILBERT, Son of *Hierom Gilbert* of *Colchester*, in *Essex*, was born there, and educated in both the Universities, but whether in *Oxon* first or in *Cambridge*, I cannot justly tell. Afterwards he travelled beyond the Seas, where, I presume, he had the Degree of Doctor of Physic conferred upon him,...[42]

Wood was clearly uninformed. At the same time, his work was used widely and uncritically; the literature concerning Gilbert is filled with statements that he (a) attended both universities, and (b) received his M. D. abroad. We shall return to the second of these errors later in discussing his alleged foreign travels.[43] Wood perhaps was prone to view Oxford as unique in the education of the worthies of England; at least this would seem justified by the title of his book. Yet elsewhere he belittles Gilbert.[44] Perhaps

[38] B. Hutchinson, *Biographia medica; or, historical and critical memoirs of the lives and writings of the most eminent medical characters who have existed from the earliest account of time to the present period; with a catalogue of their literary productions*, in 2 vol., vol. 1, London, J. Johnson, 1799, p. 356.

[39] *Dictionaire des sciences médicales. Biographie médicale*, vol. 9, Paris, C. L. F. Panckoucke, 1821, p. 420.

[40] Thompson, *op cit.* (fn. 4), p. 197.

[41] Charles Singer, "Dr. William Gilbert (1544–1603)". *Journal of the Royal Naval Medical Service*, vol. 2 (1916), p. 495.

[42] Anthony Wood. *Athenae Oxonienses. An exact history of all the writers and bishops who have had their educations in the most ancient and famous university of Oxford, from the fifteenth year of king Henry the Seventh, A. D. 1500, to the Author's death in November 1695. To which are added, the FASTI, or Annals of the said university*, in 2 vol., 2nd ed., London, R. Knaplock, D. Midwinter, and J. Tonson, 1721.

[43] The authors of at least half a dozen secondary sources have been misled by Wood into the statement that Gilbert attended both universities.

[44] In his biography of William Barlowe. Wood, *op. cit.* (fn. 42), p. 495.

65

Wood may have been misled by Gilbert's gift of a portrait of himself to the School's Gallery at Oxford.[45]

Wood's opposite number in the hierarchy of academic historical work, using the records of the University of Cambridge, was able to confirm completely Gilbert's Cambridge education, in the following terms:

> He was matriculated as a member of S. John's college in this university [Cambridge] in May 1558, proceeding B.A. in 1560–1. On 21 March 1560–1 he was admitted a fellow on Mr. Symson's foundation. He commenced M.A. in 1564, and was admitted M.D. 13 May 1569. On 21 December in the latter year he was elected a senior fellow of his college.[46]

In an addendum we find

> He was appointed mathematical examiner of S. John's college 5 Sept. 1565 and 5 Sept. 1566, and senior bursar 22 Jan. 1569–70.[46]

Venn and Venn give: "Gylbert, Will. Fellow of Joh. Pensioner. Easter term, 1558. A. B. 1560–1. Gilbard; A. M. 1564; M. D. 1569."[47]

William Gilbert was a Cambridge-trained scholar and doctor of medicine.

Gilbert's Alleged Trip Abroad

We have seen (p. 65) that Wood, not knowing that Gilbert had received his M. D. at Cambridge, found it necessary to account for his unquestioned possession of such a degree by writing:

[45] An unsigned article, referred to in secondary sources as being by Conrad W. Cooke, in *Engineering*, vol. 48 (1889), pp. 717–718, 729–730, "William Gilbert, of Colchester," contains the following comment on the error. "The statement arose probably from the fact that by his will he bequeathed his portrait to the Schools Gallery at Oxford, showing that he had some special regard for the older university, from which it might reasonably have been assumed (in the absence of evidence to the contrary) that Oxford was his *alma mater*. His record at Cambridge, however, is so clearly established that there is little room for the supposition that the University of Oxford can claim any share in his education." To add to the confusion, Gilbert's will does not bear out Cooke's statement about the portrait.
[46] C. H. Cooper and T. Cooper, *Athenae Cantabrigienses*, vol. 2, Cambridge, Deighton, Bell & Co.; and MacMillan & Co., 1861, pp. 356 and 553. J. Venn and J. A. Venn, *Alumni Cantabrigienses, a biographical list of all known students, graduates, and holders of office at the University of Cambridge from the earliest times to 1900*, Cambridge, The University Press, Part 1, vol. 2, 1922, p. 215, add nothing.
[47] Venn and Venn, *op. cit.* (fn. 46), p. 282.

Afterwards he travelled beyond the Seas, where, I presume, he had the Degree of Doctor of Physic conferred upon him...[48]

It is illuminating to examine biographical accounts of Gilbert, during the eighteenth and nineteenth century, with Wood's statement in mind. In 1757 we find:

...he travelled into foreign countries, where probably he had the degree of Doctor of Physic conferred upon him;...[49]

In 1768:

...he travelled into foreign countries; where, probably, he had the degree of Doctor in Physic conferred upon him;...[50]

In 1799:

...he travelled abroad for his further improvement, and in one of the foreign universities had conferred upon him the degree of M. D.[51]

Note that Gilbert's motivation for the trip is now known and that his foreign M. D. is no longer "presumed" or "probable" but a fact. The motivation is confirmed in 1803:

he travelled abroad for improvement, and probably pursued the study of physic and graduated in it at some foreign university.[52]

In 1821:

Ayant entrepris ensuite différens voyages pour son instruction, il prit le grade de docteur hors de l'Angleterre, on ignore dans quelle université.[53]

After the terse statement "afterwards travelled into foreign countries" in 1831, by the historian of Colchester, Thomas Wright, we find in 1868:

Having decided on adopting medicine as a profession, he went to a foreign university to prosecute his medical studies, and whilst abroad received the degree of Doctor of Physic.[54]

[48] See fn. 42 and the text above it.
[49] *Biographia Britannica, op. cit.* (fn. 13), p. 2202. Wood was used by the author.
[50] Morant, *op. cit.* (fn. 13), p. 117. Morant used Wood.
[51] Hutchinson, *op. cit.* (fn. 38), p. 356.
[52] John Aikin, Thomas Morgan, William Johnston, *General biography; or, lives, critical and historical, of the most eminent persons of all ages, countries, conditions, and professions, arranged according to alphabetical order,* vol. 4, London, J. Johnson..., 1803, p. 408. *Biographica Britannica* is given as a reference.
[53] *Dictionaire des sciences médicales, op. cit.* (fn. 39), p. 420.
[54] Charles Knight, *Biography, or third division of "The English Cyclopaedia,"* vol. 3, London, Bradbury, Evans, and Co., 1868, p. 102.

It is little wonder that Gilbert is generally thought of as having left Cambridge and travelled abroad. Yet each of the "sources" quoted derive directly or indirectly from Wood – whose discussion is at the very least questionable.

This entire galaxy of statements concerning Gilbert's foreign travels may be summed up as follows: with at least one false reason for doing so, Wood stated in 1721 that Gilbert travelled abroad after completing his English education.

With the approach of the tercentenary of the publication of the *De magnete*, in 1900, and the revival of interest in Gilbert that accompanied that event, Wood's error concerning Gilbert's English education became well known and was no longer repeated, except to be refuted.[55] The belief that Gilbert travelled abroad does, however, continue, with new variations based upon new examination of the available documentary evidence. Every biographer whose accounts I have examined states that Gilbert travelled abroad after leaving Cambridge, and usually three or four years is given for the duration of the trip. Yet I know of no direct evidence for believing that he made such a trip. At the same time there is indirect evidence worthy of examination.

First, there is no record of Gilbert's whereabouts after completing his doctoral work. His fairly rapid rise in his profession from the 1580's on may be interpreted as meaning that he had not engaged in that profession, at least in London, much before the mid-1570's. This argument is of little value alone, but if one reads Gilbert's epitaph, noting that part which states

> Summis lavdibvs pariq.foelicitate per triginta pl. annos Londini exercvit.[56]

and if one is predisposed to place Gilbert's arrival in London a few years after 1569, the epitaph yields about 1573 for that arrival. We have already seen that Ambrose and William the younger were perhaps not trustworthy in so far as precise dating is concerned.

However, it is perhaps not unreasonable to suppose that Gilbert took a Grand Tour after leaving Cambridge. This view was probably even less unreasonable to late nineteenth-century interpreters. In this period of interpretation, the role of Galileo in the development of scientific methodology was quite different from what it is today, and, as we shall explore more thoroughly in the next chapter, historians seemed to find

---

[55] For example, by Richardson, *op. cit.* (fn. 17), p. 3.

[56] See Fig. 7. Mottelay, in his "Biographical Memoir" of Gilbert, *op. cit.* (fn. 29), pp. ix-xxvii, writes: "Immediately upon leaving college he travelled on the Continent, where probably he had the degree of Doctor of Physic conferred upon him, for he doth not appear to have taken it either at Oxford or Cambridge, [Reference: Morant] and where, as well as in England, he is said to have 'practised as a physician with great success and applause.'"

it necessary to establish a connection between Gilbert and Galileo. Such a direct connection cannot be made: Galileo was too young. The argument that Gilbert had to have been to Italy in order to do the work published in the *De Magnete* is a dubious one; the Platonic tradition was as strong or stronger in England than in Italy, and the methodology of Galileo and Gilbert are quite different, as was well summed up by Galileo when he wrote

> I extremely praise, admire, and envy this Author [Gilbert],... I think him, moreover, worthy of extraordinary applause... That which I could have desired in Gilbert is that he had been a somewhat better mathematician and particularly well grounded in geometry, the practice whereof would have rendered him less prone to accepting for true demonstrations the reasons he produces as causes of the true conclusions observed by himself, which reasons (freely speaking), do not knit and bind so tight as those ought to do which lead to natural, necessary, and lasting conclusions. And I doubt not that in the process of time this new science will be perfected with new observations and, which is more, with true and necessary demonstrations.[57]

Gilbert evidently had a good reputation with at least Galileo. Indeed evidence exists that the *De magnete* was known abroad, and there is internal evidence that it was written for foreign consumption, at least in part.[58] But here the question is: did Gilbert travel abroad?

One more piece of evidence — and perhaps the only one outside of Wood's unsupported statement — may be noted. In the only known extant letter of Gilbert's written in English, to William Barlow and published by him in his *Magnetical advertisements,* Gilbert wrote

> Sir, I will commend you to my L. of Effingham, there is heere a wise learned man, a Secretary of Venice, he came sent by that State, and was honourably receiued by her Maiesty, he brought me a lattin letter from a Gentleman of Venice that is very well learned, whose name is Iohannes Franciscus Sagredus, he is a great Magneticall man, and writeth that hee hath conferred with diuers learned men of Venice, and with the Readers of Padua, and reporteth wonderfull liking of my booke, you shall haue a coppy of the letter:...[59]

[57] Galileo Galilei, *Dialogue on the great world systems,* tr. Thomas Salusbury, ed. Giorgio de Santillana, Chicago, University of Chicago Press, 1953, p. 415.

[58] That Gilbert wrote it in Latin is one indication. But there are others, such as his reference in bk. 2, chap. 2, p. 56, to the effect of the weather on electrical experiments, wherein he specifies England as the location.

[59] William Barlowe, *Magnetical advertisements, or diverse pertinent observations and approved experiments, concerning the nature and property of the loadstone: very pleasant for knowledge, and most needful in practice, of travelling, or for the framing of instruments fit for travellers both by sea and land,* a new edition, with notes by William Sturgeon, London, Sherwood, Gilbert, and Piper, 1843.

Again, if one were in a proper frame of mind, this passage might be interpreted to mean that Gilbert and Sagredus were friends; it might also be interpreted to mean simply that Sagredus found the *De magnete* of sufficient interest that, when opportunity presented itself, he sent a letter to its author.

Despite the lack of evidence for an Italian connection, one may not justly ignore a statement by S. P. Thompson. S. P. Thompson, who lived in England, devoted a great deal of time and money to the study of Gilbert, und unearthed a perceptible fraction of the present factual knowledge about Gilbert, said, in March, 1903:

> Nurtured, as we have seen, in the Cambridge which had so recently been the home of Linacre and of Kaye – the Kaye who founded Caius College – Gilbert had, during his subsequent sojourn in Italy, conversed with all the learned men of his time. He had experimented on the magnet with Fra Paolo Sarpi: he had, there is reason to think, met Giordano Bruno: he was the friend and correspondent of Giovanni Francesco Sagredo.[60]

We have already seen that the last phrase of this remark rests upon slender evidence. A connection to Bruno may be surmised from certain material in the *De magnete*, and Gilbert mentions Bruno by name in his other work, the *De mundo* (see fn. 24). The Sarpi connection is probably based upon certain favorable remarks made by Sarpi about Gilbert. Fortunately Thompson did not close his remarks on Gilbert with this paragraph. Nine months later he took a quite different position:

> Of all that happened to Gilbert during his three years of foreign travel nothing is known for certain, except that he visited Italy, and made acquaintance with many of the learned men of his time. That he occupied himself with the study of the magnet in pursuit of those life-long [?] investigations which culminated in the publication of his famous book *De Magnete,* may be taken as indubuitable. But how far he devoted himself whilst in Italy to the pursuit of medical knowledge is quite uncertain. It has been conjectured that he attended at Padua the anatomical demonstrations of the celebrated Fabricius ab Aquapendente. It has also been inferred from slender clues that he followed the teachings of Mercurialis on poisons. Certain it is that he gained a familiar knowledge of the medical writers of that time,... In his writings he frequently quotes from foreign medical authorities, from the... ... From

[60] S. P. Thompson, *William Gilbert, and terrestrial magnetism in the time of Queen Elizabeth.* "This discourse on William Gilbert and terrestrial magnetism in the time of Queen Elizabeth was delivered by Silvanus P. Thompson at the meeting of the Royal Geographical Society on March twenty-third MDCCCCIII on the occasion of the tercentenary of the death of Queen Elizabeth, and is now printed by Charles Whittingham and Company at the Chiswick Press."

the Italians, too, he probably acquired the repugnance to the teachings of Paracelsus and of Albertus Magnus which asserts itself throughout his writings; while he scoffed at Arnoldus de Villanova, the great writer of the school of Salerno. Howsoever these things be, Gilbert returned to England a pronounced hater of shams and of quackery, a champion of the experimental method, and an outspoken enemy of all those who merely relied on the authority of great names.[61]

Even in this more tentative position, Thompson is arguing from meager evidence. For example, Gilbert certainly did not have to leave England to hear questions raised about the teachings of Albertus Magnus.

In the following year, 1904, in the extremely careful and scholarly paper to which we have repeatedly referred (fn. 4), delivered to the Essex Archaeological Society, Thompson said

> After about four years of foreign travel, of which nothing is known, he settled, in 1573, in London...[62]

Everything that is said about Gilbert's activities in the few years following 1569 is based upon indirect and slender evidence and is largely influenced by a belief that the experimental nature of Gilbert's work shows Italian influence – or, among the most devout, perhaps by the tacit belief that Italian science shows Gilbertian influence.

There seems to be a much more reasonable conjecture available. In the preface to the *De magnete*, Edward Wright noted that

> Optimis igitur auspicijs (doctissime D. D. Gilberte) in lucem prodeat Magnetica philosophia tua, non in nonum tantum annum (quod Horatius praecipit) sed in alterum iam fere novennium pressa,...[63]

This statement has been widely – and I think justly – interpreted to mean that Gilbert had established the work published in the *De magnete* some seventeen years before it

[61] S. P. Thompson, *Gilbert, physician: a note prepared for the three-hundredth anniversary of the death of William Gilbert of Colchester, President of the Royal College of Physicians, & physician to Queen Elizabeth.* "This note on William Gilbert as Physician was prepared by Silvanus P. Thompson for the Commemoration on December 10th, 1903, of the Three-hundredth Anniversary of his death, and is now printed by Charles Whittingham and Company at the Chiswick Press. MCMIII."

[62] S. P. Thompson, *op. cit.* (fn. 4), p. 197.

[63] *Gvilielmi Gilberti Colcestrensis, Medici Londinesis, de magnete magnetisqve corporibvs, et de magno magnete tellure; physiologia noua, plurimis & argumentis, & experimentis demonstrata*, London, Peter Short, 1600, p. v, *verso*.

was published in 1600, that is, about 1583. We shall see some supporting evidence for this view, namely, that from the 1580's on Gilbert appears to have been thoroughly engrossed in his profession of physician. Consequently it would seem reasonable to believe that the period immediately after 1569 was devoted to studies in magnetism and electricity, studies that were neglected when Gilbert took up residence in London. Those studies may or may not have been stimulated by contacts at the university, in London, or abroad.

III. Dr. Gilbert of London

The various secondary sources previously cited all agree that Gilbert settled in practice as a physician in London about 1573. I know of no evidence for this statement beyond the phrase in his epitaph, cited on p. 68, which credits him with more than thirty years' practice. Furthermore, he suddenly appears as a prominent physician in 1581: of the meager stock of documents concerning his life as a London physician, the first two appear in that year.[64] In the absence of further evidence, I would be prone to date Gilbert's appearance on the London scene – or, at least, as a prominent London physician – as somewhat later than 1573, and to think of the period from 1569 to the late 1570's as one devoted to his studies in magnetism, electricity, and cosmology. 1577, the year in which he obtained his grant of arms, would seem a reasonable date for the beginning of his London life.

At any rate, Gilbert began practice in London and became a member of the Royal College of Physicians sometime prior to 1581.[65]

Gilbert's London Home

Just where Gilbert resided in London during his first few years there is unknown, but at some later date he acquired Wingfield House.[66] Jerome Gilbert died in 1583, but if the asterisks in Thompson's list of property are trustworthy, Gilbert did not inherit

---

[64] His first office, Censor, in the Royal College of Physicians (see *infra*, above fn. 69), and a mention of him in a letter from the Earl of Shrewsbury to Thomas Bawdewyn (see *infra* above fn. 68.)

[65] William Munk, *The roll of the Royal College of Physicians of London; comprising biographical sketches of all the eminent physicians, whose names are recorded in the annals from the foundation of the college in 1518 to its removal in 1825, from Warwick Lane to Pall Mall East*, 2nd ed., vol. 1 (1518–1700), London, published by The College, 1878, p. 78.

[66] His step-mother was a Wingfield. See Figs. 4 and 5.

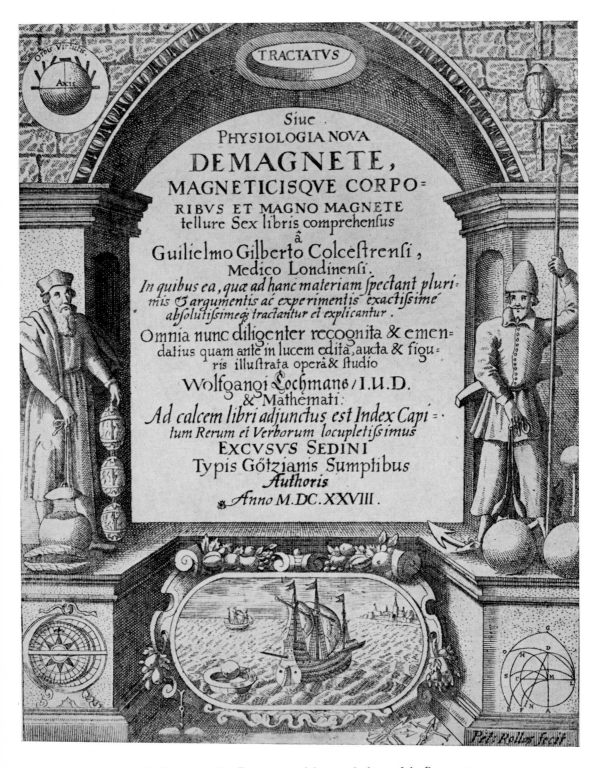

Fig. 9.   Title page of the Burndy copy of the second edition of the *De magnete*.

Tractatus, sive Physiologia Nova

DE
MAGNETE,

Magneticisq; corporibus & magno
Magnete tellure, sex libris comprehensus,
a GUILIELMO GILBERTO Colcestrensi, Medico Londinensi.

*In quibus ea, quæ ad hanc materiam spectant, plurimis
& Argumentis & experimentis exactissime absolutissi-
meq̃ tractantur & explicantur.*

Omnia nunc diligenter recognita, & emendatius quam ante
in lucem edita, aucta & figuris illustrata, opera & studio D.
WOLFGANGI LOCHMANS, I. U. D.
& Mathematici.

*Ad calcem libri adiunctus est Index capitum, Rerum & Verborum
locupletissimus, qui in priore æditione desiderabatur.*

SEDINI,
Typis GOTZIANIS,
ANNO M. DC. XXXIII.

Fig. 10. Title page of the University of Oklahoma copy of the third edition of the *De magnete*.

WILLIAM GILBERT

OF COLCHESTER,

PHYSICIAN OF LONDON,

ON THE

LOADSTONE AND MAGNETIC BODIES,

AND ON

THE GREAT MAGNET THE EARTH.

A NEW PHYSIOLOGY,

DEMONSTRATED WITH MANY ARGUMENTS AND EXPERIMENTS.

" *Electrica, quae attrahunt eadem ratione ut electricum.*"

A TRANSLATION BY

P. FLEURY MOTTELAY,

AUTHOR OF " THE CHRONOLOGICAL HISTORY OF ELECTRICITY, MAGNETISM, ETC."

———

NEW YORK:
JOHN WILEY & SONS,
53 EAST TENTH STREET.
1893.

Fig. 11. Title page of the University of Oklahoma copy of the fifth edition of the *De magnete*.

VVILLIAM GIL-
BERT OF COLCHES-
TER, PHYSICIAN OF
LONDON.

ON THE MAGNET, MAGNE-
TICK BODIES ALSO, AND ON
the great magnet the earth; a new Physi-
ology, demonstrated by many ar-
guments & experiments.

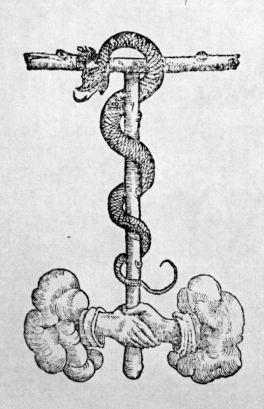

LONDON

IMPRINTED AT THE CHISWICK PRESS ANNO
MCM.

Fig. 12. Title page of the sixth edition of the *De magnete* (photographed from a copy in the author's possession).

Wingfield House from him. Perhaps he had acquired it earlier on the death of his step-mother, Jane Gilbert, daughter of Robert Wingfield. At any rate, he ultimately lived there.

Wingfield House was in St. Peter's Hill,[67] a short street or lane extending from Thames Street to Knightrider Street.

We can place a number of points of interest nearby. Only a couple of blocks' walk along Thames Street from St. Peter's Hill is Bread Street, in which lay the shop of Peter Short, printer of the *De magnete*. Just to the west of Wingfield House, with an entrance on Peter's Hill, lay the College of Arms, habitat of Robert Cooke, Clarenceux Herald, through whom Gilbert obtained his grant of arms from Elizabeth, in 1577, and the Royal College of Physicians occupied the stone house, formerly the residence of Linacre, in Knightrider Street.

Wingfield House has achieved a certain fame as the locale of a College or Society, led by Gilbert, that has acquired an unjustified definiteness in a number of modern writings and even has become the precursor of the Royal Society of London in some of them. Of this alleged College we shall have more to say later.

Dr. William Gilbert

> Bawdewyn,
>
> I HAVE thought good, receiving my Lord Treasurer's and my Lord Chancellor's letter for the payment of my subsidy, and to whom it should be paid unto, I have thought it good to send the letter unto you, which I would have you to keep safe. This gentleman, Doctor Gilbert, was sent from her by Majesty by my Lord of Leicester's means. His coming was too late, and therefore his abode short, though I would have been pleased to have had him longer. I have spoken to him to send me some biscuit bread, which is not made by common poticars, and also a serecloth, to use for my gout, which he has promised me to send. See him well recompensed, for surely, for the small talk I have had with him, I have found him a sensible man; therefore seek to be acquainted with him, and be very friendly of him. And I have written to my Lord...
> Sheffield, this 25th of January, 1581, our Lord and Master, G. SHREWSBURY.[68]

[67] John Stow, *A survey of the cities of London and Westminster: containing the original antiquity, increase, modern estate and government of those cities. Written at first in the year MDXCVIII by John Stow, citizen and native of London. Since reprinted and augmented by the author; and afterwards by A. M. H. D. and others. Now lastly, corrected, improved and very much enlarged: and the survey and history brought down from the year (being near fourscore years since it was last printed) to the present time;* ..., London, A. Churchill, J. Knapton, ... 1720, vol. 2, pp. 2, 12.

[68] Edmund Lodge, *Illustrations of British History, Biography, and Manners in the reign of Henry VIII,*

With this letter of Shewsbury's, William Gilbert, Physician, enters upon the scene, clearly making a favorable impression. In the same year, 1581, Gilbert became Censor of the Royal College of Physicians, a post that he also held in 1582, 1584, 1585, 1586, 1587, 1589, and 1590.[69] He remained an important member of that organization from this time, holding the office of Treasurer 1587–1594 and 1597–1599, Consiliarius in 1597, 1598, and 1599, Elect 1596 and 1597, and President in 1600.[70]

Thompson found, in the British Museum, a number of medical tracts bound together and inscribed "Gabrielis Harveij et amicorum." Among these is a single printed folio page, dated 1582, bearing four recipes for helping and curing "the stone in the raines." At the bottom the source of the recipes is identified as "G. G.", who might be "Guilielmus Gilbertus."[71]

More certain in origin is a document preserved in Her Majesty's Record Office and published by Thompson:

> To the Right honnourable Sir ffrauncis Walsingham. Knight & principall Secretarye to her Ma[tie].
>
> Pleaseth it yo[r] Honno[r] to be advertised That whereas wee are required by this Gent M[r] Hungait, to delyver o[r] opinions, as concerninge the cause of his desire to travyll beyonde the seas, True it is, that we have advised him therevnto, as thinkinge his beinge, for some tyme in hotte and drye Countryes, will much staye the rage and fflux of his cold and Rhumatike diseases, w[h] yb longe observation, both he and wee have founde, to abounde most, when the weather is colde and Intemperate, And thus most humblye takinge o[r] leaves wee comitt yo[r] Honno[r] to the tuition of the Almightie, London this first of Februarye 1584
>
> Yo[r] Honno[rs] most
redely to comaunde

WILLM GYLBERD
LANCELOT BROWNE[72]

Edward VI, Mary, Elizabeth, and James I, exhibited in a series of original papers, selected from the mss. of the noble families of Howard, Talbot, and Cecil, containing among a variety of interesting pieces, a great part of the correspondence of Elizabeth and her ministers with George, sixth Earl of Shrewsbury, during the fifteen years in which Mary, Queen of Scots, remained in her custody, 2nd ed., in 3 vol., vol. 2, London, John Chidley, 1838, pp. 200–201. Lodge gives as his reference "Talbot Papers, vol. G. fol. 120."

[69] Munk, *op. cit.* (fn. 65), p. 78.

[70] *Ibid.*

[71] Thompson, *op. cit.* (fn. 61), p. 6.

[72] Thompson, *op. cit.* (fn. 61), pp. 7–8.

Gilbert appears again as an attending physician in 1588, this time for the wife of Michael Hennage, keeper of the Records in the Tower, in childbirth. The Honywood evidences record.

> 1588. Ultimo die mensis Apr. ult⁰ die Martis hora quinta pomeridiana nata e in aedib' meis predictis filia mea Katherina Heneag, que die Jouis proxima sequen suscepta est de sacro fonte pro uxorem Johannis Spurling, Susan Honiwood vices agen (sic) et Wilhelmi Gilbert, medicinae doctor.[73]

In 1588 England and Spain went to war. This war came to a formal end in 1604, but England's superiority was established with the defeat of the 132-vessel "Invincible Armada" in July 1588, and its destruction by storm off the Hebrides. English preoccupation with the state of the fleet prior to the Armada was understandable, and in March the Privy Council asked for aid from the College of Physicians, transmitting to them the following letter:

> A letter to the President of the Colledge of the Doctors of Physick that whereas a dysease and sicknes begann to encrease in her Majesties Navye, for remedie of the dyseased and for staie of further contagion their Lordships thought meet that some lerned and skillfull phisicions should presently be sent thether; and for that their Lordships hard that good reporte of the sufficiency, learninge and care of Dʳ Gilbert, Dʳ Marbeck, Dʳ Browne and Dʳ Wilkinson, as they were thought very fytt persons to be employed in the said Navye to have care of the helthe of the noblemen, gentlemen, and others in that service, therefore he was required forthwith upon the receipt of their Lordships' letters to call before him the forenamed Doctors, and to make choyse of any two of them, whoe were to be willed to put them selves presently in a readynes to goe downe to the Navye, and to carry with them a convenyent quantytie of all soche drogues as should be fyt for medycine and cure; and uppon their repaier and conference with the Lord Admyrall soche order should be taken for their entertainment as should be to their contentment.[74]

In the annals of The Royal College of Physicians for 10 Oct 1589 there appears a reference to a "Dispensatorium" or pharmacopoeia to be undertaken by the Society.[75] Assignments of various topics are made in the annals and we read therein "Pilulae... Per D. D. Gilbert et Turner." Then, for 23 December, 1589 occurs the following entry:

[73] Honywood evidences. *The Topographer and Genealogist*, vol. 2(1853), p. 173.

[74] *Acts of the Privy Council of England*, new series, vol. 16 (1588), London, Her Majesty's Stationery Office, 1897, pp. 5–6.

[75] Munk, *op. cit.* (fn. 65), v. 3, pp. 372–373, quotes the entries from the annals.

In his Comitiis omnes Collegae, unusquisque pro se, in scriptis representabant id quod excogitarunt pro novo Dispensatorio et Usuali Londinensi Collegii consenu publicando. Totum autem hoc opus, ut perfectius et limatus exeat in vulgus, sex Collegis iterum examinandum assignatur. Examinatores autem sunt hi Dr. Forster, Dr. Johnson, Dr. Turner, Dr. Gilbert, Dr. Browne, Dr. James.[76]

Five years later the third and last mention of Gilbert in this connection – and the last mention of the pharmacopoeia in the annals for twenty years – appears under the date of 13 December 1594:

Assignati sunt ad examen Dispensatori nostri, Dr. Johnson, Dr. Gilbert, Dr. Browne, Dr. James, Dr. Turner, Dr. Akins, Dr. Wilkinson, Dr. Paddy.[77]

These three glimpses of Gilbert within the College bear out the belief that he was an important member of his profession. The professional associations established by these excerpts from the annals might well serve as a guide to unearthing further information about Gilbert in English libraries and manuscript collections.

In January 1597, according to the Hatfield Manuscripts,[78] Gilbert attended Lady Cecil in her last illness. With Gilbert was one Richard Wesson or Weston, identified as a servant, who was accused of the theft of a jewel which disappeared at this time. The name is not a new one: Gilbert's mother had been married to Richard Weston before her marriage to Jerome Gilbert (see Fig. 4); her son, Gilbert's half-brother, was named Richard Weston and he in turn had a son of the same name. Since Gilbert was 53 at the time of this visit to Hatfield and since his stepbrother was older, the "servant" may well have been Gilbert's nephew.

In 1597 a new source of information appears, in the form of the gossipy letter-writer, Gilbert's younger contemporary, John Chamberlain (1553–1627). A Londoner, born and bred and protesting whenever he was away from the city, with sufficient personal means to do as he wished, Chamberlain spent the major part of his life in the shadow of St. Paul's, in the homes of his friends. His letters are an invaluable record of his times – we would probably know more about Gilbert if we had earlier letters, but none are known before 1597. "From 1597... they provide, as do the letters of no one of his

---

[76] *Ibid.*, p. 373.

[77] *Ibid.*, p. 373. The pharmacopoeia was not issued until 1618, when two "first" editions were published.

[78] The account here is taken from Thompson, *op. cit.* (fn. 61), p. 12, who gives as his reference "Hatfield MSS. Cal. vol. vii."

contemporaries, an almost continuous commentary on the outstanding men and events of the time."[79]

Chamberlain refers to "our Doctors opinion" in the first of his extant letters, dated 11 June, 1597, to Dudley Carleton.[80] The opinion is a somewhat obscure witticism to the effect that the treasurer of an expedition being organized against Spain will not be much troubled with "receit."

In July, 1598, Gilbert attended Lord Burghley on his deathbed,[81] and Thompson also tells us

> In 1599 Dr. Gilbert was made President of the Royal College. In the same year he attended Lady Derby for an attack of ague. His report on her case, written to Sir Robert Cecil, the only known letter in Gilbert's autograph, is preserved among the Cecil manuscripts at Hatfield.[82]

Since his first letter of 1597, addressed to Dudley Carleton, Chamberlain had written 30 more by the summer of 1600, all filled with gossip and information of every sort, including a number of items that may have well come from a physician with an elite practice. But Gilbert is not mentioned again until the 32nd letter, dated 10 October, 1600, wherein Chamberlain writes:

> This towne is as empty as yf yt were dead vacation, no body at the Doctors, no body in Powles [St. Paul's], *solitudo ante ostium* in Little Britain,...[83]

The following February there is more news: in his 36th letter, dated 3 February, 1600–01 he tells Carleton[84]

> The Quene hath maid choice [of our] Doctor for her phisition, but he is not yet sworne. I dou [bt our] colledge wilbe dissolved, and some of us sent to seeke our fortune.[85]

This brings to an end one period in Gilbert's life, that of practicing London physician, and introduces a new one, in which he is physician to the Queen. But before turning to

[79] *The letters of John Chamberlain*, Volume I, ed. N. E. McClure, *Memoirs of The American Philosophical Society*, vol. 12, part 1, Philadelphia, 1939, vol. 1, editor's introduction, p. 1.
[80] *Ibid.*, letter 1, p. 31.
[81] Thompson, *op cit.* (fn. 61), p. 17. Reference: "Hatfield MSS. Cal., viii, p. 277."
[82] Thompson, *op. cit.* (fn. 61), p. 18.
[83] Chamberlain's Lettres, *op. cit.* (fn. 79), letter 32, p. 106.
[84] The brackets in the extract are Chamberlain's editor's.

his relationship to Elizabeth, we shall explore another point: the "colledge" to which Chamberlain refers.

Gilbert's Household

Three weeks after the letter in which he announced Gilbert's appointment as physician to the Queen to Carleton, over a date of 24 February 1600–01 Chamberlain tells him:

> I was out of the way when your letter came, and when the messenger gave warning of his sodain departure, for the covie is now dispersed, and we are driven to seeke our feeding farther of, our doctor being alredy setled in court, and I redy to go to Askot,...[86]

And, in his next known letter to Carleton, dated 27 May 1601, Chamberlain apologizes for his lack of faithfulness in correspondence, adding

> ...without hope of amendes; for I know not how to redeems that is past with further diligence, being (since the dissolution of our societie) become altogether a contriman...[87]

Chamberlain has used three terms, apparently synonyms, in these three letters: "colledge," "covie," and "societie." The last half century has seen a great deal built upon these three words. With, to my knowledge, no other evidence than the above quotations from Chamberlain, we are told that

> ...Wingfield house was frequented by numerous friends and acquaintances who formed a kind of College or Society around Gilbert as their head.[88]

And,

> [At Gilbert's house]... there used to assemble a Society or College of men interested in the secrets of Nature. This may be regarded as the earliest Scientific Association in England and perhaps the earliest in Europe.[89]

[85] *Ibid.*, letter 36, p. 117.
[86] *Ibid.*, letter 37, pp. 118–119.
[87] *Ibid.*, letter 38, p. 122.
[88] Thompson, *op. cit.* (fn. 61), p. 4.
[89] Singer, *op. cit.* (fn. 41) p. 496. Singer wrote at the beginning of this article that he was so indebted to Thompson's work that the article "may be regarded as mainly extracted from his writings." This may or may not be an apology for hurried preparation, but by 1916 Thompson's understandable enthusiasm for Gilbert's place in the history of science should have been tempered a little, not expanded upon.

It is interesting that in a well-documented work the following is undocumented:

> There was... [a] learned society that met at Gilbert's house on St. Peter's Hill.[90]

Indeed we sometimes even find the members of the group identified, presumably an easy task once the nature of the Society is known, since a scientific society meeting at Gilbert's could be expected to include all persons interested in medicine, navigation, magnetism, cosmology, and natural philosophy in general who were in contact with Gilbert in any way.

There does not appear to be a shred of evidence, beyond Chamberlain's remarks, for assuming the existence of any sort of an organization at Gilbert's house or involving Gilbert. Chamberlain, as revealed in his letters, is a strange person to place in a scientific society, and if he were meeting with such a group it is strange that he would not have mentioned the topics of discussion and incredible that he would not have discussed the persons involved. Yet he does not discuss any of the persons presumably involved in this first of scientific societies.

We have, as have the modern sources from which we quoted, used "society" in a modern sense. But modern usage was not current in Chamberlain's day: for the use of the word "college" in "the general sense of meeting of companions, reunion, club" the Oxford English dictionary[91] gives no examples prior to the eighteenth century. From the fourteenth century the word "college" was used to speak of "a society of scholars," although usually – but not invariably – in connection with a University. But from the fifteenth century on, "college" also had the meaning of a "company, collective body, assemblage," and it may well have been this that was intended by Chamberlain.

Of Chamberlain's second term for Gilbert's group there seems little doubt: "covey," outside of its usual meaning of a family of partridges is given only one other meaning: "*fig.* and *transf.* A family, party, or set (of persons or things),"[92] the earliest example given by the *Oxford English dictionary* being from 1590.

---

[90] W. Hale-White, *Bacon, Gilbert and Harvey, being the Harveian oration delivered before the Royal College of Physicians of London, October 18th, 1927,* London, John Bale, Sons and Danielsson, Ltd., 1927, p. 47.

[91] *The Oxford English dictionary, being a corrected re-issue with an introduction, supplement, and bibliography, of A new English dictionary on historical principles founded mainly on the materials collected by The Philological Society,* Oxford, Clarendon Press, 1933, vol. 2, pp. 622–623. The notes here on the meanings of Chamberlain's terms are necessarily fragmentary and ignore other meanings of those words that appear in the dictionary.

[92] *Ibid.,* vol. 2, p. 1109.

As for Chamberlain's third term, "society," its usage in the sense of "A number of persons united together for the purpose of promoting some branch of study or research by means of meetings, publications, etc." is a mid-seventeenth century phenomenon, as is the usage to mean "A number of persons meeting together, esp. for the purpose of discussion or debate, conviviality or sociability." But in Chamberlain's era, the term was used to mean: "A corporate body of persons having the same residence."[93]

Admittedly we are on difficult ground here in attempting to determine just what Chamberlain was talking about. There seems, however, no reason whatsoever for attributing meanings to his words that did not come into existence until long afterwards, and any attempt to establish an otherwise unmentioned and unknown scientific organization from these words is, in my opinion, completely unjustified. I find myself in full agreement with Chamberlain's editor who, at each of the three words, carefully added a footnote to inform the reader that Chamberlain was writing of Dr. Gilbert's household.

Gilbert and Elizabeth

We need not rely solely on Chamberlain's gossip concerning Gilbert's appointment as physician to the Queen. The appointment appears in the Court Calendar:

43 *Eliz.* 21 Apr. *Wm. Gilbert offic. unus.* medicor^m. ad. vit. Pr. S.[94]

Gilbert's position is referred to in the title of Thomas Blundeville's book.[95]

William Barlowe, whose intellectual contact with Gilbert is certified by the letter to Barlow from Gilbert (p. 69), referred to Gilbert in 1618 as "physician unto our late renouned Soveraigne Queen Elizabeth, of happy memory."[96]

Two other seventeenth-century sources introduce new elements into the Gilbert-Elizabeth relationship. First, Gilbert's epitaph contains the lines

HINC AVLA ACCERSIT' IN SVMMV REGINAE ELIZABETHAE FAVOREM
RECEPTVS FVIT CVI VT SVCCESSORI REGI JACOBO SERVIVIT
ARCHIATROS.[97]

[93] *Ibid.*, vol. 9, pp. 360.
[94] As quoted by Thompson, *op. cit.* (fn. 61), p. 21.
[95] Namely, "one of the ordinarie Physicians to her maiestie..." Thomas Blundevile (Blundeville), *The theoriques of the seven planets,...*, London, Adam Islip, 1607.
[96] Barlowe, *op. cit., ed. cit.* (fn. 59), "Preface to the Reader," p. xi.
[97] See. Fig. 7.

The term "archiatros" definitely implies "chief physician" and it has frequently been so interpreted. Morant, in his widely-used work,[98] spoke of Gilbert as Elizabeth's chief physician, thereby introducing this term into the large number of biographies derived in part or in full from Morant. Cooke, toward the end of the nineteenth century, combined and reconciled the two traditions – quite falsely – writing

> He became one of the physicians in ordinary to Queen Elizabeth,... and in February, 1600, he was appointed Chief Physician to the Court. The date of the appointment is fixed by a letter from John Chamberlain...[99]

The appointment (p. 84) does not bear not any claims for a primary position for Gilbert among the Queen's several physicians. Thompson has found two additional pieces of evidence for Gilbert's "ordinary" position:

> The patent-roll itself has been examined. It sets out the appointment, with emolument "centum libros,"... and is for the term of his natural life. ... One hundred pounds per annum appears to have been the regular stipend of each of the Queen's physicians in ordinary, though not the invariable amount.[100]

Thompson also cites entries from the roll of the Queen's New Year Gifts, 1602–3, which show that Gilbert was not favored over the other Court physicians at this, Elizabeth's last New Year's.[101] Indeed, one might at least suspect, from her behavior at her death, that physicians did not occupy a particular place of honor in her mind.

The second additional seventeenth-century document is a half-page commentary on Gilbert written by Thomas Fuller (1608–1661), which includes the statement that Gilbert

> ...was physician to queen Elizabeth, who stamped on him many marks of her favor, besides an annual pension to encourage his studies.[102]

Fuller gives as his source Gilbert's "near kinsman Mr. William Gilbert of Brental-Ely in Suffolk." A glance at Fuller's birthdate encourages some skepticism as to the closeness of the relationship. He would not have consulted with Gilbert's "near kinsman"

[98] Morant, op. cit. (fn. 13), p. 117.
[99] Cooke, *op. cit.* (fn. 45), p. 730.
[100] Thompson, *op. cit.* (fn. 61), pp. 21–22.
[101] *Ibid.*, p. 23.
[102] Thomas Fuller, *op. cit.* (fn. 6), p. 515.

much before the 1630's at the earliest. From the pedigree of Fig. 6 that person was quite certainly either the son or grandson of William Gilbert the Younger, and probably the latter, and it is difficult to see how he could have been born much before the end oft he century. Elizabeth's motivation is then the clearest sort of hearsay – perhaps faithfully and correctly transmitted as a family tradition, but certainly hearsay. Furthermore, it seems certain from the evidence hitherto presented that Elizabeth had no more of a desire to encourage Gilbert's studies than those of any other of her physicians. Nor is there any indication from contemporary records that she "stamped on him many marks of her favor." Yet the widely quoted Wood (1721)[103] repeats Fuller, as does Morant (1768),[104] and by the end of the eighteenth century we find that Gilbert

> practised in the metropolis with great success and applause, which, being observed by queen Elizabeth whose talent it was to distinguish persons of superior merit, she sent for him to court, appointed him her physician in ordinary, and gave him an annual pension to encourage him in his studies. In these, as much as his extensive practice would permit him, he applied himself chiefly to consider and examine the various properties of the loadstone; and...[105]

The *De magnete* had very likely been published before Elizabeth "sent for him to court."

It is perhaps inevitable that sooner or later the term "pension" as used by Fuller should be interpreted in modern times to have its modern meaning, namely, payment for *past* services. Since Gilbert's appointment was for life and hence only terminated at Elizabeth's death, one quickly realizes that "pension" can only mean "legacy." Thus in 1900 we attain the clear misinterpretation:

> He was received, says Morant, with the highest favor by Queen Elizabeth, whom he served as chief physician, and from whom he received a legacy, the only legacy she left to anyone.[106]

And, in 1927

> ...the story that she left him a legacy shows her liking for him.[107]

[103] Wood, op. cit. (fn. 42), p. 321.
[104] Morant, *op. cit.* (fn. 13), p. 117.
[105] Hutchinson, *op. cit.* (fn. 38), p. 356.
[106] Richardson, *op. cit.* (fn. 17), pp. 33–34. Morant's full statement on the subject was "chief Physician to Queen Elizabeth; who had so high a value for him, that she allowed him an annual pension, to encourage him in his studies." Morant, *op. cit.* (fn. 13), p. 117.

In summary, Gilbert was clearly a physician of note in London, as evidenced by his offices in the Royal College of Physicians. He was selected as one of the Queen's physicians in ordinary and was rewarded in the usual manner for his duties. He was probably present at her death, although it could not be said that he attended her, for she did not look with favor upon the advice of her doctors. We have a graphic account of her last days from Chamberlain, who notes "I had a goode meanes to understand how the world went," presumably through Gilbert, and we may at least fancy that via Chamberlain we look at the dying Queen through Gilbert's eyes when we read

> ...she could not be won or perswaded neither by the counsaile, Divines, phisitians, nor the women about her once to tast or touch any phisicke; though ten or twelve phisitians that were continually about her did assure her with all manner of asserverations of perfect and easie recoverie yf she wold follow theyre advise. So that yt cannot be saide of her as yt was of the Emperor Adrian that *turba medicorum occidit* regem, for they say she died only for lack of phisicke.[108]

Gilbert's Personal Appearance: Portraits and Statues

There exists only one description of Gilbert for which any claim of authenticity can be made. Thomas Fuller wrote

> He had (saith my informer) the clearness of Venice glass, without the brittleness thereof; soon ripe, and long lasting, in his perfections... One saith of him, "that he was stoical, but not cynical," which I understand reserved but not morose;... ...His stature was tall, complexion cheerful; an happiness not ordinary in so hard a student and retired a person.[109]

We have already noted (p. 86) that Fuller's "informer" was more likely drawing on family traditions than on firsthand information.

I know of four portraits and two statues of Gilbert.

One statue is on the city hall at Colchester,[110] and presumably is a stylized version of fairly recent vintage. The second is in the Chapel of St. John's College, Cambridge. A photograph and description has been published, but the latter tells nothing of the statue's origins.[111]

---

[107] Hale-White, *op. cit.* (fn. 90), p. 40.

[108] Chamberlain's Letters, *op. cit.* (fn. 79), letter 62, pp. 188–189.

[109] Fuller, *op. cit.* (fn. 6), p. 515.

[110] A drawing is in Benham, *op. cit.* (fn. 26).

[111] [   ], "William Gilbert of Colchester," *The Electrical World and Engineer, a weekly review of current progress in electricity and its practical applications*, vol. 42 (2nd half, 1903), p. 480.

Two of the portraits are of modern origin, and both hang in the Colchester Town Hall. One was commissioned by Benham and painted by Frank Daniell. The other, painted by Arthur Ackland Hunt, shows Gilbert performing electric demonstrations in the presence of Queen Elizabeth, Sir Walter Raleigh, Sir Francis Drake, and Cecil Lord Burghley;[112] Hunt was reported as saying that he was incited to paint the picture by Sir Benjamin Richardson.

One portrait, which has been referred to previously (fn. 36) and which was without doubt authentic, has been destroyed. Wood wrote

> The Picture of this famous Doctor drawn to the Life, is hanging in the School-Gallery at *Oxon*, which shows him to have been of stature tall, and of a cheerful Complexion.[113]

Before destruction of this portrait it was copied in copper engraving and published[114]. It is this engraving that served as a model for the two modern paintings, and probably for the two statues as well.

Thompson found a full-length oil painting of Gilbert, on a wooden panel, at a bookseller's in London, and purchased the portrait.[115] It was later published by Charles Singer,[116] but the present whereabouts are not known to me. Thompson believed this portrait to be authentic.

Finally, in a drawing by Camden of Queen Elizabeth's funeral procession there is one group of figures entitled "clerks of parliament and doctors of medecine."[117] The figures are not portraits, but Thompson apparently felt that one particular one could be identified as Gilbert.[118]

Other Relics and Contemporary Mentions of Gilbert

After finding the Gilbert signature at the Record Office (p. 78), Thompson had it

---

[112] "The Gilbert Tercentenary Commemoration," *Journal of the Institution of Electrical Engineers, including original communications on electricity and electrical science,* vol. 33 (1903–1904), p. 69.

[113] Wood, *op. cit.* (fn. 42), col. 321. Morant repeats Wood's statement.

[114] S. and E. Harding, London, 1796. Republished in Harding's *Biographical Mirror,* vol. 2, London, 1798, according to secondary sources. I have not been able to verify this publication. See frontispiece.

[115] J. S. Thompson and H. G. Thompson, *Silvanus Phillips Thompson, D. Sc., LL.D., F.R.S., his life and letters,* New York, E. P. Dutton and Company, 1920, p. 231.

[116] Singer, *op. cit.* (fn. 41).

[117] Thompson and Thompson, op. cit. (fn. 115), p. 235, gives the passage from a letter from F. G. Kenyon to Thompson informing the latter of this cartoon.

[118] *Ibid.,* p. 235.

reproduced and sent to libraries.[119] Presumably as a result of this act, four Gilbert signatures were found in the books of St. John's College.[120]

In the 1893 English translation of the *De magnete*,[121] Mottelay reproduced the title page of a copy of the 1600 *De magnete*, inscribed "Dedit Guil. Gilbertus Jo. Sherwood proprijs manibus," belonging in 1893 to Chas. L. Clarke of New York. In addition, on a fragile inserted slip Mottelay reproduces an inscription from another copy, "Londini. ex dono authoris 8: Junij. 1600."

Thompson later found not only another autographed copy of the *De magnete*, given to Lancelot Browne,[122] but also a 1542 copy of Aristotle, *Stageritae de Naturali Auscultatione,...* with Gilbert's name, among others, on the title page and marginal notes, some in Gilbert's hand.

The relics which have been found of Gilbert are thus few indeed, and for good reason: by his will[123] Gilbert gave his books, globes, instruments, and minerals to the Royal College of Physicians, to he placed in the library of their building.[124]

The College of Physicians, like Wingfield House, was destroyed by the Great Fire of London.

Three other incidental contemporary comments on Gilbert should be mentioned here. First, Thomas Blundeville referred to him as "skilled in chemistry."[125]

Second, John Owen (1560?–1622), the epigrammatist, embalmed Gilbert twice:

> *Ad D. Gilbertum*
> Stare negas terram; nobis miracula narras;
> Haec cum scribebas, in rate forsan eras.[126]
> *Medice cura teispum. Ad Gilbertum.*
> Ut teipsum cures frustra, Gilberte, moneris;
> Est tibi nam semper maxima cura tui.[127]

Third, Gilbert's later contemporary, the geographer Richard Hakluyt (1552?–1616) wrote in 1600:

[119] *Ibid.*, p. 234.
[120] *Ibid.*, p. 234.
[121] See fn. 29.
[122] Thompson, *op. cit.* (fn. 112), p. 69.
[123] Two copies are in Somerset House, London.
[124] The building of the college was very near Gilbert's home.
[125] According to secondary sources. I have been unable to find this reference.
[126] *Epigrammatum Ioannis Owen Oxoniensis Cambro-Britanni libri tres,* 4th ed., London, Simon Waterson, 1612, bk. 1, epigram 14.
[127] *Ibid.*, bk. 2, epigram 82.

...I was once minded to have added to the end of these my labours a short treatise, which I have lying by me in writing, touching The curing of hot diseases incident to traveilers in long and Southerne voyages, which treatise was written in English, no doubt of a very honest mind, by one M. George Wateson, and dedicated unto her secred Majestie. But being carefull to do nothing herein rashly, I shewed it to my worshipfull friend M. doctour Gilbert, a gentleman no lesse excellent in the chiefest secrets of the Mathematicks (as that rare jewel lately set foorth by him in Latine doeth evidently declare) then in his owne profession of physicke: who assured me, after hee had perused the said treatise, that it was very defective and unperfect, and that if hee might have leasure, which that argument would require, he would either write something thereof more advisedly himself, or would conferre with the whole Colledge of the Physicions, and set downe some order by common consent for the preservation of her Majesties subjects.[128]

Other contemporary comments, concerned with Gilbert's scientific work, will be discussed in a later chapter.

In a letter dated 6 December 1603 to the Earl of Shrewsbury, Sir Michael Hicks wrote:

I heard as I was writing here of that Doctor Gilbert, the physician, is dead, who was my neighbor at St. Peter's Hill. He was a learned physician, and an honest. The sickness is greatly decreased in London, and the citizens do return daily in great numbers.[129]

Summary

William Gilbert was born 24 May, 1544, at Colchester, son of a well-to-do free-burgess of that town, a member of a respectable family of which William was the fourth generation. He was educated at Cambridge, having a known record there, and received his M. D. in 1569. In the mid-1570's he settled in London, having probably worked out his magnetic philosophy in the interim, at some unknown place: Colchester, London, or abroad. He practiced medicine, becoming a respected and influential member of his profession, rising to the positions of President of the Royal College of Physicians and

[128] *Hakluyt's Voyages,* "The epistle dedicatorie in the third volume of the second edition, 1600." *The principal navigations voyages traffiques & discoveries of the English nation made by sea or overland to the remote and farthest distant quarters of the earth at any time within the compass of these 1600 years,* in 8 vols., London and Toronto, J. M. Dent and Sons Ltd.; New York, E. P. Dutton & Co., 1927, vol. 1, pp. 51–52.
[129] Talbot and Cecil papers, iii, p. 79, as quoted by Thompson, *op. cit.* (fn. 61), p. 28.

physician in ordinary to Queen Elizabeth. And, as only an Englishman could have put it,

> Such his loyalty to the queen, that, as if unwilling to survive, he died in the same year with her, 1603.[130]

Presumably he died of the plague.

There is no direct evidence that Gilbert traveled abroad. There is every reason to doubt that he was in any way favored by the queen over her other physicians; she left him no legacy of which we know, and as far as we know she evidenced no interest in his work in physics. There is every reason to doubt that any sort of a scientific group met at Wingfield House.

It is unbelievable that unknown traces of Gilbert do not exist in English manuscript collections. Thompson apparently had some sort of a lead into the Talbot and Cecil papers at Hatfield, and found the several items noted previously herein. At the same time, one must be careful, in the act of focusing upon an individual, not to exaggerate his contemporary importance: it is easy to make Wingfield House the city palace of the Queen's Chief Physician, a center of natural philosophy at which contemporary scientists formed a precursor of the Royal Society; it is sobering to realize that Stow, who conducts his reader as it were on a guided tour of London, finds nothing of interest to point out in St. Peter's Hill except six alms houses.[131]

---

[130] Fuller, *op. cit.* (fn. 6), p. 515.
[131] Stow, op. cit. (fn. 67).

CHAPTER THREE

GILBERT AND ELECTRICITY

Today both electric and magnetic phenomena are bound together and explained by a single conceptual scheme, electromagnetic theory. To some degree the history of these sciences – or this science – may be characterized as a succession of syntheses and analyses of the two areas of study: before the 16th Century the amber effect was, as it were, carried along as the younger and rather useless and uninteresting brother of magnetism, both being immersed in lists of occult phenomena, examples of attraction. Gilbert separated them, an act reminiscent of the earlier separation of theology into its revealed and natural components which may be regarded as the foundation of modern natural science, and for very similar reasons.[1] In doing so, he founded the science of electricity, and it remained a science separate from magnetism for nearly three centuries.

The bases upon which we today rest our differentation between magnetostatic and electrostatic attraction had been known long before the time of Gilbert. Theophrastus (p. 22) had noted that the lodestone attracted only iron while amber and lyncurium attracted thin sheets of metal as well as straws and twigs; Plutarch had also remarked this affinity of amber for many substances (p. 23); Augustine (354 – 430) had again stressed the difference in his influential *De civitate Dei*.[2]

The second major difference between magnetic phenomena and the amber effect, the failure of amber to orient, seems an inevitable by-product of the use of the compass, and was stated at least as early as the 15th Century by Marsilio Ficino (1433 – 1499).[3] Gilbert's separation of magnetic phenomena from the amber effect is based upon very fundamental elements of his theory of magnetism and the reasons which he brings forth for evidence of the essential dissimilarity of the two phenomena are at the same time the grounds upon which he builds his theory of electricity. The main theme of his

---

[1] 'With Thomas [Aquinas] and his teacher Albert [the Great], the conception of 'natural *science*' definitely stamped itself on the thought of Western Europe, never to be forgotten again. The two things we miss in the Thomistic conception of this science are (1) the Platonic conviction that the basis of any satisfactory physical science must be sought in mathematics, and (2) the Platonic sense of the *provisionality* of all results attained in physical science...' A. E. Taylor, *Platonism and its influence*, New York, Longmans, Green and Co., 1927, p. 50.

[2] *De civitate Dei*, xxi, 4. *Sancti Aurelii Augustini episcopi de civitate Dei*, ed. B. Dombart, in 2 vol., Leipzig, B. G. Teubner, 1877, p. 494.

[3] Park Benjamin, *The intellectual rise in electricity*, London, Longmans, Green, & Co., 1895, pp. 240–241.

magnetic theory is woven throughout the first book of *De magnete*,[4] which provides historical and technical background for what is to come. Lodestones, he tells us, come in all sizes, all colors, and with all sorts of physical properties, as well as with a wide variation of magnetic power, and are found throughout the world.

> Ita inter se varij & dissimiles omnes, tum alij plus, alij minus virtute egregia, dotati. Variantur enim ex soli natura, dissimili glebaru mixtura, & humoru, pro regionis ratione & labe, in suprema hac terrae adnata substatia, ex multarum causarum confluentijs, & perpetua ortus & interitus vicissitudine, corporumq; mutationibus. Nec rarus est hic tantae virtutis lapis, nec vlla regio in qua non aliqua specie reperiatur.[5]

After again reinforcing his statement of the wide distribution of lodestones, with examples showing that "nam lapis hic virtutibus suis egregius, vt nunc per vniuersum terrarum orbem celebris; ita & vbiq; omnis illum terra profert, & quasi omnium terrarum indigena est,"[6] Gilbert returns to the mutability of the earth's surface.

> Nam licet terrestris globus varijs humoribus, & glebarum naturis, perpetua generationis & corruptionis vicissitudine ortis, per totum eius ambitum temporis diuturnitate altius in superficie efflorescit, & tanquam tegumento, & inuolucro vario, & caduco cingitur: tamen ex eius gremio plurimis sese attollit locis, a perfectiori corpore propinquior soboles: & sese mittit in luminis auras. Inualidi vero magnetes & minus robusti, humorum labe debilitati, in omni regione, in omni pago manifeste apparent: facile est inuenire ingentem eorum vim vbiq;, sine montium aut profunditatum penetratione, aut metallicorum difficultatibus & aerumnis; quemadmodum in sequentibus demonstrabimus:...[7]

For Gilbert the Earth is a giant lodestone. Since this concept is basic in Gilbert's

---

[4] *Gvilielmi Gilberti Colcestrensis, medici Londinensis, de magnete, magneticisqve corporibvs, et de magno magnete tellure; Physiologia noua, plurimis & argumentis, & experimentis demonstrata*, London, Peter Short, 1600. Hereafter referred to as '*De magnete*.' In the passages quoted, accent marks have been omitted as have marks to indicate an omitted "m" following a vowel.

[5] *De magnete*, bk. 1, chap. 2., p. 10. 'Thus varied and unlike one another, some are endowed with more, others with less, of the admirable magnetic virtue. For they vary according to the nature of the soil and the admixture of clays and humors; according to the manner and terrain of the region, in this highest layer of the earth; according to the coming together of many causes, the perpetual alternations of birth and decay, and the mutations of bodies. This stone of such power is not rare, nor is there any region in which it may not be found in some form.' The term 'ortus' is here translated as 'birth.' It should be noted in this respect that Gilbert had strong astrological leanings.

[6] *Ibid.*

[7] *De magnete*, bk. 1, chap. 2, p. 11. 'For although it is understandable that the terrestrial globe, of

thought, all phenomena he investigated must be related to it. At the same time there is clearly an abundance of earthy material that is non-magnetic. Gilbert concluded that the existence of such material is a surface phenomenon, to be accounted for by the known and clear processes of decay and mutation on the surface.

This dichotomy proposed by Gilbert may be viewed as a redrawing of the long-standing Scholastic boundary between terrestrial and celestial, which he would have us change to a boundary between the pure earth and the products of mutation that lie over it: the world is to be divided into the magnetic and the non-magnetic. It is of interest that the purer region remains, in Gilbert's cosmology, the region that is concerned with celestial phenomena.

At the same time, the separation is no longer simply one of regions, for the overt products of the Earth's womb are seen by us to be mixed in with the products of surface decay that characterize the region in which we live. Gilbert's conceptual scheme in a sense brings man into contact with the celestial region of older cosmologies, and enables him literally to lay his hands upon the key to the operation of the universe – not quite unsullied, for the lodestones which we can possess have been affected by the humors of the surface region, but they still possess a great deal of the fundamental virtue of the Earth. We shall see that Gilbert is thus able to transform astronomy from an observational science to an experimental one – or at least able to see that such a transformation is within the grasp of man.

There is an immediate difficulty in Gilbert's conceptual scheme for magnetism, since in speaking of these products of the Earth's womb as "a perfectiori corpore propinquior soboles," in attempting to elevate iron to a preëminent position, he must offset the clear knowledge that iron is not even one of the noble metals. Thus he is forced to the position that

> Quare male a plurimis dicitur in auro esse terram puram, in ferro vero maxime impuram:quasi vero terra vera, tellusq; ipsa, adeo sit res (nescio quibus subtilitatibus) depurata.[8]

various humors and natures of soils rising from the perpetual alternations of growth and decay, is, in the lapse of time ever changing everywhere, deeper into its surface, and is being covered as it were with a cover, a varied and perishable wrapping. Still from her womb there arises, in many places, an offspring closer to the more perfect body, and it makes its way into the light of day. Indeed the weak and less powerful lodestones, crippled by the wavering humors, are visible in every region and district. It is easy to find enormous numbers of these everywhere, without penetrating mountains to great depths, or the difficulties and toil of mining, as we shall demonstrate later:...'

[8] *De magnete*, bk. 1, chap. 7, p. 21. 'Wherefore it is incorrectly said by many that in gold is pure earth, but in iron exceedingly impure; as if indeed true earth [the element] and the Earth [the globe] itself, insofar as there is such a thing (which is of unknown fineness) were depurified.'

In support of this view, Gilbert devotes an entire chapter to "Ferrum quid sit, & ex qua materia, & eius vsus."[9] For, he tells us,

> Quare ferrum tunc melius intelligemus quid sit, cum causas & materiam metallorum quales illae sint, aliter atq; ante nos alij putauerunt, declarabimus.[10]

His own views on the generation of iron, simply a modification of classical views to give iron a predominant role, follow. He notes that lodestone, "qui nihil aliud est quam nobilis vena ferraria"[11] is produced simultaneously with iron. There follows a lengthy ennumeration of the uses of iron. Gilbert concludes:

> Quae ideo recitaui, vt intelligatur quantus sit ferri vsus, quod omnia alia metalla plus centies superat, & indies a metallicis excoquitur, cuius in omni fere pago officinae. Hoc enim praecipuum metallum, quod multis, maximisq; humanis necessitatibus inseruit: & longe supra alia metalla omnia in tellure abundat, praedominaturq;. Quare vani sunt illi Chemici, qui putant naturam velle omnia metalla in aurum perficere: quasi eadem pararet omnes lapides mutare in adamantes, quia adamas omnes splendore & duritie superat, quia aurum splendore, grauitate, & firmitudine, aduersus omnes iniurias inuictum, excellit.[12]

I. The New Attractors

The first book of Gilbert's *De magnete* contains many arguments similar to the one just presented, arguments to demonstrate that the Earth is a giant lodestone. Throughout, iron has a unique role: iron ore is usually magnetic, iron is magnetizable. Thus the five magnetic phenomena are the manifestations of iron's special nature, and the principal

---

[9] *De magnete,* bk. 1, chap. 7.

[10] *De magnete,* bk. 1, chap. 7, p. 19.

[11] *De magnete,* bk. 1, chap. 7, p. 21.

[12] *De magnete,* bk. 1, chap. 7, p. 24. 'Which things I have recited so that it may be understood how great is the use of iron, which surpasses a hundred-fold that of all other metals, and to show how it is refined by metal workers, whose workshops are found in nearly every region. For this is the foremost among metals and it serves many—and the greatest—of human needs. And its abundancy in the Earth is far above that of all other metals and it is predominant. Therefore those Chemists are wrong who ascribe to Nature the desire to change all metals into gold. It is as if she were prepared to change all stones into diamond, because diamond surpasses all in splendor and hardness, as gold excels in splendor, weight, and strength, unconquered in the face of all damage.'

manifestation is magnetic attraction – a term that Gilbert replaced by "magnetic coition," which he applied uniquely to magnetism. The substance and the phenomenon together comprise the fundamental element of the World – ample motivation for their study. Yet before analysis and synthesis of the various elementary phenomena, the five magnetic movements, it is essential that Gilbert take account of the amber effect: otherwise the existence of this anomaly endangers his entire theoretical structure.

In the separation of, and distinction between, the two sets of phenomena, Gilbert is insistent that neither is occult, that is, both have physical explanations. His insistence necessarily forces him to consider the large number of other phenomena lumped under the name of "attraction."[13] Because of their existence and because his principal interest is in magnetism, he chooses to identify the latter, rather than the amber effect, as the new sort of physical phenomenon, unappreciated and ununderstood by his predecessors. The semantic foundation for this identification is laid in his list of *"Verborum quorundam interpretatio"* at the very beginning of the *De magnete:*

> Coitio magnetica: quia in magneticis motus non fit per facultatem attractricem, sed per vtriusque concursum aut concordantiam non vt sit vnius tantum ἑλκτικὴ δύναμις [attractive power] sed vtriusq; συνδρομή [running together], vigoris semper coitio: corporis etiam si moles non obstiterit.[14]

Here then is the motivation for Gilbert's digression, in the *De magnete,* to the amber effect: the statement that the amber effect is fundamentally different from magnetic attraction and even the coining of the term "magnetic coition" to emphasize that difference is simply not convincing. As we have discussed at some length in Chapter One, one does not observe attraction – nor does one observe magnetic coition. The *observation* in these cases is either the change in position of an object or the failure of an object to fall when it apparently lacks support. Earlier philosophers had suggested various causes for this behavior of objects, and those causes had become lumped under the generic name of "attraction." Now Gilbert proposes that the causes of the motion of iron to the lodestone and chaff to amber are so utterly different as to not admit dis-

---

[13] Some of which we have encountered in the writings of antiquity: for example, Galen's discussion of the action of cathartic drugs, the drawing of poisons by drugs, the drawing of water by grain and the sun (p. 20). Gilbert discusses some attractions and repulsions that his predecessors had associated with magnetism in *De magnete,* bk. 2, chaps. 38 and 39.

[14] *De magnete,* *vi, *recto.* 'Magnetic coition: since in magnetics motion does not occur through an attractive ability but through a joint concourse or concordance, not as if there were of one only an ἑλκτικὴ δύναμις [attractive power] but a joint συνδρομή [running together]. There is always a coition of the vigor and even of the body, if the mass does not obstruct it.'

cussion in the same terms. Yet Gilbert realizes that his reader understandably may insist upon their identity, evoking as evidence the observations of identical sorts of motion produced by lodestone and amber. Of the various modes of attack upon this ignorance, Gilbert chooses the empirical one, and enters upon a detailed study of the amber effect. The second chapter of the second book is addressed to this task, which is already revealed in its title: "De coitione magnetica, primumque de succini attractione, siue verius corporum ad succinum applicatione." Gilbert's attack upon current views would seem to me to reflect the attitude of the university-educated man in a world in which knowledge of Nature seems to be slipping somewhat into the hands of the practical man – or at least a world in which the latter is laying considerable claim to participation in such knowledge.[15]

> Ita in plurimis nonnulli, cum dausam [causam] agunt, cuius rationem reddere non possunt, magnetem & succinum, tanquam personatos aduocatos inducunt. Sed hi (praeter communem illum errorem) nescientes magneticarum motionum causas, a succini viribus longe diuersas esse: labuntur facile, & ipsi suis cogitationibus amplius decipiuntur. ...succino, de quo nonnulla prius dicenda sunt, vt qualis illa corporum applicatio, & quam diuersa a magneticis actionibus, & aliena sit (inscijs adhuc mortalibus, qui illam inclinationem attractionem esse putant, & cum magneticis coitionibus conferunt) appareat.[16]

Thus although Gilbert's main line of attack will focus upon the overt and obvious observable differences, he does not hesitate to tie his theory back to classical physics.

After a digression on the ancient names for, and ancient knowledge about, amber, during which he notes that not only does amber attract, but "Quod etiam facit Gagates lapis",[17] Gilbert reiterates his views on the confusion, paying more attention to the

---

[15] For example, the most recent major discovery in magnetism had been made by Robert Norman, an instrument maker (see p. 47). And if one thing is certain about Gilbert, it is that he utterly failed to discharge his intellectual indebtedness to Robert Norman. See E. Zilsel, 'The Origins of William Gilbert's Scientific Method,' *Journal of the History of Ideas,* vol. 2 (1941), pp. 1–32.

[16] *De magnete,* bk. 2, chap. 2, p. 47. 'Thus it often happens that persons, when pleading a cause for which they are unable to give reasons, bring in lodestone and amber as masked advocates. But these [persons] (in addition to their general errors) are unaware that the causes of magnetic motions are very different from the forces of amber. They fall into error easily and are themselves greatly deceived by their own meditations. ...amber, of which some things must first be said: it will become apparent what is the nature of the attachment of bodies to it; and how it differs from the magnetic action and is foreign to it (these mortals being still ignorant who identify that inclination to be an attraction [that is, occult] and compare it to magnetic coition).'

[17] Jet is a hard compacted form of coal. The amber effect had been noted for jet by Alexander Neckam, *De naturis rerum,* chap. 97. *Alexandri Neckam de naturis rerum libri duo...* ed. Thomas Wright, London,

97

authors of the confusion than before. This passage has won Gilbert a place in the lists of scientists who were following the new experimental philosophy of Galileo and Francis Bacon.[18]

> Multi sunt authores moderni, qui de succino & gagate attrahentibus paleas, alijsq; vulgo incognitis, scripserunt, & ab alijs exscripserunt; quorum laboribus Bibliopolarum officinae farciuntur. Aetas nostra multos libros protulit de abditis, de abstrusis, de occultis causis & miraculis; in quibus omnibus succinum & gagates adducuntur allicientia paleas; sed nullis rationibus ab experimentis, & demonstrationibus inuentis; tantum agunt verbis, rebus ipsis maiorem caliginem inducetibus; (scilicet) abdite, miraculose, abstruse, recondite, occulte. Quare & nullum talis philosophia fructum facit, (sed verbis tantum quibusdam graeculis, aut non vulgaribus insistit, lipporum & tonsorum nostrorum more, qui verba quaedam latina rudi popello, tanquam artis insignia ostentant, & auram popularem captant) quod ipsi philosophi plurimi nihil quaerentes, nullo rerum vsu valentes, otiosi, & inertes, nihil suis monumentis proficiunt, nec vident quae lumen suis rationibus adferre possunt.[19]

Longman, Green, Longman, Roberts, and Green 1863, p. 181. Chapter 97, in its entirety, reads 'Si decorem gagatis requiras, nigro gemmeus; si naturam, aqua ardet, oleo restinguitur; si potestatem, attritu calefactus applicita detinet, atque succinem; si beneficium, hydropicis illum portanibus beneficium praestat.'

[18] Galileo was about 10 years old when Gilbert did his work, and Bacon about 13. Yet even the most cursory examination of modern books reveals this tendency to place Gilbert among the followers of Galileo and Bacon. Thus one physics text, H. E. White's *Classical and modern physics*, New York, D. Van Nostrand, 1940, p. 222, cites a passage from *De magnete* and remarks: "So strongly does he advocate here, and carry out, himself, the experimental method that he is to be classed as a scientist with his contemporary Galileo 'the father of modern physics.'" In a general physical science textbook by E. J. Cable, R. W. Getchell, W. H. Kadesch, *The physical sciences*, New York, Prentice-Hall, 1940, pp. 2-3, we are told that in the last part of the sixteenth century Gilbert experimented in electricity and magnetism and Galileo experimented with falling bodies, dropping objects of unequal masses from the Tower of Pisa, that "with Gilbert, Galileo, and their contemporaries we arrive at the beginning of the modern period of scientific development. Thenceforth the experimental method was increasingly recognized as an effective means of investigation, and considered essential in testing the merits of hypotheses." Even in a modern history of science, A. Wolf's, *A history of science, technology, and philosophy in the 16th & 17th centuries*, New York, The Macmillan Co., 1935, p. 293, we find it said of the *De magnete* that "It is characterized almost throughout by its reliance upon the results of experiment, in accordance with the teaching of Francis Bacon,…" And in Jean Daujat's *Origines et formation de la théorie des phénomènes électriques et magnétiques*, Paris, Hermann, 1945, p. 125, "Gilbert est le contemporain, l'ami et le disciple de François Bacon,…"
It is my opinion that such comments are not simply errors in chronology but evidence of a particular philosophical orientation to the role of experiment in scientific work; furthermore it is my opinion that that orientation is outmoded.
[19] *De magnete*, bk. 2, chap. 2, pp. 47-48. "Many are the modern authors who have written about amber and jet as attracting chaff and about other facts unknown to the generality or have copied from other

To many who have regarded Galileo as the inventor of experimental physics, the passage just quoted was anomalous. Hence an intellectual relationship of Gilbert to Galileo was to be established in terms of an alleged trip to Italy during which there was a transfer of attitude–the direction of transfer depending upon the attitude of the interpreter. Gilbert's relationship to Bacon is somewhat more definite, and many biographers and historians have argued, with little effect, that Bacon's originality in scientific methodology vanishes when examined in the light of Gilbert's work and Bacon's knowledge thereof. We shall return to both of these relationships in later chapters.

In the traditional nineteenth century view, before the period of serious scholarly investigations in the history of science, it was held that appeals to experience were a seventeenth century phenomenon, and were not to be found in earlier writings. Since the researches of such men as Duhem, Thorndike and Francis Johnson, we know that expositions of the need for experiential information are much more common in the 16th Century than would have been thought to be the case by such a person as Ernst Mach. It is necessary to look more carefully and more directly at the technical scientific work of the author concerned, if one is to determine his place in and position concerning the "new experimental philosophy," and to devote less attention to his philosophical statements, which are usually very difficult for a modern commentator to interpret. And for us, therefore, Gilbert establishes himself as an empiricist not by this general statement of position but by the next passage of the *De magnete*, which is concerned with information collected empirically.

> Nam non solum succinum, & gagates (vt illi [earlier writers] putant) allectant corpuscula; sed Adamas, Sapphirus, Carbunculus, Iris gemma, Opalus, Amethystus, Vincentina, & Bristolla (Anglica gemma siue fluor) Berillus, &

writers: with the results of their labors booksellers' shops are crammed. Our age has produced many volumes about hidden, abstruse, and occult causes and wonders, in all of which amber and jet are set forth as attracting chaff. But you do not find in them ever a proof from experiment or demonstration: the writers deal only in words, a thing that introduces thicker darkness. They treat the subject esoterically, miraculously, abstrusely, recondirely, mystically. Wherefore such philosophy bears no fruit, for it rests simply on a few Greek or uncommon terms, after the manner of contemporary gossips and barbers who make a show of a few Latin words in the hearing of the ignorant rabble in token of their learning, and thus strive for popular favor. Few of the philosophers themselves investigate or have any first-hand acquaintance with anything; most of them are idle or untrained, add nothing to knowledge by their writings, and do not see the things that might throw a light upon their reasonings."
In some ways the following quotation is a more forceful statement of the empirical view: "Deploranda est humana, in rebus naturalibus inscitia, & taquam in tenebris somniantes, excitandi sunt moderni philosophi, & ad rerum vsum & tractationem educendi, ab otiosa ex libris tantum quaesita doctrina, probabilium rationum nugamentis, & coniecturis tantum suffulta." (Bk. 1, chap. 10, p. 28).

Crystallus idem faciunt. Similes etiam attrahendi vires habere videntur vitrum (praesertim clarum, & lucidum) tum ex vitro, aut Crystallo adulteratae gemmae, vitrum antimonij, & fluores plurimi ex fodinis, & Belemnites. Allicit etiam sulphur, mastix, & cera dura sigillaris ex lacca varijs coloribus tincta, composita. Allicit resina durior, vt arsenicum, sed imbecillius; aegre etiam & obscure in conuenienti coelo sicco Sal gemma, lapis specularis, & alumen rupeum. Quod videre licet, cum aer media Hyeme rigidus fuerit, & clarus, tenuisque; cum effluuia telluris electrica minus impediunt, & electrica firmius indurescunt; de quibus postea.[20]

For the detection of weak attractions Gilbert recommends the use of a *versorium,* a needle "ex quouis metallo," three or four fingers long, of light weight, and balanced on a sharp point so that it may easily turn about a vertical axis (Fig. 13).

This instrument was obviously suggested by the magnetic compass and, as far as is known, was invented by Gilbert.[21] It is the first instrument designed for and applied to the study of electric phenomena, the first electroscope, and is still used, at least for demonstration purposes. As is the case with all electroscopes, it could also be used as an electrometer, but with this difficulty: the strength of the effect produced is reflected in the *quickness of movement* of the versorium, a quantity that could only be estimated crudely. The eighteenth century forms of electroscope – electrometer – included some types in which a portion of the electroscope was simply *displaced* by the electrical action. Since displacement is amenable to direct measurement and quickness of movement is not, the eighteenth century electrician was able to measure a physical quantity which he could associate with electric action. In contrast, with his versorium Gilbert could

[20] *De magnete,* bk. 2, chap. 2, p. 48. "For not only do amber and jet (as they [earlier writers] suppose) attract small objects, but diamond, sapphire, carbuncle, iris gem, opal, amethyest, vincentia and bristolla (an English gem or spar), beryl, and crystal do the same. Similar powers of attracting are seen to be possessed as well by glass (especially clear and lucid) as well as by false gems made either of glass or of crystal, antimony glass, many fluors from mines, and belemnites. Sulphur, mastix, and hard sealing-wax made of various colors of lac also attract. Hard resin attracts, as does orpiment, but more weakly; with difficulty and obscurely, in suitably dry weather, rock salt, mica, rock alum also attract."

[21] An engraving by Johannes Stradanus (Jan van der Straet, Giovanni della Strada) shows a similar device in a room filled with magnetic and navigational devices (Fig. 14). One might well take this device to be a copy of Gilbert's drawing (Fig. 13) except that the Stradanus engraving dates from the 1580's.

It seems certain that the pivoted needle in the engraving is a magnetic compass. Yet Stradanus was in Florence most of the time from 1553 on, a member of the Academy of Florence, and it is difficult to avoid wondering where Gilbert was from 1569 to 1573. As we have seen (p. 69), if he went to the Continent, he may well have gone to Italy; if he went to Italy, he may well have gone to Florence. Gilbert was quite certainly using the versorium before the Stradanus engraving was published.

am, more indicis magnetici, cuius alteri fini appone succinum, vel

lapillum leniter fricatum, nitidum & politum, nam illico versorium conuertit se. Plura igitur attrahere videntur, tàm quæ à naturâ tantùm efformata, quàm quæ arte parata, aut conflata, & commixta sunt; nec ita vnius vel alterius singularis est proprietas (vti vulgo existimatur) sed plurimorum natura manifesta, tam simplicium suis tantùm formis consistentium, quàm compositorum; vt ceræ duræ sigillaris, & aliarum etiam quarundam ex pinguibus mixturarum. Sed vndè ista inclinatio fieret, & quænam sint vires illæ, (de quibus pauci paucissima, vulgus philosophantium nihil protulerunt) ampliùs inquirendum. A Galeno tria in vniuersum trahendi genera constituta sunt, in rebus naturalibus: Primum eorum quę qualitate elementari, calore (videlicet) trahunt: Secundum genus est eorum, quæ vacuati successione trahunt: Tertium eorum, quę à totius substantiæ proprietate attrahunt, quæ etiam ab Auicenna & alijs recitantur. Non ista quidem nobis vllo modo satisfacere possunt, neq; succini, gagatis, & adamantis, aliorumq; similium (quæ ob eandem virtutem vires obtinent) causas continent; neq; magnetis, & magneticorum omnium, quæ ab illis longè dissimili & aliena efficientiâ, ab alijs deriuatâ fontibus, virtutem obtinent. Quarè & alias inuenire motionum causas conuenit, aut cum his, (tanquam in tenebris) errare, nulloq; modo scopum attingere. Succinum verò non calore allicit, vtpote calefactum ab igne, & admotum festucis non attrahit, siue tepeat, siue caleat aut ferueat, siue ad flammam vsq; vrgeatur. Cardanus (vt & Pictorius) existimat non dissimili modo fieri, quàm a cucurbitula, ab ignea vi: sed vis attrahens cucurbitulæ non est propriè ab ignea vi: At prius dixerat rem siccam velle combibere humidum pingue, quare ad ipsum ferri. Sed ista inter se pugnantia, tum à ratione etiã aliena. Succinum enim si moueretur ad pabulum, aut si alia corpora inclinarent ad succinũ, vt ad pabulum, vnius esset deuorati diminutio, sicut alterius saturati accretio. Quorsũ tũc ignea vis attrahens desideratur in succino? Si à calore sit attractio, cur alia etiam plurima corpora, siue igne, sole, aut attritu excalefacta non attraherent? Neq; propter dissipatũ aërẽ, in aperto aëre attractio fieri potest; (quã tamen ratione pro magneticis motionibus, Lucretius

E j.   poëta

Fig. 13. A page from the first edition of the *De magnete*, showing Gilbert's versorium.

LAPIS·POLARIS, MAGNES.

Lapis reclufit ifte Flauio abditum   Poli fuum hunc amorem, at ipse nauitæ.

Fig. 14. A portion of an engraving in the series *Nova reperta* of Johannes Stradanus (late sixteenth century) showing various magnetic devices. Note the needle on the corner of the desk near the scholar's left hand (*Nova reperta*, Publication No. 8 of the Burndy Library, Norwalk, Conn., 1953).

only estimate quickness of movement. Consequently his electrical measurements are few. Nevertheless, we have seen he used the versorium as an electroscope, as a detector of weak attractions, with considerable success, compiling not only a list of amber-like attractors but a list of non-attractors as well.[22] In these lists, far more than in his attack upon the non-experimental nature of earlier writings, Gilbert establishes himself as an experimentalist.

Today, a large number of historians of science would deny Galileo the title of "experimenter," despite the claims that he founded experimental physics, a viewpoint that should be taken into account when examining the nature of Gilbert's work. In the case of Galileo the objection is at least threefold: others had relied on experiments as much or more than did Galileo;[23] Galileo did not present a mass of experimental evidence in support of his theories; third, and most important for our purposes, Galileo was able to predict theoretically, from an existing conceptual scheme for mechanics, the results of experiments and to publish those results with confidence. We have only become aware of the existence of this theoretical structure in the last few decades;[24] it has a long history and while certainly modified by Galileo, the modification was by no means a matter of fitting new facts into the structure. In brief, experiment on the part of Galileo was unnecessary to produce the results which he published, as he himself tells us.[25]

In contrast, there is no evidence whatsoever that a theoretical structure existed in the late 16th Century from which Gilbert could have deduced that a rubbed opal would cause the versorium to turn, when held near it, whereas a rubbed emerald would not.

[22] *De magnete*, bk. 2, chap. 2, p. 51.

[23] One of many is Joannes Philoponus (fl. c. 500 A. D.) who wrote of Aristotle's views on falling bodies "But this is completely erroneous, and our view may be corroborated by actual observation more effectively than by any sort of verbal argument. For if you let fall from the same height two weights..." M. R. Cohen and I. E. Drabkin, *A source book in Greek science*, New York, McGraw-Hill Book Company, 1948, p. 220. It is not necessary to reach back so far: the history of the 16th Century is filled with experimenters in mechanics.

[24] See the trilogy by A. Koyré, *Études Galiléennes*, Paris, Hermann & Cie., 1939. The transmission of knowledge from the University of Paris in the fourteenth century to Padua in the sixteenth century has been discussed by J. H. Randall Jr., "The Development of Scientific Method in the School of Padua," *Journal of the History of Ideas*, vol. 1 (1940), pp. 177-206.

[25] For example, in the Second Day of his 1632 astronomical work, Galileo's spokesman in the dialogues insists upon the validity of a prediction that he has never tested, insists that those who disagree have simply not performed the experiments because they have published the wrong results, insist that he need not perform the experiments because "I [without experiment] am assured that the effect will ensue as I tell you, for so it is necessary that it should,..." *Dialogue on the great world systems*, ed. G. de Santillana, Chicago, University of Chicago Press, 1953, p. 159. Such statements are to be found not only in this work but also in his 1638 work on mechanics.

Perhaps he learned of a few attractors from his predecessors – he certainly knew of Fracastoro's mention of the diamond as an attractor.[26] Yet there is no indication of the existence of such extensive lists of attractors and non-attractors before Gilbert. In brief, the preparation of objects by rubbing, the presentation of those objects to the versorium, and the decision as to whether the versorum turned, was a necessary stage in the compiling of Gilbert's lists of attractors and non-attractors.

Gilbert's Treatment of Earlier Theories

Once electrics are a defined class, it is possible to explain the amber effect, as demonstrated by any substance: a piece of this substance attracts when rubbed because it is an electric. The inherent circularity is worth noting: the generic term "electric" contains implicit in its usage the assumption that such a class exists, tending to focus discussion upon whether this or that substance *is* an electric and turning it away from whether such a category exists. The creation of the classes of electrics and non-electrics was a fruitful act, and these classifications have remained in science to the present time, with little modification.[27]

Once established, the concept of electric demands both an explanation of the existence of electrics and non-electrics and – at least to Gilbert – an explanation of the difference between electric and magnetic phenomena. Despite his initial insistence that they are so different that they belong to different classes of phenomena, Gilbert is aware that this insistence in itself is not convincing, and so he turns to proof, beginning with the citation of some of the earlier theories of electric attraction and their refutation from observations. The theories mentioned by Gilbert and his arguments against their validity are, briefly, the following:

---

[26] *De magnete*, bk. 2, chap. 2, p. 50.

[27] There are many examples of the effect upon thought of the invention of such classes. The concept "atom" has had enormous influence. Yet such a term may have no positive effect on the progress of knowledge or may have a negative effect, or even may have first one sort of influence and then the opposite. "Ghost" has been given as an example of a class whose creation has had a negative effect, the very existence of the term implying the existence of the entities it describes. Probably large scale agreement could not be obtained upon whether the effect of "soul" is positive or negative, so that it remains in limbo. "Element" served as an anti-Platonic influence in the High Middle Ages, to the probable detriment of physics, yet may well have preserved chemistry from negative Platonic influences. Professor I. B. Cohen has suggested a number of other such categories to me: "civilized" and "savage" are terms that have often prevented the European from comprehending new cultures encountered in the expansion of Europa; the belief in "heavy" and "light" objects braced the Aristotelian cosmology but hindered Renaissance studies in dynamics, as did the categories of "natural" and "violent" motion.

1. The classification of attractives into three classes, by Galen: attraction by heat; attraction by the succession of a vacuum; attraction by the whole substance of the object. This classification is unsatisfactory, and we must seek other causes for both electrics and the lodestone: specifically amber does not attract by heat since no matter how much it is heated it does not demonstrate attraction. Nor do other things, when heated – even incandescent solids – attract.[28]

2. Cardan's statements that amber attracts by the force of fire, like the cupping-glass, and that it attracts dry things which wish to feed on its fatty humor. In the first place these are contradictory statements. In the second place, the action of the cupping-glass is due to its air having been exhausted into the flame and the skin consequently rising to avoid the vacuum,[29] and neither the heat nor the air (as shall be seen) are responsible for motion of light objects to amber. There is no feeding, because there is no diminution or growth of the objects involved.

3. The motion of the attracted object is due to the motion of the ambient air [as suggested by Plutarch (p. 23) and others]. Manifestly burning objects are "calling in" the air, which they are consuming, but brought close to a versorium they do not attract it.

4. There is a sympathy between attractor and attracted object, as, for example, in Fracastoro's proposal that hairs and twigs move toward amber and toward diamond because they contain some principle – perhaps air – which is common to the attractor. But if he had only observed that all bodies are attracted to electrics (except burning ones), "nunquam talia fuisset meditatus." [In other words, his statement is no more than that all substances have a common principle, which is certainly not a satisfactory explanation of the causes of electrics.]

5. There is a near similarity between the electric and the attracted substance, which attempts to achieve perfection by moving to the electric. This is invalid for the same reason as (4).

6. Similarities are to be found between electric attraction and such phenomena as the drawing of moisture by plants, the emptying of a stoppered bottle of water under a pile of wheat, and the attraction of water by elephants' tusks. These are not attractions, but quite different phenomena, as are also the action of purgatives. [There is simply no analogy.]

---

[28] I. Bernard Cohen has called my attention to the tourmaline which does have a pyroelectric property. Could Gilbert have failed to note this property if he had heated a tourmaline?

[29] Both Cardan and Gilbert, be it noted, are well before the work that culminated in the production of Torricellian vacuums. The explanation here is therefore in terms of avoidance of the vacuum, rather than in terms of pressure.

II. Gilbert's Conceptual Scheme for Electricity

In presenting his own explanation of electric attraction, Gilbert cites his list of non-electrics and tells the reader that he will not understand why these particular substances — such as marble — fail to attract before having looked into the origins of things.

> Terrenam molem, siue potius telluris compaginem, & crustam, ex duplici materia consistere omnibus patet, omnesque confitentur; ex fluida nempe & humida; & ex constanti magis & sicca. Ex duplici illa natura, aut simpliciori concretione vnius, oriuntur apud nos varia corpora, quae nunc ex terrena, nunc aquea natura, maiori proportione proueniut. Quae ab humore siue aqueo, siue pingui, maximum incrementum acceperunt, aut ex illis simpliciori concretione formam induerunt; aut ab ipsis, longioribus saeculis concreuerunt; si illis durities satis firma fuerit, si fricata posteaquam polita fuerint, & cum frictione nitida permanserint; ad illa, corpora omnia in aëre posita, si non grauius pondus obstiterit, inclinant.[30]

This theory of the origin of electrics is immediately plausible in the light of their physical appearance, and it seems likely that it was their ice-like appearance that led Gilbert to this theory. However he now presses it further, into two elaborations: electrics produced from non-electrics and electrics becoming non-electrics. Glass is reduced, he writes, from sand, which does not itself attract because of impurities it contains, such as metals. On the other hand, heating electrics strongly or burning them destroys their humors. But

> Omnia igitur quae a praedominanti humido orta sunt, & firmiter sunt concreta, & fluoris speciem, & naturam inclytam retinent, in corpore firmo & concreto: alliciunt corpora omnia, siue humida, siue sicca.[31]

[30] *De magnete*, bk. 2, chap. 2, p. 51. "The mass of the Earth, or rather the Earth's structure and crust, consists of a twofold matter, namely [a matter that is] fluid and humid, and a matter that is firm and dry. From this twofold nature or from the simple concretion of one of them, arise all of the various bodies around us, which turn out now to be in major proportion of terrene nature, now of watery. Those that have received their major growth from humors, whether watery or fatty, or have taken on their form from a simple concretion of them, or were concreted from them many ages ago, if they are sufficiently hard, if they are rubbed after being polished, and if they remain brilliant after being rubbed, then all bodies presented to them, in air, will incline toward them, unless the body's weight interferes."

[31] *De magnete*, bk. 2, chap. 2, p. 52. "So all [bodies] that have sprung from a predominant moisture, and that are firmly and solidly concreted, and that retain the appearance and reknown nature of fluids, attract all objects, whether moist or dry."

At this point Gilbert reminds his reader of the true purpose of the work:

> Quae vero terreni veri corporis partes sunt, aut paululum ab eo diuersa, attrahere videntur etiam, sed longe diuersa ratione, & (vt ita dicam) magnetice; de quibus postea dicturi sumus.[32]

The over-all problem has thus been approached from two different sides: first, and more fundamentally, the World is to be considered divided into magnetics and non-magnetics, along the lines previously indicated. Then, from a different point of view, substances susceptible to attrition are to be divided into electrics and non-electrics. Magnetics are simply the pure products of the Earth's womb and engage in magnetic coition; electrics are concreted fluid, and demonstrate attraction when rubbed – or, in rare cases, without rubbing. But there remains the undistributed middle group, the nonmagnetic non-electric substances:

> Quae vero ex aqua & terra magis commixta, & vtriusque elementi simili ruina conflata sunt, (in quibus terrena magnetica vis deformata, & sepulta manet; aqueus vero humor inquinatus cum terra copiosori coiuerit, in se non concreuerit, sed terreno immiscetur) nullo modo ex se allicere quicquam quod non contigerint, aut loco dimouere possunt.[33]

Into the category of nonmagnetic non-electrics fall such substances as marbles, flints, woods, grasses, and so forth.

Gilbert's system now comprises the totality of solids. He seems to permit both magnetism and electricity to remain occult, that is, thinking of them as noncontact phenomena: such, however, is not the case for electricity, as we shall see. We shall also see that the theoretical structure he proposes is able to handle the known electric phenomena, with only a reasonable amount of distortion. Nevertheless it stands outside of the science of his day, at the moment, being unintegrated with contemporary physics. Any

[32] *De magnete*, bk. 2, chap. 2, p. 52. "Those however which are parts of the true earth substance, or differ but little from it, appear [!] to attract also, but for a far different reason and, so to speak, magnetically; of these we shall speak later."

[33] *De magnete*, bk. 2, chap. 2, p. 52. "However those that are more the union of water and earth mixed, and result from equal degradation of both elements (in which the magnetic force of the Earth is degraded and remains interred, while the watery humor, polluted by combination with a greater quantity of earth does not form a concretion in itself, but mingles with the earth), can in no way of themselves attract or move from its place anything with which they are not in actual contact." In the 1893 (and hence in the 1941 and 1952) English editions the phrase "aut loco dimouere" is translated "to repel the same," a translation which is particularly curious since Gilbert did not observe electric repulsion.

scheme which is ultimately to attempt to account for the structure of the universe could not be expected to grow from a mere differentiation or even renaming of two well-known kinds of attraction. Gilbert seems to have been well aware of the necessity for integration into the contemporary conceptual scheme of theoretical physics, for he now turns to the problems which it necessarily presents: what are the causes of electrics and magnetics? Whence the lack of symmetry between them, to account for attraction on the one hand and coition on the other?

> In omnibus mundi corporibus duae propositae sunt causae, siue principia, ex quibus ipsa corpora producta sunt, materia & forma; Electricae motiones a materia, magneticae vero a forma praecipua inualescunt, longeque inter se differunt, dissimilesq; euadunt; cum altera nobilitata plurimis virtutibus sit, & praepotens: altera obscura, & minoris potentiae, & carceribus quasi quibusdam plerunq; conclusa: quare & attritu seu frictione expergisci vim illam nonnunquam oportet, donec obscure incalescat, & effluuium reddat, & nitor corpori inducatur.[34]

"Effluvium" is a term that may mean many different things, and is nearly a generic term for the *modus operandi* of any occult action. In the present case we are told that

> Verisimile est igitur succinum expirare aliquid peculiare, quod corpora ipsa alliciat, non aërem intermedium:...[35]

This is directed against Plutarch's views (p. 23), which Gilbert has earlier explicitly mentioned.[36] The experimental proof is twofold: amber held above a spherical drop of water will pull it up into a cone, demonstrating the action upon the particles of the drop and not upon the drop as a whole, from which one may infer that the air is not pushing the drop from behind; rubbed amber held near a candle flame does not cause any wavering of the flame as would be expected if the amber affected the ambient air. Thus "Expirat a succino, & emittitur ab attritione effluuium;..."[37]

---

[34] *De magnete*, bk. 2, chap. 2, pp. 52-53. "In all bodies of the world are displayed two causes or principles, from which the bodies themselves were produced, matter and form. Electrical motions gain strength principially from the matter, but magnetical from the form. They differ widely from one another and turn out quite unlike, the one being ennobled by many virtues and prepotent, the other indistinct and of less potency and mostly confined within certain barriers. Wherefore that force must be awakened by attrition or friction until it gives out a hidden heat and an effluvium, and the body is made to shine."

[35] *De magnete*, bk. 2, chap. 2, p. 55. "It is therefore very likely that amber emits something peculiar to itself, which allures to it bodies—not the intermediate air."

[36] *De magnete*, bk. 2, chap. 2, p. 54.

[37] *De magnete*, bk. 2, chap. 2, p. 55.

> Spiritus igitur egrediens ex corpore quod ab humore aut succo aqueo con-
> creuerat, corpus attrahendum attingit, attactum attrahenti vnitur; corporiq;
> corpus peculiari effluuiorum radio contiguu, vnum efficit ex duobus: vnita
> confluunt in coniunctissimam conuenientiam, quae attractio vulgo dicitur.[38]

Gilbert, with Plato and the Greek mechanists, insists that electric action is no attraction,
nothing occult, that is, it is a contact phenomenon. For

> Quoniam enim nulla actio a materia fieri potest nisi per contactum, electrica
> haec non videntur tangere, sed vt necesse erat demittitur aliquid ab vno ad
> aliud, quod proxime tangat, & eius incitationis principiu sit.[39]

Gilbert's theory of electric action is therefore a mixture of the older theories, mechanistic and sympathetic. The action is clearly mechanical, but it arises from a sympathy:
Gilbert is unable to shake off the older view entirely. At the same time, he firmly
renounces the idea of *attraction,* and insists that electric phenomena are contact phenomena. Since the mechanism for establishing contact is not visible, it must be invisible
—but it must *be.*[40] This creed, which as we have already seen does not by any means
originate with Gilbert, has been the single most enduring and effective concept in the
history of electricity. Gilbert's thinking in this respect is a forerunner of what is to come
in English thought. An evaluation of the extent to which Gilbert may be regarded as
a precursor of seventeenth-century English mechanism cannot be made until his theory
of magnetism has been examined in detail.

The electric effluvia, he tells us,

> quae propria sunt & peculiaria, & sua, diuersa a communi aëre, ab humore
> genita, motu calorifico ab attritu & attenuatione excitata, tanq materiales
> radiͿ q̄ retinet & attollunt paleas, festucas, & ramenta, donec extinguutur, aut
> euanescunt; ... Differentia inter magnetica & electrica: quod magnetica omnia
> mutuis viribus concurrent; Electrica corpora alliciunt tantum, allectum non

[38] *De magnete*, bk. 2, chap. 2, p. 56. "Therefore a breath going out from a body which is concreted
from humour or watery liquid reaches the body that is to be attracted, unites it to the attracting body.
Attracting and attracted bodies being placed in contact by the characteristic radiation of effluvia, one is
made from two: united they come into the most connected harmony, which is commonly called attraction."
[39] *De magnete*, bk. 2, chap. 2, pp. 56-57. "For since no action can be performed by matter except
through contact [and] these electrics are not seen to touch, but of necessity something is given out by the
one to the other which touches it closely and is the beginning of is excitation."
[40] This is not to be interpreted as a claim that Gilbert was the first to revive the mechanistic viewpoint
concerning attractions. This is a subject that needs investigation.

immutatur insita vi, sed materiae ratione sponte appulsum incumbit: Corpora feruntur ad electrica recta linea versus centrum electrici: magnes magnetem tantum in polis directe appellit, in alijs partibus oblique, & transuersim, quomodo etiam adhaerent & appendunt. Motus electricus est motus coaceruationis materiae: magneticus est dispositionis & conformationis.[41]

Thus an excited electric produces no alteration in the attracted object, through any sort of infusion of the effluvium into that object; the latter is, simply because of its substances, seized by the spoke-like effluvia and drawn to the electric.[42] This is not contrary to Gilbert's hypothesis that all things are attracted to excited electrics, although it might seem to imply that magnetics would not be so drawn. For a magnetic would be attracted simply because of its substance, solely because it consists of matter, which is quite independent of its also having the magnetic form prerequisite to magnetic coition.

III. Gilbert's Experimental Philosophy

Any scientific research is both a consolidation of older knowledge and an attempt to modify that older knowledge, and hence contains both conservative and radical aspects. When the latter border upon the revolutionary, as is the case in Gilbert's conceptual scheme for electricity, the inevitable rejection must be met by either claiming that the apparently revolutionary ideas are not at all novel, or by insisting that they are so revolutionary as to justify ignoring the past. Gilbert uses the former and more common approach: his ideas are revolutionary in physics but not in philosophy. Indeed, he closes his preface with a claim for the utmost conservatism:

[41] *De magnete,* bk. 2, chap. 2, p. 60. "which are especial and peculiar and unique, differing from common air, produced from humor, excited by calorific motion, by rubbing and extensive refining, they are as material rods [spokes] which hold fast and lift up straws, chaff and twigs, until they [the effluvia] are extinguished or vanish;... The distinction between magnetics and electrics: that all magnetics run together by their mutual force; electric bodies merely allure. The enticed object is not altered by the incorporated force, but exerts itself by its own reason of substance to an approach. Bodies are carried to an electric along a straight line toward the center of the electric. A magnet brings a magnet directly only to the poles, to other parts [it brings it] obliquely and transversely, in which way they adhere and hang. Electric motion is a motion of accumulation of matter; magnetic [motion] is one of arrangement and forming."
[42] The pertinent passage of the quotation has received quite different translations in the two published English editions. This passage, "electrica corpora...appulsum incumbit" appears in the 1893 Mottelay edition as "electric bodies attract the electric only, and the body attracted undergoes no modification through its own native force, but is drawn freely under impulsion in the ratio of its matter (composition)." The 1900 Gilbert Club edition reads "electrics only allure; that which is allured is not changed by an implanted force, but that which has moved up to them voluntarily rests upon them by the law of matter."

Priscis illis & quasi primis philosophiae parentibus Aristoteli, Theophrasto, Ptolemaeo, Hippocrati, Galeno suus semper honos tribuatur, a quibus dimanauit sapientia ad posteros; sed ętas nostra plurima detexit & in lucem attulit, quae illi etiam si viuerent libenter amplecterentur. Quare & nos ea quae longa experientia inuenimus, probabilibus hypothesibus exponere non dubitauimus,...[43]

Despite this claim of conservatism, Gilbert is unable to avoid here once more his insistence upon demonstrable hypotheses. Previously he has explained his lack of appeal to ancient authority by an insistence upon lack of jurisdiction if not of competence:

Multa in rationibus & hypothesibus prima facie, duriora forsan videbuntur, cum sint a communi opinione aliena; non diffido tamen quin postea ex demonstrationibus ipsis authoritatem tandem nanciscentur. Quare in magnetica disciplina, qui progrediuntur magis, hypothesibus magis confidunt, & proficiunt vberius; nec facile cuiuis aliquid in magnetica philosophia certo constabit, in qua non sint cognita aut omnia, aut saltem pleraque. Physiologia haec fere tota noua est, & inaudita; nisi quod pauci admodum, de vulgaribus quibusdam viribus magneticis paucula quędam tradiderunt. Quare & veteres & Graecos auxiliarios minime aduocamus, quod neque graecula argumenta subtilius, nec graeca verba significantius veritatem demonstrare, aut melius illustrare possunt. Est enim doctrina magnetica nostra aliena ab eorum principijs plurimis & decretis.[44]

Still earlier, in an often quoted passage, Gilbert writes:

Inuentis & experimentis nostris asteriscos maiores & minores apposuimus, pro dignitatis & subtilitatis ratione. Qui eade experiri voluerit, non oscitater

---

[43] *De magnete*, *iij, *recto*. "To those early and as it were first parents of philosophy, Aristotle, Theophrastus, Ptolemy, Hippocratus, Galen, be ever given due honor; by them wisdom has been diffused to their successors. But our age has uncovered and brought to light much which would be willingly accepted by them, if they were living. Wherefore we also have not hesitated to set forth in reasonable hypotheses that which we have discovered by long experiment." "probabilibus" is translated as "provable" in the 1892 edition, "demonstratible" in the 1900 edition.

[44] *De magnete*, *ij, *verso*, *iij, *recto*. "Much in our reasonings and hypotheses will at first perhaps seem difficult, being foreign to common opinion. I do not doubt but that they will eventually acquire authority from the demonstrations themselves, for in the magnetic discipline they who are most advanced have the greatest trust in and profit the most by hypotheses. Nor can anyone with surety achieve anything certain in magnetic philosophy unless all or at least nearly all is known. This *physiologia* is nearly entirely new and unheard of, except for that very little common knowledge concerning the magnetic force which a few [authors] have handed down. Wherefore we rarely quote as aids either ancient or Greek writers, for neither subtle Greek arguments nor Greek words can demonstrate the truth distinctly nor make it known better. For our magnetic doctrine is alien to most of their principles and decrees."

111

& inepte, sed prudenter, artificiose & apposite corpora tractet; ne ille (cum res non successerit) inscius nostras arguat inuetiones: nihil enim in istis libris depromptum, quod non exploratum, sępissimeq; actu & transactum apud nos fuerit.[45]

Here the experimental philosophy that has played such an important part in discussion of the scientific revolution of the sixteenth and seventeenth centuries is not only clearly enunciated in the primitive form of appeal to experiment, but in a more developed form of an appeal to repetition of the author's experiments. But here as elsewhere in this period, we are handicapped by a lack of knowledge of the terminology. There is so little detailed knowledge of this period that it is difficult to establish the fine points of the meanings of terms in an era in which their meaning was shifting rapidly. Rather than attempting to interpret Gilbert's statement of his experimental philosophy, we shall turn to an examination of these "asteriscos maiores & minores," in an attempt to decide what sort of information Gilbert felt constituted a discovery, or an experiment.

Gilbert's Discoveries and Experiments in Electricity

The chapter of the *De magnete* concerned with electricity,[46] contains 33 asterisks, of which the first two are large and the remainder are small. These asterisks appear in the margin opposite the discovery to be designated, and normally appear slightly above the mid-point of the line in which the description of the discovery begins.[47] These "Inuentis & experimentis nostris," which Gilbert wished to call to the attention of his reader, may conceivably be inherited information: absolute priority of discovery can never be established. However, there is no known trace of such an earlier investigator, and from an examination of the discoveries it will be clear that someone, presumably Gilbert, per-

---

[45] *De magnete,* °ij, *verso.* "Opposite our discoveries and experiments we have placed asterisks, larger and smaller according to the importance and subtlety [of the discovery]. He who wishes to try them, let him handle the bodies—not carelessly and ineptly—but with skill, and properly; nor let him (when things do not succeed) ignorantly accuse our discoveries. For nothing is brought forth in this book which has not been investigated and made completely certain, performed and done in our presence."

[46] *De magnete,* bk. 2, chap. 2.

[47] The 1892 photocopy of the first edition omits two asterisks on page 51. The 1893 Mottelay translation into English omits one on page 93 (page 57 of the first edition). The 1941 edition, a reissue of the Mottelay translation also omits the asterisk on page 93, but this is relatively unimportant, since the entire author's preface is omitted, so the meaning of the asterisks is not made known to the reader. The third issue of the Mottelay translation, in 1952, restores the author's preface, but omits all of the asterisks.

formed a considerable number of experiments. In any case, with the publication of the *De magnete* these electrical discoveries became available to Gilbert's contemporaries and successors. These discoveries, part of electrical knowledge from 1600, may be summarized in the following terms.

1. Not only amber and jet attract small objects: the same is done by diamond, sapphire, carbuncle, the gem iris, opal, amethyst, vincentina, bristolla, beryl, crystal, glass, pseudo-gems made of glass or crystal, antimony glass, many kinds of spars, belemnites, sulphur, mastic, hard sealing-wax of various colors. Hard resin and orpiment attract, but less strongly. Rock salt, muscovy stone, and rock alum will attract weakly, in dry weather. There exists a class of amber-like attractors: electrics.

2. Electrics attract not only straws and chaff, but everything: all metals, woods, leaves, stones, earths, water, oil — every sensible object.

3. Amber heated without rubbing will not attract.

4. Red-hot iron, flame, a candle, a blazing torch, a live coal, will not cause a versorium to turn.

5. A large polished piece of amber will attract without being rubbed.

6. Many polished gems, bone, ivory, hard woods, metals, and lodestone will not attract, no matter how much they are rubbed.

7. Crystal, mica, glass, and all electrics do not attract if they are burned or heated very hot.

8. Substances which cannot be rubbed, because of their fluid nature, will not attract.

9. Liquid resin turpentine does not attract, but when hardened into a mastic it does.

10. Moist air, from mouth or atmosphere, prevents an electric from attracting.

11. A lodestone raises large weights, an electric will not: a two ounce lodestone will raise as much as an ounce; a three-ounce piece of amber will scarcely raise a fourth of a grain of barley.

12. A piece of amber will not attract when near to a flame or live coal.

13. Solar heat will not excite an electric.

14. Solar heat concentrated with a burning mirror will not excite amber.

15. Burning sulphur and flaming hard wax made from shellac do not attract.

16. The attraction of an electric for a versorium is greater the closer they are together.

17. Amber exhales something peculiar to itself, which attracts objects themselves, and not the intervening air.

18. A piece of amber will distort a drop of water into a cone, by attraction of its parts.

19. A well-excited piece of amber will not disturb a flame, showing that the air is not affected.

113

20. If an electric is rubbed very hard, the resultant attraction may be quite weak.

21. Weather affects an electric's action, which is best when the Atmosphere is thin, and there is a North wind or, in England, an East one; during South winds and in damp weather, electrics behave poorly or do not attract at all.

22. A piece of thin silk laid over an electric will hinder its attraction.

23. A piece of thin silk interposed in the space between an excited electric and an attracted object will partially but not entirely obstruct the attraction.

24. Amber still attracts when rubbed with warm oil.

25. If a piece of amber that has been rubbed with warm oil is moistened with *aqua vitae* or spirits of wine, it does not attract.

26. Bodies floating on water tend to unite if their protruding portions are wet.

27. Bodies floating on water tend to repel if their protruding portions are dry.

28. A versorium touched with a drop of water held on a rod swiftly joins to the rod.

29. Diamond, glass, rock-crystal, and numerous other gems first grow warm when rubbed, and then with continued rubbing begin to attract.

30. Electric effluvia will attract neither flame nor objects near to a flame.

31. Electric effluvia attract smoke from an extinguished candle.

32. The rarer smoke is, the less it is attracted by electric effluvia.

33. An electric attracts objects in a straight line toward it.

A closer examination of these discoveries will justify several generalizations concerning them: they are nearly entirely experimental in origin; they are closely tied to Gilbert's theory, each experimental discovery being associated with its theoretical explanation; Gilbert was proud of the experimental nature of his work, and took every opportunity to accentuate these discoveries.

We will now briefly examine these discoveries from the point of view set forth in the previous paragraph, in the order in which they occur in Gilbert's chapter on electricity.[48]

PAGE 48

Line 16: Nam non solum succinum, & gagates (vt illi [Gilbert's predecessors] putant) allectant corpuscula; sed Adamas, Sapphirus, Carbunculus, Iris gemma, Opalus, Amethystus, Vincentina, & Bristolla (Anglica gemma siue fluor) Berillus, & Crystallus idem faciunt. Similes etiam attrahendi vires habere videntur vitrum (praesertim clarum, & lucidum) tum ex vitro, aut Crystallo adulteratae gemmae, vitrum antimonij, & fluores plurimi ex fodinis, & Belemnites. Allicit etiam sulphur, mastix, & cera dura sigillaris ex lacca varijs coloribus tincta, composita. Allicit resina durior, vt arsenicum, sed imbecillius; aegre etiam & obscure in conuenienti coelo sicco Sal gemma, lapis specularis, & alumen rupeum.[49]

That this list is empirical in origin is certain, for comparison with his list on page 51. (of the *De magnete*) of non-electrics shows that neither his theory nor any contemporary theory – nor for that matter, any later theory – could serve to classify these substances into electrics and non-electrics.

> Line 27: Alliciunt haec omnia non festucas modo & paleas; sed metalla omnia, ligna, folia, lapides, terras, aquam ipsam, & oleum; omniaque quae sensibus nostris subijciuntur, aut solida sunt:...[50]

As is the case with his list of electrics, Gilbert has exaggerated the ignorance of his predecessors, for the attraction of the known electrics for substances other than straw and chaff had been known at least since Theophrastus. At the same time, this list of attracted substances is certainly empirical, although its extension to "omniaque quae sensibus nostris subijciuntur" is of course a theoretical operation.

PAGE 49

> Line 22: Succinum vero non calore allicit, vtpote calefactum ab igne, & admotum festucis non attrahit, siue tepeat, siue caleat aut ferueat, siue ad flammam vsq; vrgeatur.[51]

Since an electric must be rubbed to produce attraction – except in a very few rare cases – and since the rubbing is inevitably accompanied by heating, it is plausible to assume that heating is a close associate of the excitation. This is a problem that disturbed electricians before and after Gilbert, and one that he returned to again and again. He is able to justify the failure of objects heated by methods other than attrition by the *ad hoc* hypothesis that only heating by rubbing properly prepares the electric. The heating continues to play a predominant role in his thinking. The argument thus seems unconvincing, even to Gilbert, evidence of the experimental origin of this information.

[48] All references are by page and line to the first (1600) edition of the *De magnete*.
[49] *De magnete*, bk. 2, chap. 2, p. 48. This passage is translated in fn. 20.
[50] "These all not only attract straws and chaff, but all metals, woods, leaves, stones, earths, water itself, and oil; all that is subject to our senses or is solid."
[51] "Amber truly does not draw by heat, inasmuch as it does not attract when heated by a fire and brought near to straws, whether tepid, warm or hot or even driven all the way to burning."

PAGE 50

> Line 6:   Bacillum enim ferri candentis, aut flamma, aut candela, aut taeda
> ardens, aut Carbo, cum admouentur festucis, aut versorio, non
> attrahunt; cum tamen manifesto aërum successione aduocant, quia
> illum tanquam lucernae oleum absumunt.[52]

The difficulty with which Gilbert accepts the failure of heat to produce attraction makes
certain the experimental nature of this information. At the same time, the consuming of
air by these objects is being introduced as an argument against Lucretius (p. 18): hot
objects certainly draw air, but the effect is not sufficient to move a straw or a versorium,
so to attribute electrical atraction to a movement of air by an emitted effluvium is
unjustified.

PAGE 51

> Line 15:   Succinum in maiore mole politum si fuerit allicit, in minori &
> impuriori sine frictione non videtur allicere.[53]

As far as is known, Gilbert did not attempt to test the length of time during which an
object would remain electrified: here, it apparently does not enter his mind that the
large piece of amber might have become electrified by attrition at some earlier time, so
it is necessary that he modify the definition of electric which we have been using. Indeed
he has done so, probably deliberately, avoiding the question of attrition and defining
electrics as substances that behave like amber, rather than substances that attract when
rubbed. The discovery here asterisked is in conformity with modern electrical theory,
but is also in conformity with Gilbert's theory. Nevertheless, in the light of his list of
non-electrics, which follows immediately, there is good reason to believe that he engaged
in somewhat lengthy experimentation on the attractive behavior of various objects when
rubbed and when not-rubbed.

> Line 18:   at multa poliuntur tam gemmae, quam alia corpora, non tamen
> alliciunt, nullisque frictionibus expergiscuntur; nullas sic acquirunt
> vires, smaragdus, achates, carneolus, margaritae, iaspis, chalce-

[52] "For a glowing-hot iron rod, or a flame, or candle, a blazing torch, or glowing coal, when brought near
to straws or a versorium do not attract; at the same time they nevertheless clearly call in the air in
succession, for they consume it as a lamp consumes oil."
[53] "A good-sized piece of well-polished amber attracts without being rubbed; smaller and impure pieces
do not seem to attract without attrition."

donius, alabastrum, porphyrius, corallium, marmora, lapis lydius, silices, haematites, smyris, non ossa, aut ebur, aut durissima ligna, vt ebenum, non cedrus, iuiperus, aut cupressus, non metalla, argentum, aurum, aes, ferrum, non magnes vllus, quanquam egregie poliuntur, & nitescunt plurima.[54]

PAGE 52

Line 9:   Crystallus, lapis specularis, vitrum, & electrica omnia si vrantur, aut torreantur non alliciunt: humoris enim primordia, a feruoribus pereunt, & immutantur, & expirant.[55]

This is a pattern statement of Gilbert's: "This is true of a, b, c, and everything." The most reasonable interpretation is that a test was made for a, b, c, and extended to the entire class by analogy.

Line 27:   Quae vero ex humore magis consistunt, nec a natura firmius concreta sunt, (vnde nec attritionem ferunt, sed aut diffluunt & mollescunt, aut non leuigantur, vt pix, resina mollior, camphora, galbanum, ammoniacum, stirax, Assa, beniamin, Aspaltum, praesertim in calidiori coelo) ad illa, corpuscula non feruntur. Nam sine attritione, proprium & genuinum non emittunt spiritum, & effluuium, electrica plurima.[56]

If an electric is defined as a substance that attracts when rubbed, this discovery is tautological, merely an extension of the list of non-electrics by default: no experimentation is necessary to determine that substances that cannot be rubbed do not attract when rubbed. Once again we can see that Gilbert was disturbed by the manner in which some electric objects displayed attraction without attrition, and found it necessary to

[54] "but many gems when polished, as well as other bodies, nevertheless do not attract, and they are not at all aroused by friction; so, no power is acquired by emerald, agate, carnelian, pearls, jasper, chalcedony, alabaster, porphyry, coral, marbles, touchstone, flint, bloodstone, emery; nor do bones, or ivory, or the hardest woods, like ebony, nor cedar, juniper, or cypress; nor do metals, silver, gold, brass, iron, nor any lodestone, although many of them are well polished and bright."

[55] "Crystal, mica, glass, and all electrics, do not attract if burned or parched: their primordial humor perishes by heat, is changed, and given off."

[56] "Indeed, those things which consist mostly of humor, but are nevertheless not firmly congealed by nature (so that they do not bear rubbing, but either melt and soften or cannot be polished, such as pitch, soft resin, camphor, galbanum, ammoniac, storax, asafetida, benzoin, asphalt, especially in warm weather), to these things small objects are not borne. For without attrition, most electrics do not emit their proper and natural breath and effluvium."

117

examine other substances that might well be electric according to this theory of the origin of electrics and non-electrics. Soft resin has precisely the sort of physical characteristic that would cause it to be an electric, according to Gilbert's theory: hence its failure to attract must be due to its not being rubbed. Certainly he has experimented here, and the next asterisked discovery, immediately following his passage just quoted, further confirms this belief.

> Line 33: Resina terebinthina liquida, non allicit; teri enim non potest; at si concreuerit in mastichen, allicit.[57]

Gilbert's only way out of this peculiarity is to assume that rubbing is the normal method of exciting electrics, and that very good electrics may attract without being rubbed, a hypothesis that agrees with the general behavior of the electric substances that he tests. His working definition of an electric thus becomes "a substance that attracts when rubbed — except sometimes it may attract without being rubbed, if it is a large piece of a very good electric, and if it is finely polished."

PAGE 53

> Line 7: …vapidus aër efflatus, vel ab ore, vel ab aëre humidiore, virtutem suffocat; Si vero vel charta, vel linteum interponeretur motus nullus erit.[58]

The effect of moisture, which has plagued electricians forever, is certainly an experimental result, and it seems likely that Gilbert conducted specific tests of this effect, once he had phrased it in his own mind, since moisture plays such an important part in his entire conceptual scheme. He, of course, did not observe "virtutem suffocat."

The shielding effect of paper and linen is a rather curious discovery, and we know today that the phenomena involved are extremely complex: our modern theory is unable to predict with preciseness the results of this shielding. Furthermore Gilbert later records[59] that a piece of silk will only partially shield the effect: this too he marks as a discovery. Finally, such shielding is in contradiction to his theory, which considers the effluvia as

---

[57] "Liquid turpentine resin does not attract; it is not possible, to rub it; but if hardened into mastic, it attracts."

[58] "…spoiled air blown, either from the mouth or from humid air, stifles the virtue; indeed, if either a piece of paper or a sheet of linen be interposed [between, say, electric and versorium], there will be no motion."

[59] *De magnete*, bk. 2, chap. 2, p. 56.

destructible while in the process of being emitted but not so – or at least less so – after emission. Only thus is he able to explain the many pairs of nearly identical experiments in only one of which the electric attracted.

> Line 14: Magnes pondera magna attollit, vt si magnes sit duarum vnciarum & robustus, dimidium vncie aut vnciam totam allicit. Electricum minima tantum attrahit pondera, veluti succinum trium vnciarum affrictum, vix quartam partem grani hordei attollit.[60]

The importance of quantitative methods in modern science has tended to cause stress to be placed upon examples of quantitative work early in the history of a science. At the same time it is important to remember that it is easy to interpret a 16th or 17th Century statement like Gilbert's in modern terms and arrive at a meaning quite foreign to that of the original. Famous examples of dubious quantitative statements are Galileo's reproduction of the time of descent of a ball on an inclined plane many times, within a tenth of a pulse beat, and Perier's reproduction of the Torricellian experiment many times with a variation of less than a line [$1/12$ inch] in the height of the mercury column. In these cases we are today able to judge the variation in experimental results sufficiently to know that these experiments are not reproducible with such precision. Further, we know that in each case they knew in advance of the performance of any such experiment what the result would be, and it is likely that in each of those two cases the quantitative nature of the reported result is little different from quantitative aspect of a pedestrian's report: "that car only missed me by a hair's breadth."

As for Gilbert's quantitative comparison of a piece of amber and a lodestone, there is more difficulty in attempting a modern comparison: the Torricellian experiment may be performed with apparatus little different from that used by Perier, but such factors as the humidity of the air and the surface conditions of the rubbed substances are so important as to make a precise verification of Gilbert's numerical results unlikely. At the same time there is no reason to believe that these results were not stated for emphasis, rather than as results in the modern sense of the term, for it had been long known that the amber effect was generally weaker than magnetic attraction.

Finally – and most important – this discovery is completely ineffective in the ultimate quantification of magnetism and electricity. It is stated to separate, to analyze, not to

---

[60] "A lodestone raises great weights, so that if there is a magnet of two ounces and strong, it will draw to itself a half ounce or a whole ounce. An electric attracts a weight of much less, as for instance a three-ounce piece of amber rubbed will raise scarcely a fourth part of a grain of barley."

correlate and codify: here we are presented with one of the many dissimilarities between the two sets of phenomena, whereas the quantification of magnetism and electricity could come only from quantitative consistencies between sets of phenomena. It is when two physical quantities – such as force and distance – are found to present an invariant relationship that quantification is achieved, but here Gilbert is showing that two physical quantities – the forces of attraction and coition – are *not* related.

> Line 24: magnu vero frustulum electri aut gagatis politum, … si flammae aut carboni leuiter admoueatur, vt similiter incalescat, non inuitat corpuscula: quia a calidi inflammati corpore, quod calidum emittit halitum, caligine obducitur, & alienus impingitur halitus, qui plurimum a succini natura abhorret:…[61]

The envelopment of the electric by a vapor that is alien to its nature is not an explanation that is very well in accord with Gilbert's basic theory, but is somewhat *ad hoc*, so that we may presume that this discovery is experimental. The explanation offered, namely that the emission from the flaming object is not the proper sort of emission, that it is out of sympathy with electrics is one that later electricians used, under somewhat similar circumstances.[62]

> Line 31: …ex radijs solaribus calor non praeparat electricum,…
> Line 35: …feruor a lumine Solis per speculum ardens excitatus, nullum succino calefacto vigorem infert: dissipat enim & corrumpit omnia electrica effluuia.
> Line 37: Perinde sulphur accensum, & cera dura ex lacca confecta, inflammata non alliciunt; calor enim ex frictione soluit corpora in effluuia, quae flamma absumit.[63]

Gilbert continues his inquiry into heating by means other than friction. From these remarks it seems likely that he never was able to completely persuade himself that

[61] „indeed, a large polished piece of amber or jet…if brought lightly near to a flame or [live] coal so that it likewise becomes warm, will not entice small objects: because, it becomes covered with a vapor, from the hot flaming body, which emits a hot exhalation, and is struck by that body's vapor, which is very alien to the nature of the amber."

[62] For example, Francis Hauksbee the elder suggested that the effluvium from one electric could not pass through another electric.

[63] "…heat from the sun's rays does not excite an electric,… …the heat from the light of the sun, aroused by means of a burning mirror, excites no power in the heated amber: for it dissipates and ruins all the electric effluvia. Likewise, lighted sulphur and flaming hard wax made from lac, do not attract; for heat by attrition dissolves bodies into effluvia, which flame consumes."

heating by any method did not release the electric effluvia. Now, however, he has accounted for the failure to attract in such cases by two assumptions: the envelopment of the electric in an alien vapor—and he has shown experimentally that water on the surface will stifle the attractive effect; and, the destruction of the effluvium, the necessary mechanical connection between attractor and attracted, by heat.

PAGE 54

Line 38: sed cum celerius applicantur versorio fricata electrica, tum primum maxime appellit versorium, magisq; in propinquo allicitur.[64]

This discovery is presented as an argument against the view that attraction is due to some sort of an oscillatory motion of the effluvia. Gilbert argued that "Si quia tenuiora effluunt, & incrassata reuertuntur, (vt in spiritalibus) tunc potius motum haberet corpus ad electricum paulo post principium applicationis;…" Of more importance, both in his own work and in that of his successors, is the observation "Magisque in propinque allicitur." The similarity here to magnetic attraction is undoubtedly one of the factors that led him to the necessity of treating the amber effect, and the same similarity influenced 18th Century attempts to find force laws for electric and magnetic attraction. Since Gilbert's general theory of the dissimilarity of magnetic coition and electric attraction would have been supported by the lack of variation of force with distance in the electrical case, this discovery is empirical.

PAGE 55

Line 19: Verisimile est igitur succinum expirare aliquid peculiare, quod corpora ipsa alliciat, non aërem intermedium: Corpus vero ducit ipsum manifesto in aquae globosa gutta posita supra siccum; nam succinum appositum in conuenienti distantia, proximas conuellit partes, &

Line 23: educit in conum: Alioquin si ab aëre ruente adduceretur, gutta tota inclinaret. Quod vero aërem non trahit, sic demonstratur: sit tenuissima candela cerea, quae flammam minimam, & claram concipiat: appone huic

Line 27: succinum, vel gagatem planum, latum, bene praeparatum, & frica-

---

[64] "but when rubbed electrics are quickly applied to the versorium, then immediately the versorium is driven to it and the closer it is, the more it is attracted."
Gilbert may have intended a play upon words here, since his term "versorium," although invented by him in the present sense, was used in antiquity in connection with gear for bringing about a ship, and "appello" was used in the sense of making port.

tum secundum artem, intra duos digitos, vel quamuis distantiam
conuenientem; succinum tale quod longe, lateq; alliceret corpora,
flammam tamen non commouet, quod fieri, si commoueretur aër
necessum esset: flamma enim fluentem aërem sequeretur.[65]

The observation that the portions of a drop of water are affected and not their totality
is a significant piece of information, in agreement with his conceptual scheme but not
likely to have been predicted by it without at the very least some experiental evidence.
The elimination of the air as an intermediary is important to the future course of
electrical science. Plutarch had been able (p. 23) to transfer the occult electrical phenomena quickly to a familiar basis by presuming that the emission from an excited electric
operated upon the air, which then produced the observed motions by familiar and
mechanical action. From 1600 on the action remains occult: the ultimate test of electric
attraction in vacuum, attempted by the experimenters of the Accademia del Cimento and
successfully achieved by Robert Boyle, is an extension of the already clearly established
occult nature of the electrical action.

At the beginning of the last passage quoted, Gilbert states a discovery that is of a very
different sort from the others that we have seen. This is certainly not a report of an
observation, and probably may be taken as evidence of the reality of the effluvium to
Gilbert.

PAGE 56

Line 5:   ad ipsa etiam electrica plurima, si durius affricentur, imbecillis, aut
nulla fit corporum inclinatio; Optima, quando affrictio lenis fuerit,
& celerrima; ita enim tenuissima euocantur effluuia.[66]

This is a generalization from many experiences, undoubtedly of empirical origin: with-

---

[65] "Therefore it is probable that amber gives off something peculiar to itself, which attracts bodies
themselves, not the intermediate air. Indeed it is plain that it attracts the body itself, in the case of a
spherical drop of water placed on a dry surface; for amber, placed at a suitable distance, pulls away
the nearest parts, and draws the drop into a cone. On the other hand, if it were drawn by the rushing
air, the entire drop would yield. Indeed, that it [the amber] does not attract the air is thus demonstrated:
take a very thin wax candle, which makes a small and clear flame; bring up to it a broad and flat piece
of amber or jet—within some convenient distance, such as two fingers'—that has been well prepared and
also skillfully rubbed. Such a piece of amber would attract bodies far and wide, but nevertheless does
not move the flame, which it would necessarily do if the air were moved, for the air would follow after
the air current."

[66] "For many electrics if rubbed hard will make bodies incline toward themselves only weakly or not
at all. It is best when the rubbing has been gentle and very rapid; for it is thus that the finest effluvia
are evoked."

out a scale of values these ideas concerning the best method of exciting an electric inevitably remain vague and cloudy – now as then.

Line 12:   ...quae aegre alliciant in claro coelo, in crasso nihil comoueat:...[67]

Just what is meant by these two sorts of weather has been explicitly laid out in the previous lines, where Gilbert writes: "Effluuia, ex subtili fusione humoris existunt, non ex improba vi turbulenta; presertim in ijs quae ex pingui concreuerunt; quae tenuissimo aëre, spirantibus ventis septentrionalibus, & apud nos (Anglos) orientalibus, effectum habent certiorem, firmioremque: Meridionalibus vero, & vdo coelo, infirmum admodum;..." The "vdo coelo" catches the modern eye. Gilbert probably reckoned the moisture important because of his earlier-noted discovery that water on the surface of an object suppresses its attractive property (p. 118). Indeed he connects the two discoveries, writing

> ...in succino, Gagate, & sulphure, quia non tam facile concipiunt in superficie aërem humentem, multoq; largius soluuntur, non tam cito supprimitur vis illa, atq; in gemmis, Crystallo, vitro, & huiusmodi, quae flatum humidiorem in superficie incrassatum colligunt.[68]

Yet at the same time it should not be forgotten that Gilbert also stressed the heaviness of the atmosphere even more, mentioning it in the passage which he chose to mark as a discovery.

Line 22:   Ita & sericum rarum, tenuissimumque, vulgo *Sarsnet,* cito supra succinum, postquam fricatum fuerit, impositum,

Line 24:   attractionem corporis impedit: At si in medijs interuallis interpositum fuerit, non penitus obstat.[69]

---

[67] "...those substances or effluvia which attract with difficulty in clear weather, in thick weather produce no motion..."

[68] *De magnete,* bk. 2, chap. 2, p. 56.

[69] "There is a certain loose-textured and fine silk, commonly known as *Sarsnet,* which when quickly placed over amber, after it has been rubbed, prevents the attraction of bodies. But if it is placed in the intervening space, it does not wholly obstruct it."

In the Gilbert Club edition, London, 1900, the discoveries marked by the asterisks are assumed to be different from those listed here. The asterisk for line 24 has been moved up to line 22, and the asterisk for line 22 has been moved up opposite the previous phrase, namely, "scilicet, quia aliud est in exortu ipso supprimere, aliud emissum restinguere." This interpretation seems to me to be incorrect for the following reasons: with the single exception of the emission of effluvia, the discoveries marked by

This passage immediately follows the statement "scilicet, quia aliud est in exortu ipso supprimere, aliud emissum restinguere." and is presumably offered in support of that view. Nevertheless this discovery seems to contradict an earlier one (p. 118) concerning the shielding by means of a piece of paper or linen placed between the objects.

> Line 27: ...oleum quod leue, purumq; est, non impedit [the effluvium];
> Line 28: nam etsi calido digito oleo imbuto succinum affricetur, tamen trahit.[70]

Gilbert explains these phenomena in terms of the physical properties of the oil – although not those particular properties we would note today – and the assumption concerning the ease of suppression of the effluvia at the electric and away from it. His explanation is not very convincing, in the light of his theory, which is evidence of the experimental nature of these discoveries.

PAGE 57

> Line 19: Perinde [to the way in which electrics tend to unite] vniri corpora contendunt, & mouentur in superficie aquarum: veluti, bacillum quod immittitur paululum in aquas C [Fig. 15]; manifestum quod E F bacillum, quod propter corticem H natat in aqua, & finem habet tantum F, vdum supro superficiem aquarum, attrahitur a bacillo C, si bacillum C, vdum fuerit paululum supra aquae superficiem: veluti gutta adiuncta guttae, attrahitur, & subito vniuntur.[71]

Gilbert can hardly be claiming the discovery of "gutta adiuncta guttae, attrahitur, & subito vniuntur.", and the motion of the floating rods is little more than this. Marking this "discovery" as such would seem to indicate a tendency on Gilbert's part to over-

---

Gilbert with asterisks are observables; the general format of the *De magnete* places the asterisk at the beginning of the statement of the discovery (although of course an earlier phrase may be necessary to make the statement intelligible), and the first of these two asterisks is opposite the line containing "Ita & sericum rarum,..." There is circumstantial evidence for believing that Gilbert supervised the printing of the *De magnete* and it seems likely that he would have paid careful attention to the location of the asterisks.

[70] "...oil which is light and pure does not impede it [the effluvium] for even if amber is rubbed with a warm finger dipped into oil, it nevertheless attracts."

[71] "In a like manner [to the way in which electrics tend to unite] bodies floating on the surface of water strive to unite and move, even as the rod C [Fig. 15] which is immersed a little into the water. Clearly the rod EF, which floats, in water, because of the cork H, and has only the wet end F above the surface of the water, is attracted by the rod C, if the rod C be wetted a little above the surface of the water: just as one drop next to another is attracted and they are united."

emphasize his discoveries, an indication of pride in them that is already demonstrated by his prefatory remarks (p. 112).

> Line 29: Sin vero bacillum totum supra aqua siccum fuerit non amplius attrahit, sed fugat virgulam E F.[72]

Any tendency for the dry sticks to "flee" one another was probably simply a result of bumping, which may imply a lack of careful observation on Gilbert's part. This "repulsion" which he reports in this water-analogy is also of interest because he did not know of electric repulsion. If Gilbert had not marked this a discovery, it might well be inter-

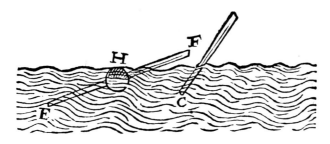

Fig. 15. Gilbert's water analogy (*De magnete*, p. 57).

preted as simply an emphatic statement that the floating objects do not cohere when dry, but in the presence of the asterisk it seems necessary to consider this fleeing as an observed phenomenon.

Nevertheless, the repulsion occurs only in the absence of moisture, and it is likely that Gilbert would have thought of it—if at all, in this sense—as analogous to a lack of humor, and hence as bearing no relation to any electric phenomena.

PAGE 58

> Line 4: Solida appellunt ad solida mediante humido: Exempli gratia, Tange finem versorij, cum bacilli fine in quo gutta aquae eminentiam habet; vt primum versorium tetigerit eminentiam guttulae, statim valide corpori bacilli celeri motu adiungitur; sic humida concreta in aëre resoluta paululum (mediantibus ad vnitionem effluuijs)

---

[72] "But if the entire above-water portion of the rod be dry, it is no longer attracted, but flees the stick."

alliciunt; nam aqua humidis, aut humore laxo perfusis in aquae summitate, effluuij vim habet.[73]

Gilbert is willing to press the analogy to the limit, ascribing to water the force of effluvia. His seizure of this rather commonplace phenomenon of cohesion of droplets as an important analogy is further indication of his conviction that moisture is an essential element in electric phenomena—despite the "killing" of the electric property by a coating of water.

PAGE 59

Line 19: At adamas, vitrum, crystallus, & aliae gemmae plurime duriores, & valde concretae incalescunt primum, deinde diutius teruntur primo tempore, & tunc etiam bene alliciunt; nec enim aliter soluuntur.[74]

It seems likely that Gilbert tested this hypothesis for the substances named, and then extrapolated to the class of hard and compact gems. Throughout his recorded observations there is displayed an understandable tendency for him to do this.

Line 26: manifestum enim est quod effluuia destruuntur a flamma, & calore igneo; quare nec flammam nec corpora flamme propinquiora prouocant:...[75]

[73] "Solids draw solids through the medium of liquid. For example, touch the end of a versorium with the end of a rod having a protruding drop of water [on it]: as soon as the versorium touches the outermost part of the droplet, it immediately is joined to the body of the rod by a swift motion. Thus concreted liquids resolved a little, in the air (through the mediation of the unifying effluvia) allure, for the water of a wet spot or moisture spread on an object floating on top of water, has the force of an effluvium." The phrase "sic humida...alliciunt" appears in the 1893 edition as "So do bodies concreted from liquids when melted a little in the air exercise attraction, their effluvia being the means of unition" and in the 1900 edition as "So concreted humid things attract when a little resolved into air (the effluvia in the intermediate space tending to produce unity)". In the former the "melted" is a reasonable translation of "resoluta" although I do not believe that Gilbert intended this. Nevertheless it seems certain that he thought of the heating, by attrition, as essential to resolution of the effluvia.
In the 1900 translation of the phrase, the interpretation of "in aëre" as "into air" seems very doubtful: again, if this translation is valid, the interpretation of the phrase must be considerably modified.
[74] "But diamond, glass, crystal, and many others of the harder and very well concreted gems, first become warm. Thereafter when well rubbed for some time, they allure well. Nor can they be set free in any other way."
[75] "It is manifest indeed that the effluvia are destroyed by flame and igneous heat; on which account, they do appeal neither to flame nor bodies near to a flame."

Although the second phrase of this statement is experimental, it is merely repetition of earlier discoveries: :furthermore, it is not the one indicated by the asterisk. Here then Gilbert is certainly marking a non-experimental discovery, the destruction of effluvia by fire or heat.

Line 31: Fumu tamen excitatu extincto lumine allectant: & quanto magis fumis ille superiora petens extenuatur, tanto infirmius inclinat, nimis enim rara non deducuntur,

Line 34: tandemq; cum iam fere euanuit, nihil inclinat, quod versus lucem facile cernitur: Cum vero in aërem transiuerit fumus, non mouetur, vt antea demonstratur.[76]

PAGE 60

Line 13: Corpora feruntur ad electrica recta linea versus centrum electrici: magnes magnetem tantum in polis directe appellit, in alijs partibus oblique, & transuersim, quomodo etiam adhaerent & appendunt.[77]

Summary

Gilbert's study of the amber-effect is of a magnitude far greater than any previous one. Despite his persistent claims of conservatism throughout the *De magnete*, his work in the second chapter of the second book establishes a new science, electricity. A new technique in the sciences was coming to fruition: the isolation of a field of study from broader issues, and Gilbert's work in electricity was the major factor in the isolation and hence the establishment of that area of study. His discoveries furnished a broad foundation for further work; his theory of electrics provided a theoretical basis suggesting new experiments and made available a great variety of substances for study and use in electrical experiments. Gilbert's work on electricity was assimilated and somewhat modified during the seventeenth century and provided the starting point for the eighteenth century fluid theories and the invention of the concept of electric charge.

It is interesting that all this is a digression to Gilbert. His intense interest in electric phenomena is principally to eliminate them so that he may safely pursue his primary topic of study: magnetism.

---

[76] "Nevertheless, they [effluvia] allure the smoke emitted from an extinguished light, and the more that smoke is spread out in going upward, the more weakly is it deflected; this is to be expected, for substances that are too rare are not attracted. And finally, when it is almost vanished, it is not deflected at all, which is easily determined [looking] toward the light. Indeed when it has passed over into air, it will not be moved, as previously demonstrated."

[77] This passage is translated in fn. 41.

CHAPTER FOUR

GILBERT AND MAGNETISM

Although Book One of the *De magnete*[1] is intended to be chiefly historical, Gilbert does not seem to be able to avoid digressing to his own experimental discoveries. The technical background which he provides concerns

> Qvae in lapide ipso manifesta sunt plurima, antehac cognita, non tamen bene explorata,...[2]

In summary his important points in Book One are the following.

Each celestial sphere is assigned a pair of poles by astronomers; similarly there are two preëminent poles of the Earth, constant relative to the diurnal rotation; likewise the lodestone has poles, north and south, definite points.[3]

Our demonstrations will be with spherical lodestones since this spherical form, the most perfect form, agrees most with the terrestrial globe, and is best suited to experimental use.[4]

Turn a strong, solid, uniform and flawless lodestone into a smooth sphere: much may be learned from this Earth-like stone, which we name μικρόγη [mikroge] or *terrella*.[5]

To find the terrella's poles (arranged like the Earth's poles): lay bits of iron wire on the terrella and with chalk mark their length on the terrella, and such lines will trace the meridian circles, which intersect at the poles; or, use a magnetized wire mounted on a pivot and free to turn – a magnetic versorium – which when held near to the terrella tangent to its surface will point along the meridian circles; or locate the poles directly with this versorium by finding the places where it will point directly toward the center of the terrella [See Fig. 16].[6]

---

[1] *Gvilielmi Gilberti Colcestrensis, medici Londinensis, de magnete, magnetisqve corporibvs, et de magno magnete tellure; Physiologia noua, plurimis & argumentis, & experimentis demonstrata,* London, Peter Short, 1600.

[2] *De magnete,* bk. 1, chap. 3, p. 12. "Many things are manifest in the lodestone itself, previously known but not yet well investigated,..."

[3] *Ibid.* Compare the views on this page and the next with Peregrinus' ideas (p. 40).

[4] *Ibid.*

[5] *De magnete,* bk. 1, chap. 3, pp. 12-13.

[6] *De magnete,* bk. 1, chap. 3, pp. 13-14.

If a terrella is placed in a round wooden dish which is then floated in a tub of water, the dish will turn until the south pole of the terrella points to the north. The terrella receives this power from the Earth.[7]

A terrella floated in a wooden dish will orient even when the axis is not in the horizontal plane—the axis may even be eighty degrees away from the horizontal.[8]

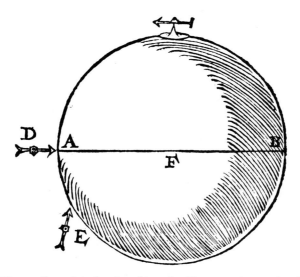

Fig. 16. The terrella, and the location of its poles. The magnetic versorium (compass needle) on top of the sphere is pointing along a meridian circle; the versorium at D points directly to the center of the sphere and hence to the pole A, in contrast to the versorium at E (*De magnete,* p. 13).

It is the *south* pole of the terrella that points to the *north,* contrary to all who have written about the lodestone, to all instrument makers and navigators. The whole magnetic philosophy is ill-cultivated.[9]

The lodestone attracts iron. Likewise, lodestone attracts lodestone: opposite (unlike) poles attract, like poles repel, and a floating stone will be turned by one held nearby according to these rules.[10]

[7] *De magnete,* bk. 1, chap. 4, p. 14.
[8] *De magnete,* bk. 1, chap. 4, pp. 14-15.
[9] *De magnete,* bk. 1, chap. 4, p. 15.
[10] *De magnete,* bk. 1, chap. 5, pp. 15-16.

129

Elongated lodestones, with the poles at the ends, tend to adhere to one another, with unlike poles in contact. Similarly, if such a stone is divided into two, by cutting midway between the poles, each side of the cut is a new pole, unlike the other pole in that half of the stone. The two halves will tend to combine and to restore the original continuity.[11]
Lodestone not only attracts iron, but also iron ore, and attracts it the more the more metal the ore contains. There is no theamedes [see p. 25]; Albertus Magnus observed badly when he wrote of a lodestone that attracted iron on one side and repelled it on the other.[12]
Crude, rich iron ore normally attracts other iron ore, although weakly.[13]
Stony ores and certain others neither attract or are attracted by lodestone, but if heated ten or twelve hours and then cooled as described in Book Three they will be attracted by lodestone and will themselves come together.[14]
Iron ore has poles; less perfect ones when treated with fire acquire polar strength — *verticity* as we call it.[15]
Worked iron, not magnetized by a lodestone, attracts other worked iron, although weakly. This may be shown by the method of the figure [see Fig. 17] or by bringing a piece of iron near to a long iron rod hanging balanced from a silken cord.[16]
All good and perfect iron, if drawn out [into a rod] acts like lodestone or iron rubbed by a magnetic body, and orients north-south. This can easily be shown experimentally.[17]
Lodestone, iron magnetized by lodestone, and iron that is unmagnetized by a lodestone will, in a given locality, point to the point of variation, not to the North [see p. 43]. The direction of pointing is thus not put in by the impress of any particular stone [that is, the direction of pointing is a property of the place, not a property of the magnet].[18]
Wrought iron has in itself fixed North and South parts, verticity, and poles. But it differs from iron ore and lodestone in that iron balls only weakly acquire and show verticity, while elongated pieces at once show the force.[19]
Lodestone and iron have some medicinal properties, although there has been much quackery on this subject.[20]

[11] *De magnete*, bk. 1, chap. 5, pp. 16-17.
[12] *De magnete*, bk. 1, chap. 6, p. 18.
[13] *De mangete*, bk. 1, chap. 9, p. 27.
[14] *De magnete*, bk. 1, chap. 9, pp. 27-28.
[15] *De magnete*, bk. 1, chap. 10, p. 28.
[16] *De magnete*, bk. 1, chap. 11, pp. 29-30.
[17] *De magnete*, bk. 1, chap. 12, p. 30.
[18] *De magnete*, bk. 1, chap. 12, p. 31.
[19] *De magnete*, bk. 1, chap. 13, pp. 31-32.
[20] *De magnete*, bk. 1, chap. 14 and 15, pp. 32-35.

Lodestone and iron ore are the same.[21]
Iron ore and prepared iron may be used as well as may weak magnets, in all magnetic experiments. Native iron ore fresh from the mine sometimes displays attraction.[22]
Lodestones are in no way weakened through being used to magnetize iron.[23]
The terrestrial globe is magnetic and is a lodestone.[24]

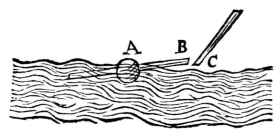

Fig. 17. The iron wire B, supported by the cork A, will be moved by the iron wire C, although they do not touch and neither wire had been magnetized with a lodestone (*De magnete*, p. 29).

I. The Terrella

Today the spherical magnet is an anachronism in magnetostatics, and except for certain special and limited applications we think of a permanent magnet as having the form of a right cylinder or an elongated right parallelepiped – perhaps curved into a "horseshoe" shape – with two poles, one near each end. The "virtue" of the magnet is measured in terms of two concepts, *pole strength* and *magnetic moment*. The pole strength is the same for each of the two poles and is defined in terms of a series of operations in which the forces acting upon magnets are measured for various separations. The magnetic moment is defined as the pole strength (of either pole) multiplied by the separation of the poles. Increasingly magnetic moment is becoming a primary quantity, pole strength being a secondary quantity in many areas of physics, but in dealing with macroscopic magnets moment is still a derived quantity.

[21] *De magnete*, bk. 1, chap. 16.
[22] *De magnete*, bk. 1, chap. 16, p. 36.
[23] *De magnete*, bk. 1, chap. 16, p. 38.
[24] *De magnete*, bk. 1, chap. 17.

In such modern permanent magnets the important quantities are therefore the strength of the poles and their separation. It may therefore seem strange that Gilbert should shape his lodestones into the spherical form, or at least a display of Gilbert's ignorance of the important magnetic quantities. It is neither. In his discussion of polarity, Gilbert discusses in a semi-quantitative manner the virtue of various lodestones and the factors upon which that virtue depends, and makes a rather strong case for the superiority of elongated non-spherical lodestones. In a chapter entitled "Vigor in magnete quomodo inest,"[25] he writes:

> Ferrum magnes non ab omni parte aeque rapit; vel non similiter ad omnem partem magnetis confluit magneticum; quia puncta sua habet magnes (id est) veros polos, in quibus virtus eximia excellit.[26]

But, he warns,

> Iam intelligere oportet, & firma memoria retinere, quod vertices praeualent propter vim totius; ita vt (quasi diuiso imperio per aequinoctialem) iste omnes in septentriones intendant vires: Ille vero aduersa ratione in meridie, tam diu quam sunt vnitae partes, vt in sequenti demonstratione [See Fig. 18]. Sic enim, per infinitas curuas ab omni puncto aequatoris diuidentis sphaeram in duas partes aequales; & ab omni puncto superficiei ab aequatore in Boream; & ab aequatore in Austrinum polum, tendit vis omnis ad polos seorsim. Ita verticitas est ab aequinoctiali circulo ad polum vtrinque. Talis in integro potestas posita est. Ab A immittitur vigor in B, ab A B in C, ab A B C, in D, & ab illis simul in E. Similiter a G in H, & ita deinceps, quamdiu totum vnitum fuerit. At si frustulum A B resectum fuerit (quanquam iuxta aequatorem) tamen tam validum erit in actionibus magneticis, atque C D, aut D E reuulsum aequali quantitate a toto. Nulla enim pars in toto praecipua dignitate excellit, nisi propter alias partes adiunctas, a quibus totum absolutum & perfectum euadit.[27]

---

[25] *De magnete*, bk. 2, chap. 5.

[26] *De magnete*, bk. 2, chap. 5, p. 71. "The lodestone does not with all its parts equally drag the iron, nor do magnetic bodies equally flow to all parts of the lodestone, because the lodestone has its points, that is true poles, in which an exceptional virtue is eminent."

[27] *De magnete*, bk. 2, chap. 5, pp. 73-74. "Now it is necessary to understand and firmly keep in mind that the vertices are strong because of the force of the whole, so that (the empire as it were being divided by the equinoctial) all the forces of this [half] tend northward, all those in the opposite [half] tend southward, so long as the parts are united, as in the following demonstration. [See Fig. 18]. For the whole force tends separately to the poles, along an infinity of curves from all points of the equator which divides the sphere into two equal parts, both from all surface points of the equator to the North [pole]

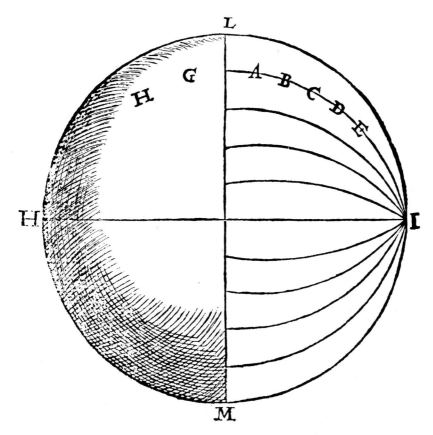

Fig. 18. In a terrella with poles at H and I, A transmits its vigor to B, AB to C,
ABC to D, etc., so that the preëminence of the pole I is due to a concentration of the force of the entire lodestone at I, rather than due to any
particular power residing in the point I. (*De magnete*, p. 73.)

and from the equator to the South pole. So the verticity is from the equinoctial circle both ways to the
pole. Such is the power placed in the whole [stone]. From A the *vigor* is transmitted into B, from AB
into C, from ABC into D, and from them likewise into E. Similarly from G into H and thus successively,
as long as the whole is united. But if the piece AB be cut out (although it is near the equator) yet the
effect in the magnetic action will be as if CD or DE, equal quantities, were torn away from the whole.
For no part exceeds in worth in the whole except by union with the other parts, by which an absolute and
perfect whole results."

The coordinate system for the terrella is naturally patterned after the Earth's.
Continuing this semiquantitative approach, Gilbert attributes the vigor of each point
of the terrella to a combined action of all portions of the hemisphere (dividing the
terrella symmetrically with respect to the poles) further from the pole than the point in
question [Fig. 19]. Thus the point C demonstrates the action of the section ACH, if a
piece of iron is brought to C. The iron will be acted upon more strongly at F since at
that point the section FGH is effective, and of course at E the entire hemisphere is
effective.

After a digression to the nomenclature and terminology of the terrella – which is defined
in complete analogy to that of the Earth – Gilbert returns to the concentration of power
at the poles, "Cur in polo ipso coitio firmior sit, quam in alijs partibus medijs inter
aequatorem & polum; & de proportione virium coitionis in diuersis terrae & terrellae
partibus."[28] The confluence of power to any particular point of the lodestone is now
expressed semiquantitatively in slightly different terms. If an elongated piece of iron
is brought to a terrella [Fig. 20] it will stand normal to the surface only at the pole; at
all other points there is a dip from the tangent plane, from the magnetic horizon, that
increases from zero at the equator to 90° at the poles.

> Ita quo minus ad corpus conuertitur, eo minus, & debilius coit, adhaeretq;.
> Veluti A B poli: ferri obelus, siue frustum magneticum C allicitur in parte E;
> non tamen apprehensus finis tendit ad centrum magnetis, sed oblique vergit
> versus polum, chordaque deducta a fine illo oblique, vt tendit corpus attrac-
> tum, breuis est: habet igitur roboris minus; tum etiam conuersionem minorem.
> Sed vt a corpore in F maior procedit chorda, ita actus firmior; in G etiam
> longior; in A polo longissima (diameter enim via est longissima) in quem
> omnes vndiq; partes auxilia conferunt, in quo tanq totius regionis arx &
> tribunal constituitur, non dignitate aliqua sua, sed quia vis insidet illi ab
> omnibus alijs partibus attributa; quemadmodum milites omnes imperatori suo
> subsidium ferunt.[29]

[28] *De magnete*, bk. 2, chap. 14.
[29] *De magnete*, bk. 2, chap. 14, p. 82. "Therefore the less it turns toward the body, the less and weaker
is the coition and adhering. Thus if A B are poles, an iron bar or magnetic fragment C is attracted at
part E. Yet the end held does not tend to the magnetic center, but obliquely toward the pole, and a chord
drawn from that end obliquely, [in the direction that] the attracted body tends, is short. Therefore it has
less strength and likewise less inclination. But as a larger chord proceeds from the body at F, its action
is firmer. At G [the chord is] still longer. At the pole A it is the longest (for the diameter is the longest
path), in which all the parts everywhere provide aid, in which as it were stands the stronghold and
tribunal of the entire region, not in itself dignified, but because a force takes root there that is contributed
by all the other parts, just as every soldier forms a reserve to his own commander."

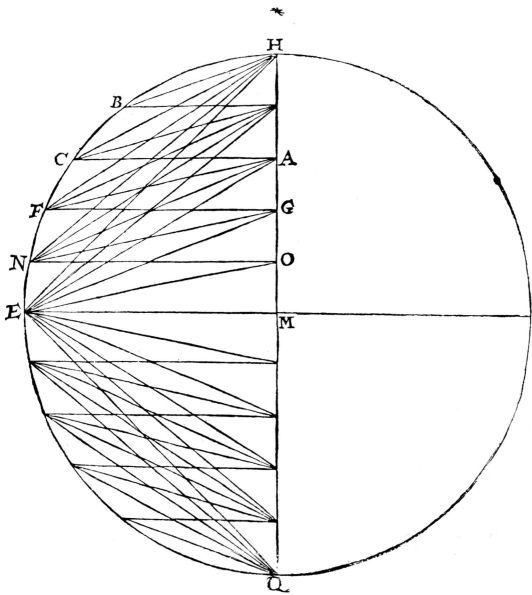

Fig. 19. At each point, B, C, F,..., of the surface there is an effect due to the portion of the half-terrella further from the axis than the surface point (*De magnete*, p. 74).

135

From this view Gilbert is led directly to the statement that:

> Quare & longior paulo lapis magis trahit quam sphaericus, cum longitudo
> sit extensa a polo in polum; etiamsi fuerint eiusdem minerae lapides, &
> eiusdem ponderis & magnitudinis. Longior via est a polo in polum in longiore
> lapide, & collatae ab alijs partibus vires non adeo sunt fusae, vti in rotundo
> & terrella, & in angustum magis conueniunt, & vniuntur, & vnita vis fortior
> excellit eminetque.[30]

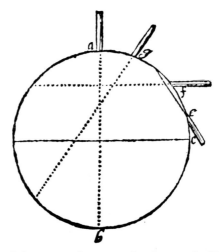

Fig. 20. The dip of the compass demonstrated with a terrella (*De magnete*, p. 82).

This viewpoint is supported, as Gilbert tells us, by the fact that elongated lodestones
with poles not at the ends are very weak, of a "abiecti & contemnendi generis."[31]
Nevertheless, Gilbert's theory that the lodestone achieves its power and virtue as a
sample of the Earth itself is so overbearing that this clear factual evidence is not
effective in turning his mind from the spherical form; the greater attraction per unit

---

[30] *De magnete*, bk. 2, chap. 14, p. 82. "For this reason a slightly elongated stone attracts more than a
spherical one, when the length extends from pole to pole; even if the stones are from the same mine and
have the same weight and size. The path from pole to pole in the longer stone is longer, and the forces
brought together from the various parts are not so much diffused as in a round lodestone and terrella,
and in a narrow one they are brought together better and united; a united stronger force excels and is
more conspicious."
[31] *Ibid.*

weight manifested by the elongated lodestone is not of determining consequence compared to the Earth-lodestone relationship that his conceptual scheme makes so clear to him. In brief, the facts are meaningful to him only in the light of his theory, which requires the perfect lodestone to have the perfect magnetic shape, that of the Earth. In his own words:

> Sed quoniam forma sphaerica, quae & perfectissima, cum terra globosa maxime consentit, & ad vsus & experimenta maxime idonea sit, praecipuas igitur nostras per lapidem demonstrationes, globoso magnete fieri volumus, tanquam magis perfecto & accommodato.[32]

Of course neither the spherical lodestone nor its description in terms of meridians and poles originated with Gilbert; we have seen that this same nomenclature was used by Peter Peregrinus (p. 40) in his letter, a work that Gilbert described as "satis pro tempore eruditum."[33] But Peter clearly and explicitly assigned the terminology in terms of the celestial sphere. It is the analogy to the Earth that both characterizes Gilbert's work and probably is the second most influential theoretical contribution to the science of magnetism.[34] Peregrinus knew (p. 40) that one pole of the lodestone was "north-seeking," the other "south-seeking," that unlike poles attract and that like poles repel. But once the Earth is identified as a giant lodestone Gilbert is able to write

> ...omnes ante nos de polis lapidis scribentes, artificesq; omnes & naucleros, in maximo errore versari, qui partem lapidis in septentriones inclinantem, septentrionalem polum lapidis existimant, in meridie vergentem meridionalem, quod postea falsum esse demonstrabimus.[35]

It is important to realize that this is by no means simply a triumph of a somewhat trite reform of terminology. Rather we have here a major change in the theory of magnetism:

---

[32] *De magnete*, bk. 1, chap. 3, p. 12. "But whereas the spherical form, which is the most perfect, in greatest agreement with the globular earth, and is the most suited to use and experiment, we wish therefore to use a globular magnet in our principial demonstrations with the stone, as being the most perfect and suitable." Gilbert does not seem to be explicitly appealing to perfection of the globular form, except in analogy to the Earth. Nevertheless traditional beliefs in the preëminence of the spherical shape were probably an encouragement to him.

[33] *De magnete*, bk. 1, chap. 1, p. 5.

[34] Certainly the connection between electric and magnetic phenomena stands in first place.

[35] *De magnete*, bk 1, chap. 4, p. 15. "...all those who before us wrote on the poles of the stone, and all instrument-makers and seamen, were in greatest error in thinking that the part of the stone which turns to the north is the north pole of the stone, and the part which turns to the south the south [pole]; we shall hereafter demonstrate this to be false."

whatever it may be that causes a magnet free to move to orient itself with respect to a fixed magnet, this is the cause of the orientation of the compass. We previously noted (p. 37) that the motion of iron to a lodestone and the orientation of the compass had been brought together into a single theoretical structure by the assumption that there are mountains of lodestone at the north pole of the Earth, or at least in nearby regions. This theory, while having the advantage of unifying two phenomena into a single scheme, encountered serious difficulties. If orientation is to be accounted for as simply an attraction, then a compass free to translate should move northward, which it does not. The obvious way out was to assume an equal attraction to the south: but since a lodestone mountain in the south might be expected to nullify the effect of one in the north, late medieval philosophers sought the *theamedes* (p. 25) as sort of a "counter-lodestone" in the south. The theamedes was, however, retreating into mythology with increased magnetic experimentation, although Gilbert found it necessary to frequently object to claims of observation of repulsion of iron by the lodestone-theamedes.[36] Further thought on this combined with increased experience with lodestones undoubtedly pointed to two other facets of the problem: opposite ends of a lodestone will attract and repel a specified end of a magnet, so that the lodestone mountain might be expected to be as it were self-neutralizing; the force of a lodestone becomes vanishing small at even small distances, so that some skepticism might be expected concerning the action of the lodestone mountain over many thousands of miles. Furthermore, Gilbert, who had collected considerable amounts of information concerning the variation of the compass from the geographic meridian, had strong evidence against the magnetic mountains. Not only did he know that islands did not appreciably affect the direction of orientation of a nearby compass, but he knew specifically that lodestone mines did not produce any such effect. In particular he knew that the island of Elba produced large quantities of lodestone but did not produce any effect on compasses on ships sailing nearby.[37] Yet it was clear that the compass exhibited no weakened orientation as it was removed from the pole. Gilbert writes:

> Nam in vlterioribus borealibus climatibus sub altitudine 70 aut 80 graduum (ad quae mitioribus anni temporibus, sine frigoris noxa peruenire nautae

---

[36] For example, *De magnete*, bk. 1, chap. 6, p. 18, "Neque Theamedem vllum esse, & vim magneti habere contrariam existimo." Or, bk. 2, chap. 39, p. 113: "Quod autem Fracastorius putat magnetem posse inueniri, quod ferrum abigat, propter latens aliquod in eo principium ferro contrarium, inane est."

[37] *De magnete*, bk. 4, chap. 5, p. 161. "Quod de Ilua Insula mirantur nonnulli (quae licet magnetum ferax sit, tamen versorium (siue nautica pyxidula) nullam facit in illam peculiarem inclinatione, cum prope nauigia in Tyrrheno pelago feruntur)..."

138

nostri solent) in medijs regionibus sub aequinoctiali in calidiore zona; tum in maritimis locis omnibus & terris australibus, sub maxima quae hactenus innotuit latitudine: semper magneticum ferrum viam inuenit suam, tenditque in polos eodem, modo (variationis excepta differentia) ex hac parte aequatoris (quam incolimus) atq; ex altera meridionali, magis incognita, a nautis tamen aliquatenus explorata: semperq; pyxidis lilium versus Boream dirigitur. Hoc illustrissimi nobis confirmant naucleri, & nautae etiam sagaciores plurimi. Hoc mihi indicauit confirmauitque illustrissimus noster Neptunus Franciscus Drake, & alter orbis lustrator Thomas Candish: hoc ipsum indicat terrella nostra.[38]

The last phrase is perhaps the most convincing evidence of all, to Gilbert, for in his hand he could hold a miniature Earth and show that although the attraction weakened with increased distance from the pole, along a meridian, the orientation did not, for the iron takes its orientating property from the Earth as a whole, not from the pole.

Thus the new theory banishes the theamedes, and sweeps away the magnetic mountains, and produces not only a confluence of the phenomena of movement and orientation into a unified whole, but explains the other magnetic movements as well. The sole requirement is that the Earth's poles *be* poles, preëminent points as are found in the terrella, and not solely imaginary points under the poles of the celestial sphere. As we shall explore further in a later chapter, Gilbert's conceptual scheme for magnetism is a considerable step toward rejection of the celestial poles, and establishment of the terrestrial poles as real points of importance. From this position the recognition of the diurnal motion of the Earth comes easily—at least to a Copernican.

We have yet to consider one rather serious difficulty with Gilbert's theory. He has told us that lodestone are somewhat damaged portions of the true Earth, found among the surface debris, into which they have been pushed from the true earthy core. Yet we have also been told that the power manifest at a pole is a contribution of the whole magnet. Hence we would expect that a section of a terrella or a section of the Earth would

---

[38] *De magnete*, bk. 3, chap. 1, pp. 117-118. "For in far northern climates in latitudes 70 to 80 degrees (to which, in the milder times of the year our sailors are accustomed to penetrate without injury from the cold), in the middle regions, under the equinoctal in the torrid zone, as also in all maritime regions and southern lands in the highest latitude that has yet been reached, the magnetic iron always finds its way and tends to the poles (except for the difference in variation). On this side of the equator (where we live) and in the other, the southern part, less well known, yet somewhat explored by sailors, the lily of the compass always points north. This has been confirmed to us by the most eminent navigators and the most intelligent seamen. This was pointed out and confirmed to me by our most illustrious sea-god Francis Drake and by the other circumnavigator Thomas Candish [Cavendish]; our terrella shows the same thing."

posses the same polarity as the whole. Thus in a terrella [Fig. 21] with poles at A and B, if the section EF is removed, E should have the same polarity as A – and Gilbert writes that he showed this to be the case:

> Atq; hic tamen obseruandum, quod si polus terrelle A moueretur in merediem telluris, etiam & E terminus partis solitariae excisae, nec prope lapidem admotae, per se moueretur in meridiem;…[39]

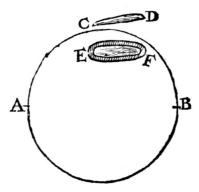

Fig. 21. If the section EF is removed from a terrella AB, E will have the polarity of A; but if a piece of iron CD is magnetized by the terrella, C will have the polarity of B (*De magnete*, p. 121).

Because of the complete analogy between the Earth and a terrella, it is clear that if a lodestone is part of the giant magnet Earth, and if the original orientation, in the Earth, of that lodestone is known, we may expect it, when set free to move, to turn 180 degrees from its original position. For since the northward end should be a north pole, and since the south pole of a terrella seeks the geographical north – the north magnetic pole of the Earth – it would seem that no other consequence of Gilbert's theory is possible. Such, however, is not the case; since the fact contradicts the theory, a new explanation is sought and found.

The fact is this:

[39] *De magnete*, bk. 3, chap. 2, p. 121. "And yet here it is to be observed that if the pole A of the terrella were moved toward the south of the earth, certainly also the end E of the cut out part alone, if not too near to the stone, would also move to the south;…"

140

Magnetem in vena sua magnum viginti librarum, obseruatis primum eius terminis & signatis, excidi & erui curauimus: postea erutum in cymba super aquam collocauimus, vt libere conuerti posset; tunc ilico facies quae septentriones in minera spectabat, in septentriones sese super vndas conuertebat, & in illo puncto tandem acquiescebat: facies enim illa despectans in minera septentriones est australis, & a telluris septentrionalibus attrahitur;...[40]

The explanation of this discrepancy is not difficult. Book One of the *De magnete* ended with a chapter entitled "Quod globus terrae sit magneticus, & magnes, & quomodo apud nos magnes lapis telluris vires primarias omnes habeat, tellus vero ijsdem potentijs in mundo directione certa constat," in which Gilbert takes some pains to make clear to the reader that we have barely scratched the surface of the layer of corrupt debris that lies over the true substance of the Earth. He points out that the maximum ocean depths are a mile [*ad mille passum*], that mines at best penetrate 500 fathoms [*orgyae*], depths that are negligible compared with the 6,872 mile diameter of the Earth [*diametri terre 6872. milliariorum*]. A lodestone dug out of a mine in the decayed surface of the Earth is not then to be likened to a section from a terrella, but to a piece of iron CD (Fig. 21) at the surface, magnetized by the terrella (Earth). The true and unattainable portion of the Earth, EF, would behave quite the opposite, as experiments with a terrella show.

II. The Five Magnetic Movements

After a brief rejection of the Aristotelian-Peripatetic qualities of heaviness and lightness[41] at the beginning of the Second Book of the *De Magnete*, Gilbert enters upon the main plan of his work:

Nunc vero aliarum motionum, a vera eius forma pendentium cause, a nobis inquirende sunt, quas in magneticis nostris corporibus manifeste vidimus, easque terrae, partibusque eius omnibus homogenicis quoq; inesse, telluri consentire & eius viribus alligari animaduertimus. Motus igitur, siue motio-

[40] *De magnete*, bk. 3, chap. 2, pp. 119-120. "Having observed a large lodestone of twenty pounds in its vein, we first marked its ends and then had it cut out and dug up. Then we placed it on a boat in water so that it was able to turn about freely. Immediately that face that looked north in the mine was turned to the north on the waves and finally settled down in that point. For that face that in the mine regarded the north is southern and is attraced by the north of the Earth..."

[41] Gilbert's entire theory was fundamentally opposed to the Aristotelian conception of the universe, as we shall see in a later chapter. See, for example, *De magnete*, bk. 5, chap. 12.

num differentiae quinq; a nobis obseruantur: Coitio (vulgo attractio dicta) ad vnitatem magneticam incitatio; directio in polos telluris, & telluris in mundi destinatos terminos verticitas & consistentia; variatio, a meridiano deflexio, quem motum nos deprauatum dicimus; Declinatio, infra horizontem poli magnetici descensus: & motus circularis, seu reuolutio:...[42]

Each of the remaining five books (2 through 6) of the *De magnete* is devoted to one of these five magnetic movements, the second book being on magnetic coition. But despite the title of the second chapter of this book, "De coitione magnetica, primumque de succini attractione, siue verius corporum ad succinum applicatione," we have seen that this chapter is entirely a digression to the amber effect. And in the next chapter, "De magnetica coitione, quam attractionem appellant, opiniones aliorum," he remains diverted, this time to earlier opinions, concerning which he was well informed. Such a diversion is necessary, Gilbert writes in reiterating his renunciation of magnetic attraction, because:

> Coitionem dicimus, non attractionem, quod male vocabulum attractio irrepsit in magneticam philosophiam, ex veterum ignorantia:...[43]

Magnetic Coition

The third chapter of Book Two affords us an opportunity to view the opinions of his predecessors as seen through Gilbert's eyes.
These, in brief, are those opinions.[44]
Epicurus [quotation] held that iron is drawn by the lodestone as straws by amber and that the atoms and indivisible particles of lodestone and iron fit together in shape and

---

[42] *De magnete*, bk. 2, chap. 1, pp. 45-56. "But now other [non-Aristotelian] motions, depending on its true form, must be investigated by us. These which we see clearly manifest in our magnetic bodies, are in the Earth itself and in all homogenous parts of it also. We have noted that they harmonize with the earth and are closely connected to its forces. Now five motions or differences of motion are observed by us: coition (commonly called attraction), the incitement to magnetic union; direction toward the Earth's poles, and verticity of the Earth toward fixed points of the world and its firm stand in that position; variation, a turning aside from the meridian, which we call a perverted motion; Declination, a descent of the magnetic pole below the horizon; and circular motion, or revolution."
[43] *De magnete*, bk. 2, chap. 3, p. 60. "We say coition and not attraction, the word attraction having improperly crept into magnetic philosophy from the ignorance of the ancients:..."
[44] In the following, page references are references to this present volume.

hence when rebounding they bring the iron with them. But, Gilbert objects, this cannot be, for this power is unobstructed even by blocks of marble.[45]

According to Aristotle, *De anima*, bk. 1, Thales (p. 15) deemed the lodestone endowed with a soul.[46] Anaxagoras held the same opinion as did Thales.[47]

In the *Timaeus* Plato [quotation] denies attraction, saying that the particles drive one another around (pp. 15–16). This, notes Gilbert, is an idle opinion.[48] Galen does not know why Plato selected the theory of circumpulsion rather than attraction, since it agrees neither with reason or experiment. He compares the attraction of medicaments to the lodestone. This, says Gilbert, is an error on his part.[49]

Lucretius (p. 18) is quoted by Gilbert, who ascribes to Plutarch an explanation similar to Lucretius'.[50] Iohannes Costaeus Laudensis is also quoted and said to have presented a theory which considered motion of iron to the lodestone as a result of combined attraction and spontaneous motion.[51] Cardan says that iron is the only metal attracted because it is the coldest. As if, writes Gilbert, lead were not as cold; this is an old woman's tale.[52] Cornelius Gemma in his *Cosmographia*, book x, holds that lodestone draws iron by invisible rays.[53]

Guilelmus Puteanus [quotation], according to Gilbert, deduces the power of the lodestone, not from an indemonstrable property of the whole substance but from its substantial form as an instrument of its efficient form. The lodestone attracts iron without a physical cause and for the sake of some good. Gilbert objects that nothing like this occurs, because of substantial form, in any other bodies.[54]

Baptista Porta [quotation] believes that lodestone is a mixture of stone and iron in

---

[45] *De magnete*, bk. 2, chap. 3, p. 61.

[46] *Ibid.* In the Mottelay translation of the *De magnete* the phrase "eo putavit magnetem anima…" is translated "deemed the loadstone endowed with a sort of life…" Gilbert felt that Thales was closer to the truth of the matter than were most of Gilbert's predecessors. See *De magnete*, bk. 2, chap. 4, p. 68: "Thaletis Milesij non absurda admodum opinio, nec vehemens delirium Scaligeri censura, quia animam magneti concessit:…"

[47] *De magnete*, bk. 2, chap. 3, p. 61.

[48] *Ibid.*

[49] *Ibid.*

[50] *De magnete*, bk. 2, chap. 3, p. 62.

[51] *Ibid.* John Coste of Lodi was a sixteenth-century translator of and commentator on Galen and Aristotle.

[52] *Ibid.*

[53] *De magnete*, bk. 2, chap. 3, p. 63. S. P. Thompson, *Notes on the de magnete of Dr. William Gilbert*, London, privately printed, 1901, gives the relevant passage: "Certe vt a magnete insensiles radij ferrum ad se attrahunt, ab echineide paruo pisciculo sistuntur plena nauigia, a catoblepa spirtu non homines solum, sed & alta serpentum genera interimuntur, & saxa dehiscunt."

[54] *De magnete*, bk. 2, chap. 3, p. 63.

conflict with one another, and the iron therein attracts other iron to acquire strength and company. Stone is not attracted because the lodestone is predominantly stone. But, answers Gilbert, iron touched by lodestone attracts iron; those are wrong, too, who think the cause is sympathy.[55] Scaliger eruditely says that iron moves to the lodestone as to its mother, to be perfected by hidden principles, as the Earth tends to the center.[56] The divine Thomas [quotation] held that the iron is somehow altered by the lodestone giving to it some quality which causes it to move. In one of his rare commendations, Gilbert calls this a by no means ill-conceived opinion that, however, is corroborated by things unbelievable concerning the lodestone and the adverse effect of garlic on it.[57] Cardinal Cusa held that in the lodestone there is some principle of the efflux of the iron, which causes the iron, by a wonderous longing, to move upward rather than its natural motion downward.[58]

> Talles feruntur de magnete attrahente opiniones (pro cuiusq; sensu) dubiae & incertae. Magneticarum vero motionum causas quae in philosophorum scholis ad quatuor elementa & primas qualitates referuntur, blattis illas & tineis terendas relinquimus.[59]

III. The Cause of Magnetic Phenomena

In Chapter One (pp. 15–16) we noted that "attraction" is not a phenomenon but a theory, and furthermore a theory that has never been intellectually satisfying for long periods. It is clear that Gilbert realized that in both the magnetic and electric cases *attraction* serves as an *explanation* of *motion,* and that he was accordingly justified in explaining the observed motions by quite separate theories for the two cases.

> Cum vero duo sint corporum genera, quae manifestis sensibus nostris motionibus corpora allicere videntur, Electrica & Magnetica;...[60]

---

[55] *De magnete,* bk. 2, chap. 3, pp. 63-64.

[56] *De magnete,* bk. 2, chap. 3, p. 64. S. P. Thompson, *op. cit.* (fn. 53) gives the source of Scaliger's statement as *De subtilitate, ad Cardanum, Exercitatio* CII (Lutetiae, 1557, p. 156 *bis*).

[57] *De magnete,* bk. 2, chap. 3, p. 64. The passage quoted by Gilbert is from *Expositio Diui Thome Aquinatis Doctoris Angelici super octo libros Physicorum Aristotelis,...* Venice, Giunta ed., 1539, p. 96 verso, col. 2. See Thompson, *op. cit.* (fn. 53), p. 45.

[58] *De magnete,* bk. 2, chap. 3, p. 64.

[59] *Ibid.* "Such are the opinions concerning the lodestone attracting (or their sense), doubtful and uncertain. But those causes of the magnetic motions which in the schools of the philosophers are referred to the four elements and prime qualities, we leave them for cockroaches and bookworms."

[60] *De magnete,* bk. 2, chap. 4, p. 65. "Since there are in truth two kinds of bodies which seem to allure bodies with motions manifest to our senses, Electrics and Magnetics;..."

We have already seen (Chapter Three) Gilbert's explanation of the motion produced by electrics, which he summarizes thus:

Electrica naturalibus ab humore effluuijs;... incitationes faciunt.[61]

But what of Magnetics? Motion to a magnetic, Gilbert is convinced, is not amenable to explanation in terms of a material effluvium from the magnetic, that is, it is not reducible to a contact phenomenon. In the electric case one can see the interference of interposed objects which halt the motion – clear evidence to Gilbert that a material substance is being interfered with by the intermediate shielding object. In the magnetic case no such interference is observed. Hence, he concludes, the magnetic action must not involve emission of such a material effluvium.

Today we know that such interference is present if the interposed object is a magnetic. One may not conclude from this, however, that Gilbert's convictions rested upon so shaky a foundation that his theory of magnetism could have been overthrown by a simple fact unknown to him – for the fact was not unknown to him. He was well aware of the magnetic shielding produced by a plate of iron interposed between a lodestone and a test piece of iron; he devoted considerable space to a discussion of the phenomenon, writing for example:

Si magnes imbecillior fuerit, versorium vix conuertitur interposita lamina; fusus enim per extremitates vigor magnetis imbecillioris, per medium minus permeat.[62]

Nevertheless, Gilbert refused to assign a material effluvium to magnetics: his interpretation of the phenomena in terms of his cosmological views is sufficient to make him return again and again to a consideration of magnetic coition – as well as the other magnetic movements – as due to some inherent property of magnetics. These same cosmological views made it essential that he reject the foundations of Aristotelian mechanics, and indeed the entire peripatetic cosmology. Yet at the same time he is held fast in the intellectual straitjacket of the peripatetic vocabulary.[63] He writes that

[61] *Ibid.* "Electrics incite by means of natural effluvia from humors..."
[62] *De magnete*, bk. 2, chap. 16, p. 84. "If the lodestone is weak, the versorium scarcely turns when the plate is interposed; for being diffused to the extremities [of the plate], the vigor of the weak lodestone is less able to penetrate through the middle of the plate."
[63] This is not to say as the term lingers on, the older concepts do not at the same time persist. However a breaking away from those concepts may be under way without elimination of the language associated with them. Thus Galileo uses the term "impetus" without complete subscription to the impetus physics; today we use terms such as "affinity," "cause," "form," "element," in some connotations that show their direct connection to the Scholastic tradition.

145

...Magnetica formalibus efficientijs, seu potius primarijs vigoribus, incitationes faciunt.[64]

But, he hastens to add,

> Forma illa singularis est, & peculiaris, non Peripateticorum causa formalis, & specifica in mixtis, & secunda forma, non generantium corporum propagatrix; sed primorum & praecipuorem globorum forma; & partium eorum homogenearum, non corruptarum, propria entitas & existentia, quam nos primariam, & radicalem, & astream appellare possumus forma; non formam primam Aristotelis, sed singularem illam, quae globum suum proprium tuetur & disponit.[65]

Each body of the universe has its own form and a fragment of any of those bodies arranges itself to conform to that body.

> Quare magnetica natura est telluris propria, eiusque omnibus verioribus partibus, primaria & stupenda ratione, insita; haec nec a coelo toto deriuatur procreaturue, per sympathiam, per influentiam, aut occultiores qualitates; nec peculiari aliquo astro: est enim suus in tellure magneticus vigor, sicut in sole & luna suae formae;...[66]

Gilbert devotes four chapters, thirteen pages,[67] to a discussion of this magnetic form which is "singularis... & peculiaris, non Peripateticorum causa formalis, & specifica in mistis, & secunda forma, non generatium corporum propagatrix;..." Yet his negative definition is as close as one gets to a clear-cut explication of the nature of the magnetic form. Later[68] Gilbert returns to an overt animism and berates Aristotle in such terms as these:

---

[64] *De magnete*, bk. 2, chap. 4, p. 65.

[65] *De magnete*, bk. 2, chap. 4, p. 65. "This form is singular and peculiar [proper], not the formal cause of the Peripatetics, the specific cause in mixtures, the secondary form, not the propagator of generative bodies, but the form of the primary and chief globes [i.e., the celestial bodies, including the Earth]: it is a special entity and existence of their homogenous, noncorrupt parts, which we may call a primary, radical, and astral form. This is not the primary form of Aristotle, but that unique one which preserves and orders its own proper globe."

[66] *Ibid.* "Wherefore the magnetic nature is proper to the Earth, and fixed in all its true parts according to a primary and astounding plan. It is neither derived nor produced from the heavens as a whole through sympathy, influence, or occult qualities, nor from any particular star. For there is in the Earth a magnetic *vigor* of its own, just as in the sun and moon there are forms, of their own..."

[67] *De magnete*, bk. 2, chaps. 4-7, pp. 65-77.

[68] *De magnete*, bk. 5, chap. 12.

Monstrum igitur istud in Aristotelico mundo videatur, in quo omnia perfecta, viuida, animata; vnica vero terra, infoelix pars pusilla, imperfecta, mortua, inanimata & caduca.[69]

He again finds Thales' use of "anima" as a symbol representing the magnetic power quite reasonable.[70] The experimental nature of Gilbert's work is nowhere shown as clearly as in his approach to the meaning of the magnetic form in terms of operations and observables. As an example—one of many given by him—consider the following facts: iron is obtained from iron ore—perhaps even smelted from lodestone; it is usually not magnetized or weakly magnetized, although the smelting removes impurities; the iron is capable of becoming magnetized. These are the observables. Interpreted in terms of Gilbert's theory they tell us that

In ferro propter corporis fusionem cum funditur vena magnetica, aut ferrea, formae primariae virtus distincta antea, iam confusa est: sed magnes integer appositus iterum actum primarium disponit, disposita, & ordinata forma cum magnete socias vires coniungit mutuoq; magnetice in omnibus motionibus ad vnitate ambo consentiunt, confederantur, & adiuncta siue corporeo contactu, siue intra orbem disposita, vnum & idem sunt.[71]

The Sphere of Influence

Some modern writers have sometimes credited Gilbert with having at least a primitive concept of magnetic field.[72] One must tread cautiously in any such reading back of modern concepts into earlier writings, although of course there are elements of almost

[69] *De magnete*, bk. 5, chap. 12, p. 209. "Therefore the Aristotelian world would seem to be monstrous, in which everything is perfect, vigorous, animated, while the Earth alone, a barren and puny part, is imperfect, dead, inanimate and perishable." Gilbert expands at length upon this theme.

[70] *De magnete*, bk. 5, chap. 12, p. 210. See also *supra*, fn. 46, and the treatment of Thomas Aquinas, *supra*, p. 144.

[71] *De magnete*, bk. 2, chap. 4, p. 69. "In iron, on account of the fusion of the body when a magnetic ore or iron is smelted, the virtue of the primary form, previously distinct, is now confused. But an undamaged lodestone placed near again arranges its primary action, the disposed and ordered form joins its forces mutually with the lodestone. The two together harmonize magnetically in all motions toward unition, act in consort, and whether joined by bodily contact or being within their [mutual] sphere, are one and the same."

[72] One of many examples is Brother Potamian's discussion in "Gilbert of Colchester," *Popular Science Monthly*, vol. 59 (1901), p. 344. For example, "When Faraday spoke of field of force, magnetic field, lines of electric and magnetic induction, some thought the idea new, whereas not only the idea but the very terms occur with appropriate illustrations in *De Magnete*."

every modern concept in almost every earlier book, if one is willing to accept vague enough allusions.

The concepts of magnetic and electric fields expounded by Michael Faraday in the 19th Century may be considered in great measure as devices for eliminating action at a distance and restoring the study of electric and magnetic phenomena to the realm of contact phenomena.[73] In this sense then Gilbert's magnetic form is quite remote from Faraday's field. Gilbert's influence in this direction lay in his insistence upon the region around the magnetic as being a region of interest. In a chapter entitled "De potentia virtutis magneticae, & natura in orbem extensibili," he writes:

> Fvnditur virtus magnetica vndequaque circa corpus magneticum in orbem; circa terrellam sphaerice; in alijs lapidum figuris, magis confuse & inaequaliter.[74]

It is important to emphasize that this virtue is by no means the property of the space that it becomes in later science.

> Nec tamen in rerum natura subsistit orbis, aut virtus per aërem fusa permanens, aut essentialis; sed magnes tantum excitat magnetica conuenienti interuallo distantia.[75]

For this discussion of the sphere of influence Gilbert refers to the figures reproduced in Figs. 22 and 23. Later he returns to this subject, "De formali actu magnetico sphaerice effuso."[76] Here he suggests that if through a point near a lodestone a circle (for a circular lodestone) be drawn that is concentric with the center of the lodestone, that a magnetic placed at the point will behave as though it were at the surface of an imaginary lodestone bounded by that circle. Thus for a lodestone bounded by the smallest circle (Fig. 24) LF, a compass at E will behave, according to Gilbert, as though it were on the surface of a lodestone bounded by the largest circle, ABCD, and will therefore point–as predicted by a theory to be discussed later–toward the equatorial point D. This "mapping" of the region about a magnet its a characteristic operation in

---

[73] See Al-kindi's remark, *supra*, pp. 40-41.

[74] *De magnete*, bk. 2, chap. 7, p. 76. "The magnetic virtue is spread out around the magnetic body in all directions in a sphere; around a terrella it is spherical; in stones of other shapes it is more confused and irregular."

[75] *Ibid.*, p. 76-77. "Nevertheless there exists in nature no orb or permanent or essential virtue spread out through the air. But a lodestone only excites magnetics at convenient distances."

[76] *De magnete*, bk. 5, chap. 11.

148

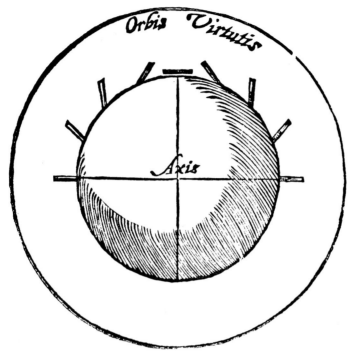

Fig. 22. The sphere of influence about a spherical lodestone (terrella)
(*De magnete*, p. 76).

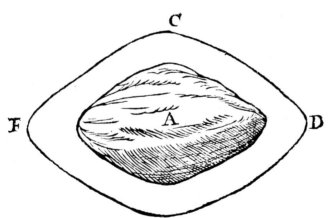

Fig. 23. The sphere of influence about a nonspherical lodestone
(*De magnete*, p. 77).

149

modern pedagogy for elementary magnetostatics, wherein it bears the title of "mapping the field." Yet it is as necessary to be careful of reading modern terminology back into older works as to watch for the continued existence of archaic terms. Gilbert is not, either here or in other places where he does such mapping (Fig. 25), mapping a magnetic field: he is exploring the sphere of influence. His exploratory technique remains with science to modern times, but the concept of sphere of influence undergoes radical modification in the 19th Century.

It is not clear how far out from the magnet Gilbert thought the sphere of influence to extend. In some places he seems to deem it finite, as when he writes of that sphere

> Veluti in longiore lapide A [see Fig. 25] vigor extenditur ad termimum ambientem FCD aequidistantem vndique a lapide A.[77]

Yet elsewhere, in discussing Fig. 24, he writes

> In his (vt in omnibus quos infinitos imaginari possumus) orbibus,...[78]

It is probable that in this case "omnibus quos infinitos" refers to the large number of spheres that may be imagined within a finite distance of the stone. At any rate the question is not of great importance: Gilbert knew that the lodestones with which he experimented had at best an insignificant effect at large distances; he also knew that the Moon and Earth were close enough together to influence one another.[79]

IV. Summary

Within half a century of the publication of the *De magnete*, Gilbert's distinction of "magnetic coition" in terms of the joint action of the two objects concerned, in contrast to the unsymmetrical attraction of an object by an excited electric, has become unsatisfactory; the lack of symmetry in the electric case had been disproved, eliminating this difference between the action of electrics and magnetics.[80]

---

[77] *De magnete*, bk. 2, chap. 7, p. 77. "As in the elongated stone A, the vigor extends to the surrounding limits FCE everywhere equidistant from the stone A."

[78] *De magnete*, bk. 5, chap. 11, p. 205. "In these spheres (as in all those which we may imagine without end)..."

[79] *De magnete*, bk. 6, chap. 6, p. 232.

[80] By the Accademia del Cimentio.

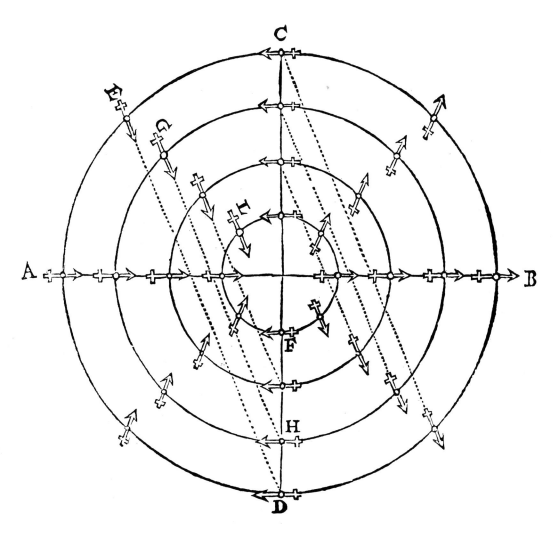

Fig. 24. Behavior of a compass, within the sphere of influence, at varying distances from a terrella (*De magnete,* p. 206).

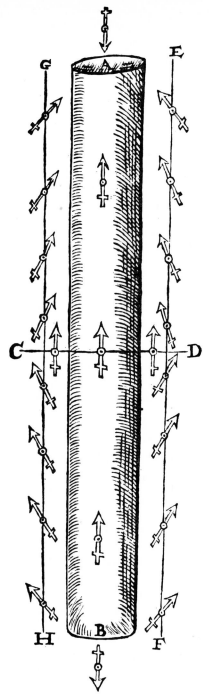

Fig. 25. Behavior of a compass near an elongated lodestone
(*De magnete*, p. 164).

Gilbert denies the presence of a material medium in the magnetic case because of the ability of magnetics to act through objects that stifled the electric virtue. He is thereby driven back to an animistic position which at best is able to say that a magnet simply possesses the property of acting at a distance upon a magnetic. The view of action at a distance is by no means one that science has always immediately rejected, although scientists have never liked it: within a little more than a century of the publication of the *De magnete*, the property possessed by matter of acting gravitationally at a distance is being hailed as the key to the understanding of the universe. The extent to which a theory may be unreasonable and yet acceptable depends upon the breadth of the usefulness which may be found for it. We may therefore no more ask for a further explanation of Gilbert's magnetic form than we may ask for elaboration of the Newtonian property of gravitational action at a distance. An understanding of Gilbert's importance and influence in science must therefore stem from an examination of what could be done with his conceptual schemes for electricity and magnetism, rather than from an attempt to understand his magnetic form.

We may summarize the logical structure of Gilbert's magnetic theory in the following terms. At the base is the belief that each of the major objects in the universe possesses its own peculiar magnetic properties, form. From this the analogy between terrella and Earth is deduced, as well as certain speculations concerning cosmology. From the former Gilbert is able to account for the magnetic phenomena which he can observe, and from the latter he is able to provide certain cosmological theories that are of considerable interest to some of his contemporaries and immediate successors. His explorations of magnetic phenomena, in terms of his theory, result in the accumulation of a large body of facts. His belief that the terrella is a little Earth enables him to both experiment in the field of astronomy and to experiment at home with the world-wide behavior of the nautical compass. It is in the accumulation of facts and the contributions to the sciences of astronomy and navigation that we must look for Gilbert's notable magnetic contributions.

CHAPTER FIVE

GILBERT, NAVIGATION AND COSMOLOGY

In the sixteenth century England was becoming great and powerful and navigation and seamanship were important and essential elements in her rise to power. The prior development of the compass as an instrument of sea trade is unquestionable and the accentuated interest in the compass at the same time as the beginnings of European world expansion cannot be simply coincidence. To this clear and certain general European influence one must add, in Gilbert's case, the additional English influence. One of the few contemporary documents we have relating to Gilbert is concerned with the English fleet (p. 79); that document concerns the health of the fleet shortly before the defeat of the Armada, which occurred when Gilbert was 44. In the *De magnete* Gilbert refers to Drake and Thomas Cavendish (p. 139) in a manner that sounds suspiciously as though he is bragging about the acquaintance.

Gilbert pursued a navigational dream – a dream that we know was illusory, but one that showed immense promise to a seafaring nation, namely, the determination of position at sea. The illusion lay in Gilbert's hope to determine such positions through the variations of the compass from the meridian and from the horizontal. Briefly, the variation from the meridian was expected to yield longitude and the variation from the horizontal, the dip, to yield latitude. The first of these was the vastly more important one, for latitude could at least in principle be determined from astronomical observations, when the weather was clear. But by Gilbert's day it was already certain that theoretical prediction of the variation from the meridian would be uncertain and that empirical techniques would have to be used.

I. The Variation from the Meridian

It had long been known that the bare compass needle did not aline itself with the meridian, and compasses were normally constructed by fixing one or more needles to a compass card in such a way that the north-point on the card indicated North, although the needles would not (p. 45). Gilbert's hope for use of the variation lay in the knowledge that the variation itself varied from place to place.

Gilbert's source of knowledge was two-fold: data from seamen; experiments with the terrella. As is so often the case in science, the "real" facts from seamen combined with Gilbert's theory of magnetism to heavily influence what he saw when he experimented with the terrella.

Book Four of the *De magnete* is entitled "De variatione," and begins with clarifications of terminology and definition. From the general theory of the concordance of the compass and the Earth it is clear to Gilbert that the variation is an *error*.

> Qui de magneticis motionibus ante nos scripserunt, nullam differentiam posuerunt inter directionem & variationem, sed vnam volunt & simplicem esse magnetici ferri conuersionem. Sed directio vera, est ad verum meridianum corporis magnetici motus,...[1]

The view that the variation is not an error is rejected by Gilbert as being absurd. He cites as evidence the manner in which not only the needle, magnetized iron, and the compass show the variation "sed etiam in sua cymba terrellam, venam ferream, & ferreos lapides, & terras magneticis apte preparatas."[2]

The symmetry of both the terrella and the Earth with respect to their equators leads Gilbert to reject any preëminence of North over South. The variation at a particular point is therefore to be conceived and observed in terms of the nearer pole; there is no "point respective" in the north. Thus in the northern hemisphere the variation is the deviation of the northmost (magnetically south) end of the compass; but in the southern hemisphere the variation is the deviation of the opposite end, since it is the one that indicates the nearer pole. The distinction is important, for although the *angle* of variation does not depend upon which end of the needle is observed, Gilbert's explanation of the phenomenon does.

After briefly reminding his reader once more that earlier writers—mentioning them by name—were ignorant concerning the topic of variation, Gilbert enters upon his theory of the phenomenon. Since the terrella or Earth gives to the compass its directivity, the large-scale irregularities and deviations from spherical form, in the Earth, could be expected to produce irregularities and deviations in the orientation.

---

[1] *Gvilielmi Gilberti Colcestrensis, medici Londinensis, de magnete, magneticisqve corporibvs, et de magno magnete tellure; Physiologia nova, plurimis & argumentis, & experimentis demonstrata,* London, Peter Short, 1600. (Hereafter this work is referred to as *"De magnete."*) Bk. 4, chap. 1, p. 151. "Those who have written before us concerning magnetic movements have made no distinction between direction [orientation] and variation, but think both simply to be one, a turning around of the magnetic iron. But the true direction [orientation] is the motion of the magnetic body to the true meridian,..."

[2] *Ibid.* "... but also a terrella in its boat, iron ore, ironstone, and properly prepared magnetic earths."

Consider a continent on the Earth. A compass placed to the west of the continent might be expected to show an easterly deviation, since to the normal directivity of the spherical Earth there is added the additional non-symmetrical directivity of the continent. This does not produce as much deviation as might be expected from a first consideration, however. It is important, Gilbert tells his reader, to keep firmly in mind that the deviation from the meridian is not due to either attraction or coition.[3] The Earth as a whole *directs* the compass needle. The continent of our example then does not pull the needle to one side but merely enters into the process of directing it; but because of the asymmetry of the situation, the result is a directing a little to one side of the meridian. Since the directing is toward the nearest pole, it is the end of the needle nearest the pole that is deviated toward the continent. In Gilbert's words,

> Veluti apud nos Anglos Londini vndecim gradibus variat & 1/3: In alijs quibusdum locis aliquanto maior est variatio, non tamen multo pluribus partibus in vlla vnquam regione remotus est ferri finis a meridiano. Nam vt a vera terrae verticitate semper dirigitur ferru; ita continentis terrae (quemadmodum totius terreni globi) polaris natura pergit versus polos: atque etiamsi moles illa magnetica corpora a meridiano diuertat; eadem tamen conformat, & disponit earundem terrarum (sicut etiam totius telluris) verticitas, ne in Eurum maiore aliquo arcu conuertatur.[4]

This hypothesis is a consequence, if not a unique one, of Gilbert's general theory of orientation. At the same time, as we have seen (pp. 46–47), it conforms to the original and gross navigational evidence, namely, that the compass varies to the east off the Atlantic Coast of Europe and then swings back to the meridian as the observer moves west past the Azores, and then beyond the meridian to a westerly variation, presumably due to the approach to the Americas.

Experimental evidence from the terrella is brought to bear on this same problem

> Demonstratur hoc ipsum manifeste per terrellam, hoc modo: sit lapis rotundus aliqua parte imperfectior, & marcore labefactatus (talem habuimus parte

---

[3] *De magnete*, bk. 4, chap. 6.

[4] *De magnete*, bk. 4, chap. 7, 163. "As with us English at London it varies eleven degrees and 1/3: in some other places the variation is a little greater, but in no other region is the end of the iron removed much more from the meridian. For as the iron is always directed by the true verticity of the Earth, so the polar nature of the continent land (just as all of the terrene globe) proceeds toward the poles; and even if that mass diverts magnetic bodies from the meridian, yet the verticity of that same land controls and directs them, so that they do not turn east by any greater arc."

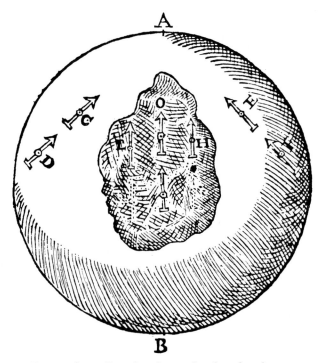

Fig. 26. A terrella with a depressed and weakened region
representing an ocean (*De magnete*, p. 155).

quadam cariosa, ad similitudinem maris Atlantici, siue Oceani magni) pone
fila ferrea longitudinis granorum duorum hordeaceorum super lapidem, vt
in sequente figura [Fig. 26]. A B, Terrella partibus quibusdam imperfectior,
& virtute in circumferentia, inaequalis: Versoria E, F, non variant; sed
directe polum A respiciunt: posita sunt enim in medio firmae & valentis
partis terrellae, longius ab imperfecta: superficies punctis & lineis transuersis
insignita, imbecillior est. O (versorum) etiam non variat (quia in medio
imperfectae partis) sed in polum dirigitur, non aliter atq; iuxta occidentales
Azores in tellure. H & L (versoria) variant, ad proximas enim saniores partes
inclinant.[5]

---

[5] *De magnete*, bk. 4, chap. 2, pp. 155-156. "This is manifestly demonstrated by use of a terrella in this
way: let there be a round stone imperfect in any part and weakened by decay (such a one we had with
a certain part corroded to resemble the Atlantic Sea, or a great ocean), place on the stone iron filaments

This is one of the demonstrations of the validity of Gilbert's theory by experiment with a terrella. In other such demonstrations he uses terrellas with various bumps and protuberances, and finds that they all bear out the theory, at least in its general outlines.

But unfortunately the navigational evidence neither bears out the earlier and cruder evidence of easterly variation off Europe and westerly variation off America in the Atlantic, nor does it support the obvious hope that a simple relationship between the magnitudes of the variation and the longitude might be found. It is in a chapter entitled 'An longitudo terrestris inueniri possit per variationem'[6] that Gilbert comes to grips with this problem, 'Gratum hoc opus nautis esset, & geographiae maximum incrementum adferret.'[7] But, he adds, Porta's hope that there is a one-to-one correspondence between longitude and variation is a 'spe vana.'

> ...variatio varijs modis incerta semper est, tam propter longitudinem, quam latitudinem, & propter accessum versus terras magnas, terrenarumque eminentiarum magis praeualentium habitudinem; nec meridiani alicuius regulam sequitur,...[8]

This is of course by no means contrary to Gilbert's hypothesis. Yet predictions of the variation at given places on the Earth from that theory can now only be expected to yield qualitative results. These results would of course have some value: thus in the inverse case Gilbert is able to write:

> Iam vero a pyxidulae deuiatione ratio apparet manifesta vie in orientem per Scythicum oceanum apertae; nam cum versorium variationem habeat tam amplam in Zephyroboream, non in aliqua magna distantia continentem tota illa via versus ortum sese extendere manifestum est. Igitur maiore spe mare

the length of two grains of barley-corn, as in the following figure [Fig. 26]. A B [is] a terrella somewhat imperfect in parts and of unequal power on the circumference. The versorium E, F, do not vary, but regard the pole A directly, for they are in the center of the firm and storng parts of the terrella, far from the imperfect [part] which is weaker and is marked with dots and transverse lines. O (a versorium) also does not vary (because it is in the center of the imperfect part) but is directed to the pole, no different from just off the Western Azores on the Earth. H and L (versoriums) vary, inclining toward the sounder parts near to them."

[6] *De magnete*, bk. 4, chap. 9.

[7] *De magnete*, bk. 4, chap. 9, p. 166. "This work would be welcome to seamen, and would bring the greatest advance to geography."

[8] *De magnete*, bk. 4, chap. 9, p. 167. "...the variation is in various ways always uncertain, both because of longitude and latitude and because of the approach to great [masses of] land and the appearance of the dominant land prominences; nor does is follow the rule of any meridian..."

versus Eurum tentandum & lustrandum, pro transitu ad Moluccas per Euro-
boream potius quam Zephyroboream.[9]

One would imagine that Gilbert was proud of this deduction.[10]

Gilbert has accounted for the variation with the framework of his conceptual scheme
for magnetism. At the same time he has failed to achieve a means of determination of
longitude theoretically, that is, he is unable to compile a table or nomograph which, in
conjunction with measured values of the variation, will yield the longitude of the
observer. Indeed he has hinted that local variations in the power of portions of a
spherical lodestone – that is, lack of magnetic homogeneity – indicate a similar variation
in the Earth. Consequently construction of a scale-model Earth, a terrella with all
depressions and elevations faithfully reproduced, would be a waste of time, since these
variations in homogeneity are not reproducible. But now Gilbert gives us firm evidence
of his at least partial motivation by practical interests:[11] he presses beyond the limita-
tions of theoretical work into empirical determination of the relationships between
longitude and variation. His theory tells him that the variation at a given place is un-
changing with time;[12] therefore he concludes that the solution to the problem of longitude lies in the compilation of *accurate* tables of variation at various positions on the
surface of the Earth. To this end he presents detailed instructions for the construction
of the necessary instruments and their use in the determination of the variation. A table
of the right ascensions and declinations of 'Stellae Lucidæ & spectate, quae non longe
distant ab aequatore,...' is included. Gilbert definitely hoped that seamen would compile
the necessary data, guided by the *De magnete*, and that the data would ultimately yield
a method of determining longitude from the local variation. His vision was not idle,
but it was fruitless.

[9] *De magnete*, bk. 4, chap. 16, p. 180. "Now from deviation of the compass there appears manifest the
reason for a passage to the east through the Arctic Ocean. For since the versorium has so great a
variation toward the north-west, it is manifest that no continent extends any great distance of the whole
of that way toward the East. Therefore with greater hope can we attack and examine a sea toward the
East for a passage to the Moluccas by the north-east than by the north-west." This statement appears in
a chapter entitled "De variatione in Noua Zembla."

[10] Yet other factors such as ice and colonies were rapidly to reduce the importance of both north-west
and north-east passages.

[11] Gilbert has been examined at length from a Marxist point of view by Edgar Zilsel, "The Origins of
William Gilbert's Scientific Method," *Journal of the History of Ideas*, vol. 2 (1940), pp. 1-32. In this
extremely interesting and illuminating article Zilsel investigates Gilbert's connections with artisans,
laborers, and seamen, and throws a good deal of light on sources of information that are not acknowledged by Gilbert. The connections are sometimes made by Zilsel only by placing undue stress on some
rather casual passages in Gilbert.

[12] *De magnete*, bk. 4, chap. 3, pp. 159-160: "Variatio vniuscuiusque loci constans est."

159

II. The Variation from the Horizontal

> Iam tandem peruenimus ad nobile illud experimentum, & motionem admi-
> randam magneticorum, conuertibili sua natura infra horizontem descenden-
> tium: cuius scientia, terrestris globi & magnetis (siue ferri magnetici) mirabilis
> apparet, & per nostram doctrinam manifesta combinatio, concordantia, &
> mutuus consensus.[13]

Thus does Gilbert begin his discussion of the other variation of the compass, the dip
of the needle when it is free to turn about a horizontal axis.[14] As with his other experimental work, Gilbert seems anxious that the reader should reproduce his experiments,
and he describes in meticulous detail the construction and use of an instrument for
measuring the angle of dip. This is no 'thought-experiment' or illustrative example, but
is definitely intended for guidance of an experimenter.

Then Gilbert turns to the explanation of this phenomenon:

> Huius tanti, & tamdiu omnibus mortalibus incogniti effectus, talis causa certa
> & verissima existit.[15]

Here again we arrive at the moment of ennunciation, and again, as in the case of the
magnetic form (p. 146), the revelation is anticlimatic:

> Magnes lapis mouetur & conuertitur, donec eius polus alter versus septen-
> triones incitatus, in destinato horizontis puncto acquiescat; hic qui versus
> boream consistit (vt ex praecedentibus regulis, & demonstrationibus apparet)
> meridionalis est, non borealis, quem ante nos omnes existimabant esse bore-
> alem, ob conuersionem eius in illam horizontis partem.[16]

---

[13] *De magnete,* bk. 5, chap. 1, p. 184. "Now at last we arrive at that noble experiment and admirable
movement of magnetics, the turning by their own nature to sink below the horizon. It is made clear by
this knowledge and shown through our teaching that the terrestrial sphere and the lodestone (or
magnetized iron) combine, concord, and mutually agree."

[14] *De magnete,* bk. 5. The effective discovery (invention) of the dip was due to Robert Norman (p. 47).
Zilsel, *loc. cit.* (fn. 11) presents effective evidence that Gilbert had a far greater intellectual debt to
Norman than is apparent from the *De magnete.*

[15] *De magnete,* bk. 5, chap. 1, p. 187. "Of this effect, so great and so long unknown to men, the following
appears to be the certain and true cause."

[16] *Ibid.* "The lodestone is moved and turned until one of its two poles being urged toward the north
comes to rest in a determined point of the horizon. This [pole] which takes its place toward the north
(as appears from the foregoing rules and demonstrations) is the southern one, not the northern, though
all before us thought it to be the northern because of its turning to that [northern] part of the horizon."

160

The explanation is not a very satisfying one: indeed it is no explanation at all, but a complete tautology. At the same time there seems no doubt but that Gilbert felt that the variation from the horizontal was closely associated with and a part of the general orientation of the compass. This orientation is due to its magnetic form (p. 146) which it possesses solely because of its origin as part of the Earth. The orientation – in three dimensions – is then a conformation of the whole magnet to the whole Earth, as Gilbert has so carefully demonstrated with the terrella. The 'failure' of the compass to remain in the horizontal plane is thus not to be regarded at all as a failure; it is simply the orientation into the proper position for conformity. Beyond this Gilbert's theory does not extend.

Since the dipping needle is horizontal at the equator and vertical at the poles, and hence turns through 90° as it is moved along a meridian through 90° of latitude from equator to pole, it is reasonable to equate the angle of depression below the horizon to the latitude. But this hypothesis is not borne out by the experimental evidence: such a simple relationship between latitude and dip is not to be found.

Gilbert's belief in the fundamental character of magnetic phenomena drives him to seek the simple relationship between the angles of dip and latitude that all of his instincts as a scientist tell him must exist. His later contemporary, Johann Kepler (1571–1630) demonstrated precisely the same behavior as Gilbert when seeking simple relationships concerning planetary motion. Both Gilbert and Kepler achieved theories that demonstrated to them the simplicity and the wonderous order within Nature. These theories – often called 'empirical laws' – in each case are not derived from any higher level of theory, other than the belief in order and simplicity. At the same time they must not be regarded simply as brief statements of the data. In each case they *are* theories, invented to account for the phenomena, expressed in mathematical language.

In Gilbert's case, the empirical law took the form of a nomograph relating the latitude and dip. There is no indication that he made extensive use of data from observations on the Earth's surface, and it is probable that his data was obtained largely from experiments with the terrella.

In the prefatory address in the *De magnete* Edward Wright (1558?–1615) wrote:

> ...si nihil aliud haberent hi tui de Magnete libri praeter solam hanc latitudinis ex declinatione magnetica inuentionem, a te nunc primum in lucem prolatam, eos tamen naucleri nostri Britanni, Galli, Belgae, Dani ex oceano Atlantico, in mare Britannicum, aut fretum Herculeum tenebroso coelo ingressuri, non modico auro aequiparandos meritissime indicarent.[17]

[17] *De magnete,* iiij *verso.*

161

The hopes of Wright and Gilbert were not fulfilled: Gilbert's theory is not adequate to predict useful values of either the variation from the meridian or from the horizontal, and empirical techniques are also unable to yield useful determination of position from the variation and dip. The fruitful path toward determination of position at sea lay through use of astronomical observations.

III. Cosmology

Scattered through the first five books of the *De magnete* are remarks that indicate both Gilbert's general cosmological outlook and a belief that his magnetic theory has astronomical applications. There is no doubt but that he believed that the Earth turns diurnally upon its own axis.[18] Gilbert opens his discussion of the polarity of lodestones and identification of the poles by writing:

> Telluris polus alter versus Cynosurae astru conuertitur, certumq; in coelo punctum constater respicit, (nisi quod ex astris fixis promotis in longitudinem immutatur, que motum nos in tellure agnoscimus, vt postea demonstrabimus:)...[19]

Gilbert assures the reader that not only is the constancy of orientation of the Earth's axis magnetic in origin, but that its particular orientation may be explained in terms of his theory of magnetism. Just as a lodestone, free to move, will conform to the Earth, so the Earth – if it were possible to disturb the orientation of its axis – would return to the proper alignment.[20] Furthermore

> Cur vero terrestris globus altero polo in illas partes, & versus Cynosuram conuerso, constantior permanere videretur; aut cur polus eius 23 gradibus, minutis 29 cum variatione quadam non satis adhuc ab Astronomis explorata ab eclipticis polis variaret, a magnetica pendet virtute: Anticipationis aequi-

---

[18] See *supra,* chap. 4, above fn. 69, the strong remarks on those who would make the world a dead inert thing.
[19] *De magnete,* bk. 1, chap. 4, p. 14. "One pole of the Earth turns toward Cynosura [Ursa Minor] and steadily observes a fixed point of the heaven (except that it is not moved by the advance of the fixed stars in longitude, which motion we recognize in the Earth, as we will demonstrate later)."
[20] *De magnete,* bk. 3, chap. 1, p. 117.

noctiorum, & progressionis stellarum fixarum, mutationis denique declinationum solis & tropicorum causae ex magneticis virtutibus petendae sunt:...[21]

It has already been remarked that, in his discussion of magnetic form, Gilbert hinted at a different form associated with each of the heavenly bodies including the Earth.[22] Later, when discussing the effect of a lodestone through an interposed object, he notes that this

> ...demonstratur etiam in alioru corporum præcipuorum a primaria forma efficientijs. Luna cum telluris internis partibus (supra omnia astra) propter propinquitatem & forme similitudinem conuenit; Luna motus aquarum & aestum maris efficit, repleta littora & exinanita bis facit, a puncto aliquo certo coeli delato sydere ad idem punctum per diurnam reuolutionem: motus ille aquarum incitatur, & intumescunt maria, & residunt, non minus cum Luna sub horizonte fuerit & in imo coeli, qua si supra finitorem eleuata esset. Ita tota interposita moles terrestris cum infra terram est, non resistit actionibus lunae, quin in quibusdam coeli positionibus, cum sit infra finitorem, maria nostris regionibus finitima mouerentur, & eadem concussa eius potentia (licet nec radijs percutiantur, nec lumine illustrentur) surgerent, accederent magno cum impetu, & recederent. Sed de aestus ratione alias: hic tantum attigisse limen quaestionis sufficiat.[23]

Here certainly exist the foundations of arguments concerning cosmology: each planet, star, and satellite[24] has its own proper magnetic form; the magnetic form of a satellite

---

[21] *Ibid.*, p. 117. "For why the terrestrial globe seems to remain steadily with one pole in those parts, turned toward Cynosura, or why its pole should vary 23 degrees 29 minutes, with a variation not yet sufficiently investigated by the Astronomers, from the poles of the ecliptic, depends upon magnetic virtue..."

[22] See *supra*, chap. 4, above fn. 66.

[23] *De magnete*, bk. 2, chap. 16, p. 86. "...is demonstrated also in the efficiencies of other distinguished [principal] bodies having primary form. The Moon (more than all the stars) agrees with the internal parts of the Earth because of its nearness and likeness of form. The Moon causes the movements of the waters and tides of the sea; twice it fills the shores and empties them, from any particular point in the sky marked by stars to that same point by the diurnal revolution [Note the avoidance of specifying *what* revolves diurnally]. That motion of waters is incited and the seas rise and fall no less when the Moon is below the horizon and in the lower heavens than if it is elevated above the horizon. Thus the whole terrestrial mass, interposed when it [the Moon] is underneath, does not oppose the lunar action; when it is in certain positions in the sky, as below the horizon, the seas around us are moved and stirred by its power (though not struck by its rays or illuminated by its light), they rise, come up with great impetus, and recede. But of the reasons of the tides elsewhere; here it suffices merely to have touched on the threshold of the question."

[24] Gilbert knew only of the Moon; but a decade after the publication of the *De magnete* the "miniature

163

is similar to that of its planet so that interactions might be expected. Ascription of a magnetic nature to the Moon's influence on the waters of the Earth may seem surprising. But it is necessary here to remember a most basic element of Gilbert's magnetic theory: the Earth is characterized by the magnetic form. Since the waters are earthy, Gilbert would expect them to be magnetic. He had found evidences in plenty to support his belief that the lack of magnetic virtue in surface matter on the Earth does not arise because that matter is non-magnetic but because its magnetic form had been somehow damaged, so that its magnetic actions are weakened – perhaps to the point of being undetectable. Thus iron has the damaged form restored by contact with a lodestone; stone ores lacking the magnetic virtue may acquire it – that is, have it restored to them – by certain actions. Many clods of earth and clays are magnetic. And the atmosphere also shows signs of participation in the most fundamental property of the Earth:

> Ferro in Lucanis pluit, anno quo M. Crassus intereptus est. Affirmant etiam ferream massam, recremento similem, ex aëre decidisse in syluis Nethorianis, prope Grinam,...[25]

After recounting several other examples of this sort, Gilbert adds:

> Caetera vero metalla pluisse vnquam, non commemoratur; neque enim de caelo aurum, argentum, plumbum, aut stannum, aut plumbum album, decidisse visum est.[26]

Of course it would not have mattered if other metals had fallen from the sky, for, as we previously noted in another example from Gilbert, theories are not so easily overturned or given up. Gilbert gives here additional confirmation for this view, for he tells his reader that rains of copper have been observed – and explains that there is no contradiction, by noting that copper 'non multum a ferro differt.' But this leads him into another difficulty, since copper differs from iron in what he insists is the most important and truest property, the magnetic one. This, in turn, is explained away by the inferiority of copper in the plastic properties of casting and working. In brief, Gilbert knows of

Copernican system" of the Medicean Stars was discovered by Galileo. This not only enabled generalization from "Moon" to "satellites" but enabled the planets to be thought of as satellites of the Sun.
[25] *De magnete,* bk. 1, chap. 8, p. 26. "It rained iron in Lucania the year that M. Crassus was destroyed. They tell too of a mass of iron, like slag, falling from the air in the Nethorian forest near Grina,..."
[26] *De magnete,* bk. 1, chap. 8, p. 27. "It is not recorded that it ever rained other metals; for never have gold, silver, lead, or tin or zinc been seen plunging from the sky."

the magnetic nature of the Earth and its components, and all evidence supports his theory.

The Sixth Book of the De magnete

The sixth and last major subdivision of the *De magnete* is concerned with the last of the magnetic movements, circular movement, and brings Gilbert squarely into cosmological arguments. In the first two chapters of this book he reminds his reader of the equivalence of Earth and terrella for experimental purposes, and of the fixed orientation of the Earth's axis. In the last three chapters of the book, chapters 7–9, he examines the obliquity of the ecliptic and the precession of the equinoxes, accounting for the former teleologically in terms of the necessity of seasons, and notes the latter as a phenomenon that produces changes in earthly phenomena through variations in star light – that is, in astrological terms.

The heart of his cosmological arguments are in the 3rd, 4th, 5th, and 6th chapters of this book. In a manner that we have seen before Gilbert opens the discussion with an appeal to authority, an insistence that he is not a revolutionary but a conservative. After citing ancients who held that the Earth moves, he writes:

> Sed posteaquam philosophia a plurimis tractata, & diuulgata fuit, opiniones ad vulgi ingenia fictae, aut Sophisticis argutijs suffultae, plurimorum mentes perstrinxere, & multitudinis consensu, torrentis instar praeualuere.[27]

Copernicus, Gilbert tells us, 'vir literaria laude dignissimus,' was the first to study the phenomena of moving bodies by new hypotheses.

With some elasticity in his interpretation of the history of cosmology, Gilbert is able to claim

> Vetus est igitur opinio, & ab antiquis vsque deducta temporibus, nunc vero magnis cogitationibus aucta, terram diurna reuolutione 24 horarum spatio totam circumferri.[28]

[27] *De magnete*, bk. 6, chap. 3, p. 214. "But after that, philosophy being studied by many and becoming commonly known, theories adapted to the common mind, or supported on Sophistic arguments, laid hold of the minds of many and, the multitude consenting, prevailed like a torrent."

[28] *De magnete*, bk. 6, chap. 3, p. 215. "It is then an ancient opinion and rescended from ancient times, although now greatly developed by reflection, that the earth turns around in a diurnal rotation in a space of 24 hours."

This we must accept, Gilbert tells us, or else believe that the entire universe whirls about diurnally in the opposite direction. Gilbert counters: This is absurd – the argument common to Copernicans. This interesting inversion of the geocentrist's position is indicative of a new frame of mind that is to play an increasingly important role in cosmology, namely, the identification of the heavens with the Earth. In Gilbert's terms, if a *primum mobile* is to sweep the universe about the Earth in diurnal motion, it must have great physical strength, and it must therefore be composed of material substance.[29] It then becomes more absurd to think of such a great material sphere turning than to think of the relatively small, albeit material, Earth performing that motion. The argument is of course invalid against a geocentrist who believes that the heavens are composed entirely of a quintessence lacking the physical properties of earthy substance. The quintessence becomes, to Gilbert, an aetherial fluid between material stars and planets and the heavenly bodies are immersed in it, not part of it.

To this argument Gilbert adds a second: the stars are not all at the same distance from the Earth,[30] so that it is senseless to think of them as attached to a great crystaline spherical shell; the physical structure of the geocentric system thus, in Gilbert's mind, collapses.

The varying distance of the stars from the Earth was a very important argument to Gilbert.

> ...quomodo permanebunt in tanta vasti orbis, corporis incertissimi, vertigine. Obseruatate sunt ab Astronomis stellae 1022; praeter has innumerabiles, aliae sensibus nostris apparent exiguae quidem, in alijs caligat sensus, vixque, nec nisi ab egregia oculorum acie percipiuntur, nec quisquam est qui optimis praeditus oculis, silente Luna, & rarissimo aëre, non sentit plurimas propter magnam distantiam exiguis luminibus incertas, & vacillantes: Quare & multas esse, & nulla oculorum acie comprehendi vnquam, credibile est. Quantum est igitur ad longissime remotas illas fixas incomprehensum spatium, quanta phantasticae illius sphaerae, ampla & immensa profunditas? quam longe a terra disiunctissimae stellae separantur, elonganturque supra omnem visum, artem omnen, & cogitationem? Motus iste igitur quam erit monstrosus?[31]

[29] *De magnete*, bk. 6, chap. 3, p. 216.

[30] Gilbert undoubtedly obtained this, directly or indirectly, from Thomas Digges. See F. R. Johnson, *Astronomical thought in Renaissance England: A study of the English scientific writings from 1500 to 1645*, Baltimore, The Johns Hopkins Press, 1937, chap. 6.

[31] *De magnete*, bk. 6, chap. 3, pp. 215-216. "...how do they remain in such a vast whirling sphere, of such uncertain substance! 1022 stars have been observed by astronomers; besides these, innumerable others appear weak indeed to our senses, while with others our perception is misty and they scarcely can be perceived by those with the best eyes. Nor is there anyone endowed with excellent sight that will

This insistence upon the varying distance of the fixed stars has caused Gilbert to be credited by some later writers with the 'discovery' of that varying distance.[32] This is certainly not the case. Thomas Digges (?–1595) had published the first book of Copernicus' treatise, in extract form and had added thereto a number of ideas, without distinguishing between them and those of Copernicus (see fn. 30). Among these new ideas, published with at least the implication that they were Copernicus' own, was precisely this one of the varying distances of the stars. As Johnson has phrased it:

> By far the most important addition which Digges made to Copernicus, however, was his assertion that the heliocentric universe should be conceived as infinite, with the fixed stars located at varying distances throughout infinite space. Copernicus... although bringing the question of the infinity of the universe into his refutation of his Aristotelian opponents, had refused to commit himself on this subject. ... Digges, however, clearly perceived that, the moment the rotation of the earth was conceded, there was no longer any necessity for picturing the stars as attached to a huge, rotating sphere at a definite distance from the earth. ... He was the first modern astronomer of note to portray an infinite, heliocentric universe, with the stars scattered throughout infinite space.[33]

Digges' book was published in 1576, 24 years before the *De magnete* and at approximately the time that Gilbert was doing his work.

Gilbert adds two other arguments to the one concerning the absurdity of the celestial sphere. First, not only is the Earth less likely to break up in moving than does the sphere, but forces—magnetic ones—to hold the Earth together are known.[34] Second, there is no reason to suppose any resistance to be offered to the motion of the Earth:

not feel, when the moon is obscure and the air is its thinnest, that there are many more which, on account of their great distance, are weakly luminous and vacillating. Whereby it is believable that there are many of these and that they can never be taken in by any eye. Accordingly how far is the incomprehensible space to the most remote fixed stars, how wide and high is that imaginary sphere? How far from the Earth are these furthest stars, beyond all vision, knowledge, and thought? And therefore how monstrous would that motion be?"

[32] For example, "...Gilbert's realization that the fixed stars are at various distances, a discovery he was the first to make." Rufus Suter, "Dr. William Gilbert of Colchester," *Scientific Monthly*, vol. 70 (1950), p. 261. Or, "...Gilbert's one contribution to the science of Astronomy, in his remark that the fixed stars (previously regarded as fixed in the eighth of the celestial spheres at one common distance from the central earth) were in reality set in the heavens at various distances from the earth." S. P. Thompson, *William Gilbert and terrestrial magnetism in the time of Queen Elizabeth*, Chiswick Press, 1903, pp. 13-14.

[33] Johnson, *op. cit.* (fn. 30), p. 164.

[34] *De magnete*, bk. 6, chap. 3, p. 219.

it moves in a space devoid of bodies,[35] and has no weight,[36] since weight is merely a representation of the tendency of objects toward their origin and has no meaning when applied to the Earth as a whole.

> Ex his igitur rationibus, non probabilis modo, sed manifesta videtur terrae diurna circumuolutio, cum natura semper agit per pauciora magis, quam plura; atq; rationi magis consentaneum vnum exiguum corpus telluris diurna volutatione efficere potius, quam mundum totum circumferri.[37]

Gilbert goes on immediately to sidestep the question of the annual motion:

> Reliquorum terrae motuu rationes praetereo, iam enim agitur tantum de diurno, quo ad solem reuoluitur, & naturalem diem (quem nycthemeron vocamus) efficit.[38]

The arguments presented thus far are mostly familiar Copernican ones. In the next chapter of the sixth book, Gilbert brings his magnetical ideas to bear upon the Earth's behavior. Having argued that there is no celestial sphere in a physical sense and that the universe does not turn about the Earth, so that the Earth itself must turn to account for the diurnal motion, Gilbert now turns to positive arguments for that motion. These are weak. From the motion of a lodestone set free to move Gilbert argues the fixed orientation of the Earth's axis:

> Hoc facit exiguus lapis quatuortantum vnciarum; eundem etiam habet motum tam expedite, si fuerit magnes robustus aliquis centum librarum: similem quoque conuersionem obtinebit maximus magneticus mons, si largo flumine aut mari profundo veheretur: & tamen multo magis magneticum ab aqua impeditur, quam tellus tota ab aethere. Idem faceret tota terra, si Borealis polus distraheretur a vera sua directione; recurreret enim polus Borealis circulari totius circa centrum motu versus Cynosuram.[39]

[35] *De magnete,* bk. 6, chap. 3, p. 219.

[36] *De magnete,* bk. 6, chap. 5, p. 230.

[37] *De magnete,* bk. 6, chap. 3, pp. 219-220. "Therefore for these reasons the diurnal rotation of the Earth seems not merely probable but certain, for Nature always acts with the fewest than with more. Moreover, it is more agreeable to reason that the one small body of the Earth should make a diurnal rotation than that the whole universe should be whirled around."

[38] *De magnete,* bk. 6, chap. 3, p. 220. "I pass by the reason of the other movements of the Earth, for here only the diurnal is treated, by which it turns around to the sun and produces the natural day (which we call nycthemeron)."

[39] *De magnete,* bk. 6, chap. 4, p. 222. "A little stone of only four ounces does this [orientates]; it would

This is reasoning by analogy, for the turning of the lodestone to conform to the Earth is not equivalent to the Earth turning into its rightful position. Such reasoning by analogy has often been very useful in scientific work, despite the lack of logical sanction. However, Gilbert's next conclusion is still more weakly founded.

> Atque iste magnetis motus circularis ad positionem suam iustam, & naturalem, ostendit totam terram habilem esse & idoneam, proprijsque viribus satis instructam, ad circularem motum diurnum.[40]

Immediately he mentions the diurnally rotating terrella of Peter Peregrinus (p. 40), and with some wistfulness he remarks:

> Quod tamen nobis adhuc videre non contigit; de quo motu etiam dubitamus, propter lapidis ipsius pondus, tum quia tellus tota vt mouetur a se, ita etiam ab alijs astris promouetur: quod proportionaliter in parte quauis (vt in terrella) non contingit.[41]

Galileo wrote of this that he wished Gilbert had not lent his ear to the diurnal rotation of the terrella, adding that there was no reason why the terrella should so move.[42]

The other principal argument advanced by Gilbert in this fourth chapter of the last book is a teleological one: the Earth turns for its good, providing the necessary alternations of day and night.

The fifth chapter is concerned completely with objections to the rotation of the Earth and answers to them that are typical of Gilbert's Copernican contemporaries. The

---

have a motion just as quick if it were a powerful lodestone of one hundred pounds. The largest magnetic mountain would have a similar turning if borne on a large river or deep sea: yet the lodestone is much more impeded by the water than would be the whole Earth by the aether. The entire Earth would do the same if the north pole were diverted from its true direction; for that north pole would return, with a circular motion of the whole about the center, toward Cynosura [Ursa Minor]."

[40] *De magnete*, bk. 6, chap. 4, p. 223. "Moreover this circular movement of the lodestone to its right and natural position makes plain that the whole Earth is suited and adapted to and sufficiently equipped by its own forces for diurnal circular motion."

[41] *De magnete*, bk. 6, chap. 4, pp. 223-224. "It has never befallen us to see this; indeed we doubt this motion, because of the weight of the stone itself as well as because the whole Earth as it is moved of itself so also it is pushed by the other stars. This does not happen proportionally in any part (as in the terrella) of it."

[42] Galileo Galilei, *Dialogue on the great world systems*, in the Salusbury translation, ed. G. de Santillana, Chicago, The University of Chicago Press, 1953, p. 422. "...I will speak of one particular suggestion to which I could have wished that Gilbert had not lent an ear; I mean that of admitting that, in case a little lodestone could be exactly librated, it would revolve in itself; because there is no reason why it should do so."

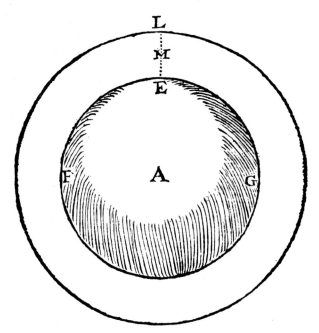

Fig. 27. An object dropped from L strikes the Earth at E, directly
below L, despite the diurnal motion of the Earth, for the
Earth's sphere of influence turns with the Earth (*De
magnete*, p. 229).

sphere of influence of the Earth, coupled with his belief in the inherently magnetic
nature of all motions not due to contact,[43] enables Gilbert to strengthen the Copernican
arguments concerning projectile motion. The geocentrists asked this question persist-
ently, in two forms: how can a stone dropped from directly above a spot on the Earth's
surface strike that spot, if the Earth is moving during the time of fall? Why will a
projectile, fired in both cases with the same charge of gunpowder from a cannon
elevated the same amount, go equally far to the west and to the east (measured on the
surface of the Earth) if the Earth is turning under the projectile while it is in flight?
Gilbert's answer is that the stone or projectile remains within the sphere of influence
of the Earth, that that sphere turns with the Earth. Accordingly an object M (Fig. 27)

[43] Electrical motions, be it remembered, have been reduced to contact phenomena by Gilbert.

falling from L to E toward the center A, simply falls in the straight line LE, whether the Earth is presumed to be turning or not.[44]

In the sixth chapter of the sixth book of his work Gilbert presents the views that were so eagerly taken up by early seventeenth-century Copernicans. Again he finds a marvelous order in the universe, an order reflecting the firm control of magnetic forces, so that the time of one revolution of the Earth is constant and

> Nulla enim ars curiosa, aut per Clepsydras aut per horologia arenaria, aut per ea quae ex rotulis denticulatis composita, ponderibus, aut intensae laminae chalybeae vi incitantur, differentiam aliquam temporis inuenire potest.[45]

Such marvelous regularity is not only found in the motion of the Earth:

> Ob eamque causam, Saturnus ampliorem habens cursum, longiore tempore circumfertur; breuiore autem Iupiter, & Mars adhuc multo celerius; Venus vero noue mensibus, Mercurius 80 diebus, ex Copernici hypothesibus; Luna circa terram ad solem 29 diebus, horis 12, minutis 44.[46]

In one special case Gilbert is able to find what seems to him to be a striking relationship. The Moon is about 29-5/6 Earth diameters away and completes a trip once around its orbit in a month, that is in 29-1/2 days and 44 minutes. Gilbert has not been entirely fair with these numbers (as he well knows). A point on the Earth executes its diurnal movement in one day, and Gilbert implies that the Moon – about 29 times as far from the center of its orbit as the Earth – executes its orbital motion in about 29 times as long. But the point on the Earth is not one diameter from the center but one-half a diameter; the Moon is thus about 60 times as far from the center of the Earth as we are.[47]

---

[44] De magnete, bk. 6, chap. 5, p. 229. Gilbert specifically mentions "Tychone Brahe" as the author of the objections. Brahe died the year after the *publication* of the De magnete.

[45] De magnete, bk. 6, chap. 6, p. 231. "For no ingenious skill, using clepsydras or sand clocks or those [clocks] consisting of little toothed wheels driven by weights or by the force of a bent steel band, can discover any difference in the time."

[46] De magnete, bk. 6, chap. 6, p. 231. "For that same cause, Saturn having the farther course moves around it in a longer time; Jupiter however is shorter, and Mars still more quickly; Venus takes nine months, Mercury 80 days, according to the Copernican hypotheses. The Moon moving around the Earth to the Sun [that is, one lunation] in 29 days, 12 hours, 44 minutes." The Mottelay edition fails to translate "breuiore autem Iupiter," simply omitting it. This particular chapter of the De magnete is very poorly translated in that edition, with many omissions of this sort.

[47] Gilbert probably mislead Galileo by these numerological manipulations, for the Italian wrote in 1610 that the Moon was nearly sixty Earth-diameters away, and he knew the De magnete well. See Edward Rosen, "Galileo on the Distance between the Earth and the Moon," *Isis*, vol. 43 (1952), pp. 344-348.

Nevertheless Gilbert finds meaning in these numbers, and since magnetic forces decrease with separation it is not unreasonable to him to simply introduce a factor of one-half: the Moon only moves half as fast as it should under the assumption of a simple linear relation between speed and distance from the center.

> Conueniunt igitur Luna & tellus inter se proportione motus dupla; moueturq; tellus viginti quatuor horarum spatio, diurno motu; quia Luna motum habet proportionalem telluri, tellus vero motui Lunari subdupla proportione conuenientem. In minutis aliqua differentia est, quia in minutis astrorum distantiae non sunt exacte satis exploratae, nec de illis adhuc conueniunt mathematici.[48]

This harmony between Moon and Earth is to be expected, Gilbert writes, because of their closeness and similarity, because of the obvious effects [tides?] of the Moon on the Earth, and

> quod etiam Luna ex omnibus planetis, sola reuolutiones suas (quamuis etiam diuersas) ad centrum terrae summatim conferat, sitq; terrae cognata maxime, & quasi vinculis alligata.[49]

Gilbert and Copernicism

Three arguments are presented by Gilbert for his use of the synodic period of 29-odd days for the Moon instead of the somewhat smaller sidereal period. First, since a solar day is what is meant by 'day' it would be compared to a solar (synodic) month. Second,

> ...quia sol causa motus est, tam terrestris, quam Lunaris:...[50]

[48] *De magnete*, bk. 6, chap. 6, p. 232. "Therefore the Moon and the Earth agree among themselves in a double proportion of motion and the Earth moves in its diurnal motion in the space of 24 hours, because the Moon has a motion proportional to the Earth's, and the Earth has a motion agreeing with the Moon's in a proportion of one-half. There is some difference in details because the distances of the stars [i.e., the Moon, here] in detail have not been examined with sufficient exactness by astronomers, nor are mathematicians [astrologers] up to now agreed on them."

[49] *De magnete*, bk. 6, chap. 6, p. 232. "...also because the Moon, alone of all the planets, directs its revolutions (however diverse) summarily toward the center of the Earth, and is strongly related to the Earth, and as though tied to it by chains."

[50] *De magnete*, bk. 6, chap. 6, p. 232. "...because the Sun is the cause of motion, both terrestrial and lunar:..."

Third,

> ...quia (iuxta recentiorum hypotheses) mensis synodicus sit vere periodicus, propter telluris motum in orbe magno.[51]

This is a certain reference to Copernicism, not solely in the mention of the annual motion but in the appeal to the solar month as being the true period of the Moon. In a geocentric system of the world, there is no reason to relate the period of the Moon in any such way to the Sun: some relationship may be found between the periods of the various heavenly bodies, but those periods are for their motions against the background of the stars. But in a heliocentric world the Sun has the predominant role; the Earth then may be thought of as not only moving about the Sun in an annual path, but as turning once a year in performing that annual motion. Thus in approximately a twelfth of a year, one month, the Earth would have turned a twelfth of a circle in executing the annual motion. If then we observe the Moon as it moves against the stars, it will appear to complete its orbit when actually it has only completed about 11/12ths of it. This difficulty is overcome if instead of using a line from our solar system to a star as a reference direction the line connecting the Sun and Earth is used, for this line turns with the Earth in its annual motion. From this point of view—which is not our modern one—the true period is executed from the time the Moon is in one phase until it returns to that phase.

Was Gilbert a Copernican? The answer given by the *De magnete*[52] is certainly 'no,' although it requires some amplification. Gilbert was a student of the lodestone, magnetic bodies, and of the great lodestone, the Earth. The diurnal motion of the Earth fitted into the theory of magnetism that he had constructed; hence he found support for that diurnal motion in Copernicus as well as in the writings of Classical Antiquity. In only one case did he need the annual motion of the Earth, and that was for this numerological experiment with the Moon's motion. For this instant he becomes a Copernican, establishes the fundamental nature of the synodic period of the Moon, and returns to magnetism. Just as electrics are a digression from his chief interest, so is cosmology. It is Kepler and Galileo that found powerful support for Copernicism in the *De magnete*, not Gilbert.

---

[51] *De magnete*, bk. 6, chap. 6, p. 232. "...because (according to the theories of moderns) the synodic month is the true period, because of the motion of the Earth in its great sphere."

[52] Gilbert's other work, first published in the second half of the seventeenth century, needs investigation to determine Gilbert's personal attitudes in more detail. Such an investigation is beyond the scope of this volume. It should be remembered, however, that only the *De magnete* was available to Gilbert's immediate successors.

CHAPTER SIX

THE DE MAGNETE

I. Bibliography

The *De magnete* has been issued a total of eleven times, four in Latin, six in English translation, and once in Russian translation. Various ghost editions have been reported, and a total of sixteen alleged issus may be counted.[1]

The First Edition; Latin, London, 1600

The title page, [*j], *recto,* reads: GVILIELMI GIL-/BERTI COLCESTREN-/SIS, MEDICI LONDI-/NENSIS,/DE MAGNETE, MAGNETI-/CISQVE CORPO-RIBVS, ET DE MAG-/no magnete tellure ; Physiologia noua,/ plurimis & argumentis, & expe-/rimentis demonstrata./ [Printer's mark of Peter Short]/LONDINI/[Rule]/ EXCVDEBAT PETRVS SHORT ANNO/MDC.[2]

Gilbert's coat of arms appears on *j *verso* and is followed by: *ij *recto* to *iij *recto,* Gilbert's preface; *iij *verso* to *v *verso,* Wright's preface; *vj *recto,* glossary; *vj *verso* to *viii *verso,* table of contents. The main text begins on Aj *recto,* page 1, and runs through 20 ternions to page 240. Errata on page 240.

All known copies have ink emendations,[3] which may indicate that Gilbert saw the edition through the press in Peter Short's Bread Street shop, near to Wingfield House.

The Second Edition; Latin, Stettin, 1628

Prepared by the Stettin Judge (Assessor) Wolfgang Lochmann, and probably published at his own expense. The unnumbered title page is engraved and reads: TRACTATVS/ Siue/PHYSIOLOGIA NOVA/DE MAGNETE,/ MAGNETICISQVE CORPO-/

---

[1] See "Bibliography of *De Magnete*," S. P. Thompson, *Notes on the de magnete of Dr. William Gilbert,* London, Privately Printed, 1901, pp. *ij *recto* and *verso;* G. Hellmann, "Zur Bibliographie von W. Gilbert's "De magnete," *Terrestrial Magnetism and Atmospheric Electricity,* vol. 7 (1902), pp. 63-66; "Biographical Memoir" by P. F. Mottelay in the 1893 edition of the *De magnete,* pp. xix-xxii.
[2] See S. P. Thompson, "Peter Short, Printer, and his Marks," *Transactions of the Bibliographical Society,* vol. 4 (1896–1898), pp. 103-128.
[3] See Thompson, *op. cit.* (fn. 1), *passim.*

RIBVS ET MAGNO MAGNETE/ tellure Sex libris comprenhensus/ a/ Guilielmo Gilberto Colcestrensi,/ Medico Londinensi./ In quibus ea, quae ad hanc materiam spectant pluri-/mis & argumentis ac experimentis exactissime/ absolutissimeq; tractantur et explicantur./ Omnia nunc diligenter recognita & emen-/datius quam ante in lucem edita, aucta & figu-/ris illustrata opera & studio/Wolfgangi Lochmans-/I.U.D./ & Mathemati :/ Ad calcem libri adjunctus est Index Capi-/tum Rerum et Verborum locupletissimus/ ESCVSVS/SEDINI/ Typis Götziams Sumptibus/ Authoris/ Anno M.DC.XXVIII.

Verso of title page is blank.

Thompson's collation reported an unnumbered half-title page before the title. This order is reversed in the Houghton Library copy, in which the title page appears to have been pasted in. The half-title *recto* reads: 'GULIELMI GILBERTI/ Tractatus/ DE MAGNETE,' and is blank *verso*.

A third unnumbered page is an 'Amicorum acclamationes' by Lochmann, with verses; one pen change has been made in the Houghton copy. The *verso* of this page is blank. A fourth unnumbered page bears a preface, *recto* and *verso,* in the Houghton copy. Thompson's collation has this the third page.

The signatures begin with Gilbert's preface on A1, Wright's preface on A2 *verso,* the glossary on B2 with *verso* blank. Twelve engraved plates follow, with the text beginning on B3, page 5. There are 35 signatures, all fours, pagination ends with page 232 on Hh3 (misnumbered H3), *verso* is blank, and table of contents and index follow, Hh4 through Mm3 *verso.* Errata and instructions to binder on Mm4, *verso* is blank.

Some examples, including the Houghton copy, have 'Authoris' on the title page replaced by 'Ioh: Hallervordij.' Lochmann apparently remaindered the pages to Johann Hallervord, a well-known book dealer of Rostock, who altered the engraved title page.

The Third Edition; Latin, Stettin, 1633

This edition is sufficiently like the second to have been mistaken for a reissue with a new title page. It is, however, completely new, with different spacings between letters, and the titlepage is not engraved.

The Fourth Edition; Latin, Berlin, 1892

This is a facsimile of the first edition, produced by a photozincograph process. The ink emendations of the first edition have been removed and certain of the marginal asterisks are omitted. The back of the title page, *j *verso*, has had added: 'FACSIMILE-DRUCK/ BERLIN/ MAYER & MÜLLER/ 1892.'

Latin Ghosts

P. F. Mottelay, who collected without choosing, collected the title pages of the 1600, 1628, and 1633 editions; he also collected references to a number of other editions, which may be summarized as follows:

> Two British editions, five German and Dutch editions before 1628.
> A 1600 Amsterdam edition.
> A 1629 Ferrara edition, with commentary by Cabaeo.
> Sedan, Sedini, and Stettin editions of various dates.
> Frankfort editions of 1629 and 1638.[4]

Two main sources of confusion may be pointed out. First, the 'Sedini' of the second and third editions is of course 'Stettin' and nothing else. Second, Theophili Georgi in 1742 listed the following for Gilbert's *De magnete*:

> 1600, Londini.
> 1628, Frf. Hallew.
> 1636, Amst. Janson.
> 1633, Sedini.[5]

Hellmann[6] believes that Hallervord may well have been selling the remaindered 1628 edition at the Frankfort Fair; that the famous Amsterdam book dealer Janson may have obtained a number of copies of the 1633 edition; that Frankfort and Amsterdam must be regarded thus as 'Messaddressen.'

The Fifth Edition; English, New York, 1893

This, the first translation of the *De magnete*, is referred to as the 'American translation' by Thompson, who may have felt some bitterness at this anticipation of the Gilbert

---

[4] Mottelay, *op. cit.* (fn. 1), pp. xix-xx.

[5] *Theophili Georgi Buchhändlers in Leipzig, Allgemeines Europäisches Bücher-Lexicon, In welchem nach Ordnung des Dictionarii die allermeisten Autores oder Gattungen von Büchern zu finden,...*, Leipzig, Theophili Georgi, 1742, p. 143.

[6] Hellmann, *loc. cit.* (fn. 1), pp. 63-64.

Club's translation. The title page reads: WILLIAM GILBERT/ OF COLCHESTER,/ PHYSICIAN OF LONDON,/ ON THE/ LOADSTONE AND MAGNETIC BODIES,/ AND ON/ THE GREAT MAGNET THE EARTH./ A NEW PHYSIO-LOGY,/ DEMONSTRATED WITH MANY ARGUMENTS AND EXPERI-MENTS./ 'Electrica, quae attrahunt eadem ratione ut electricum.'/ A TRANSLATION BY/ P. FLEURY MOTTELAY,/ AUTHOR OF 'THE CHRONOLOGICAL HISTORY OF ELECTRICITY, MAGNETISM, ETC.'/ [Rule]/ NEW YORK:/ JOHN WILEY & SONS,/ 53 EAST TENTH STREET./ 1893.

Some examples read: London:/ Bernard Quaritch,/ 15 Piccadilly.[7]

A frontispiece facing the title page shows the Harding (Clamp) engraving of Gilbert. Following the title page is a facsimile of the title page, *recto* and *verso,* of an example of the 1600 edition, inscribed 'Dedit Guil. Gilbertus. Jo: Sherwood proprijs manibus.' Over this is pasted in a slip of paper reproducing an inscription from another example: 'Londini. ex dono authoris: 8: Junij: 1600.' with the year underlined sweepingly.

The translator's preface follows on pages v-viii, and Mottelay's 'Biographical Memoir' of Gilbert, ix-xxvii. xxvii *verso* is blank and is followed by xxxi. xxxi-xxxvi is the table of contents, xxxvii-xlv is Wright's preface, xlvi is blank, xlvii-li is Gilbert's preface, lii is blank, liii-liv is the glossary. The main text begins on page 1 and runs to 358. Pages 359-361 contain reproductions of the 1628 and 1633 editions and of Gilbert's other work, the *De mundo.*[8] Page 362 is blank, 363-368 is the index.

It is my opinion that translations are not reliable and the Mottelay one is not an exception. I have found it useful.

The Sixth Edition; English, London, 1901

In 1889 there came into existence a 'Gilbert Club,' whose origins were attributed, by S. P. Thompson's wife and daughter, to the interest in Gilbert held by Thompson and his friend, Conrad W. Cooke.[9] In that same year, in a published article, Cooke wrote:

> The Gilbert Club held its inaugural meeting a month ago, when the following were adopted by resolution as the objects of the club:

[7] According to Thompson, *op. cit.* (fn. 1), p. iv.

[8] *Gvilielmi Gilberti Colcestrensis, medici regii, de mundo nostro sublunari philosophia nova. Opus post-humum, ab authoris fratre collectum pridem & dispositum, nvnc ex duobus mss. codicibus editum. Ex museio viri perillustris Gvilielmi Boswelli equitis aurati &c. & oratoris apud Foederatos Belgas Angli,* Amsterdam, Elzevir, 1651.

[9] J. S. Thompson and H. G. Thompson, *Silvanus Phillips Thompson, his life and letters,* New York, E. P. Dutton and Co., 1920, p. 228.

(i) To produce and issue an English translation of 'De Magnete' in the style of the folio edition of 1600.

(ii) To arrange hereafter for the Tercentenary Celebration of the publication of 'De Magnete,' in the year 1900.

(iii) To promote inquiries into the personal history, life, works, and writings of Dr. Gilbert.

(iv) To have power, after the completion of the English edition of 'De Magnete,' to undertake the reproduction of other early works on electricity and magnetism, provided at such date a majority of members of the club so desire.

The following gentlemen were elected as the Council and officers for the ensuing year:

President: Sir William Thomson, LL.D., F.R.S.S.L. and E., President of the Institution of Electrical Engineers. – Vice-Presidents: The Right Hon. Lord Rayleigh, Sec. R.S. Jonathan Hutchinson, F.R.S., President of the Royal College of Surgeons. Professor A. W. Reinold, F.R.S., President of the Physical Society. Benjamin Ward Richardson, M.D., F.R.S. Professor David E. Hughes, F.R.S. Henry Laver. – Treasurer: Latimer Clark, F.R.S. – Council: W. Lant Carpenter. Professor John Ferguson, M.A., F.R.S.E. Professor George Forbes, M.A., F.R.S.S.L. and E. Professor G. C. Foster, F.R.S. Sir Philip Magnus. Professor A. W. Rücker, F.R.S. – Hon. Secretaries: Conrad W. Cooke. Professor Raphael Meldola, F.R.S.; and Professor Silvanus P. Thompson.

In accordance with the first and principal object of the club, we are glad to state that the translation of 'De Magnete' is well in hand, and it will be printed and 'got up' in such a manner as to be as like the original in appearance as it can be made, it will, in fact, be a fac-simile reprint in everything except the language in which it is reproduced.[10]

The edition appeared in 1901, although dated 1900. The title page reads: WILLIAM GIL-/BERT OF COLCHES-/TER, PHYSICIAN OF/ LONDON./ ON THE MAGNET, MAGNE-/ TICK BODIES ALSO, AND ON/ the great magnet the earth; a new Physi-/ology, demonstrated by many ar-/guments & experiments./ [Printer's mark of Peter Short]/ LONDON/ [Rule]/ IMPRINTED AT THE CHISWICK PRESS ANNO/ MCM./

The collation is identical with the 1600 edition. The intent of the committee, constituted by the Gilbert Club in 1889, was to produce 'as far as circumstances would permit, a facsimile (in English)' of the first edition. The Gilbert Club edition was printed by C. Whittingham and Co., on handmade Van Gelder paper. 250 copies were printed

---

[10] [C. W. Cooke] "William Gilbert, of Colchester," *Engineering,* vol. 48 (1889), p. 730.

and each member received a prospectus[11] offering him a copy bound in half holland, boards, at 21s, 6d, postpaid, or bound in whole limp vellum with ties at 32s, 6d, post-paid. If the member elected the latter, he might also elect to have bound with his copy, gratis, a copy of Thompson's *Notes*.[12] These notes were on the same paper and in the identical typography as the edition of the *De magnete*. The remainder of the edition was disposed of at 40s and 50s, in the two bindings, to cover Club costs.

S. P. Thompson's biographers wrote:

> The publication was anticipated by some years by the appearance in New York in 1893 of a translation by Dr. P. Fleury Mottelay. This was, however, but a small volume, and, though the work of a keen bibliographer of electrical and magnetical sciences, lacked the charm of the luxurious facsimile edition.[13]

Thompson undoubtedly felt that the Gilbert Club, largely through his efforts, had produced the *De magnete* as Gilbert would have written it in English. It would be more accurate to say that they had produced the work as Peter Short might have printed it in English, for the attention of the Club seems to have been devoted more to typography than to an understanding of Gilbert's thought. The forging of the title page date to make it exactly 1600 plus 300 years, the forcing of the translation so that the chapters begin with the identical initial letter in English and Latin—these actions make the book a beautiful one, but not an Englishing of Gilbert's thought.

The Gilbert Club clearly profited from having Mottelay's translation and I have made use of both, but neither is reliable.

The Seventh Edition; English, Ann Arbor, 1941

This is a photographic process reissue of the Mottelay translation. Pages i and ii are blank, the frontispiece and facsimile title page being omitted. Page iii, the title page, reads: The Classics of the St. John's Program/ WILLIAM GILBERT/ OF COL-CHESTER,/ PHYSICIAN OF LONDON,/ ON THE/ LOADSTONE AND MAGNETIC BODIES,/ AND ON/ THE GREAT MAGNET THE EARTH./ A NEW PHYSIOLOGY,/ DEMONSTRATED WITH MANY ARGUMENTS AND EXPERIMENTS./ 1600/ translated by/ P. FLEURY MOTTELAY/ 1892/ This

---

[11] A copy of the prospectus, together with a copy of another one, perhaps offering the remainder to public sale, is in the Houghton Library copy of the Gilbert Club edition.

[12] Thompson, *op. cit.* (fn. 1).

[13] Thompson and Thompson, *op. cit.* (fn. 9), p. 230.

WILLIAM   GILBERT

ВИЛЬЯМ ГИЛЬБЕРТ

О МАГНИТЕ,
МАГНИТНЫХ ТЕЛАХ
И О БОЛЬШОМ МАГНИТЕ-ЗЕМЛЕ

НОВАЯ ФИЗИОЛОГИЯ, ДОКАЗАННАЯ
МНОЖЕСТВОМ АРГУМЕНТОВ
И ОПЫТОВ

ПЕРЕВОД С ЛАТИНСКОГО
А. И. ДОВАТУРА

РЕДАКЦИЯ, СТАТЬЯ И КОММЕНТАРИИ
А. Г. КАЛАШНИКОВА

ИЗДАТЕЛЬСТВО АКАДЕМИИ НАУК СССР
МОСКВА · 1956

Fig. 28. The titlepage of the Burndy copy of the Russian translation of the *De magnete*.

edition is reproduced by the courtesy of/ the Peabody Institute Library, Baltimore,/ from a copy in their possession/
Page iv reads: Printed in U.S.A./EDWARD BROTHERS, INC./ Lithoprinters/ ANN ARBOR, MICHIGAN/ 1941/
Pages v-viii are the translator's preface; there are no pages ix through xxx, Mottelay's biographical memoir having been omitted. Pages liii-liv, the glossary, are also omitted. The pagination skips from 358 to 363 because of omission of the facsimile title pages.

The Eighth Edition; English, Chicago, 1952

Volume 28 of the *Great books of the western world*, ed. R. M. Hutchins, Chicago, London, Toronto, Encyclopaedia Britannica, Inc., 1952, contains translations of Gilbert's *De magnete*, Galileo's *Due nuove scienze*, and Harvey's *De motu*. The Gilbert translation is Mottelay's. Pages ix-x are a 'Biographical Note,' pages xi-xiii the contents. The translator's preface, Wright's preface, Gilbert's preface and the glossary are omitted. The main text is pages 1-121. All marginal asterisks are omitted.
The biographical note is so extraordinarily inept that the only appropriate term is a 'hack job.' It is a careless collection of the myths concerning Gilbert that have developed during the last four centuries, here indiscriminately thrown together in a self-contradictory and disgracefully inaccurate document.

The Ninth Edition; Moscow, 1956

Russian translation by A. I. Dovatur, edited with a commentary in Russian by A. G. Kalashnikov. First leaf is half title (Academy of Sciences, Union of S.S.R.; Classics of Science), verso blank. Second leaf is title page (See Figure 28), verso is series information (Classics of Sciences Series, Founded by Academician S. I. Vavilov, Editorial Board Academicians I. G. Petrovsky, ...). Third leaf has drawing of Gilbert (De Magnete, William Gilbert), verso blank. Translation begins on next page (7) and runs through page 308. Page 309 is half title (Appendix), verso blank. Pages 311 and 312 are facsimiles of title page recto and verso of first edition of *De magnete*. Pages 313 and 314 are respectively facsimiles of pages *ij and 240 of first edition. Pages 315-364 are Kalashnikov's discussion of Gilbert, his precursors and his work, and pages 365-404 are notes on the *De magnete*. Pages 405-411 are the Table of Contents to the translation and appendix; page 412 is the colophon. An errata slip is tipped in following page 412.

181

I am indebted to Bern Dibner for calling my attention to this edition and to Herbert J. Ellison for translation of portions of the work.

The Tenth Edition; New York, 1958

A photographic process reissue of the Gilbert Club translation including Thompson's *Notes,* with six leaves added at the beginning. First leaf recto reads: GILBERT/ON THE MAGNET; verso is series titlepage (The Collector's Series in Science). Second leaf recto reads: ON THE MAGNET/BY/WILLIAM GILBERT/ (Drawing of Gilbert); verso is copyright notice. Next seven pages, numbered v–xi is 'Editor's Introduction.' Verso of xi is facsimile of titlepage of second edition.
The 'Editor's Introduction' entitled 'William Gilbert and His De Magnete' is a summary of material appearing in secondary sources.

The Eleventh Edition; New York, 1958

A photographic process reissue of the Mottelay translation, with the following changes: The recto of the leaf bearing the frontispiece is a half-title reading DE MAGNETE; the titlepage of the 1893 edition has been replaced by one reading DE MAGNETE/ By William Gilbert/Translated by P. Fleury Mottelay/Dover Publications Inc., New York. The verso of the titlepage bears a note reading: This new Dover edition first published in 1958 is/an unabridged and unaltered republication of the/P. Fleury Mottelay translation published in 1893. Eight leaves of advertising have been added at the end.

Bibliographical Note

I have used the following copies of the *De magnete:* Harvard College Library's 1600, 1628, 1633, 1892, 1893, 1952; the Burndy Library's 1956; the De Golyer Collection's 1600, 1633, 1892, 1893, 1952; David Wheatland's, 1600; my own copies, 1900, 1941, and both 1958 editions.

II. The Influence of the De magnete

Gilbert's *De magnete* established electricity as a separate science, gave the electrician a wide choice of working substances, strongly accentuated a mechanistic effluvium

theory of electricity, insisted that the Earth is a great magnet, offered a means of determining position at sea, provided a physical basis for the Copernican Theory, and suggested mechanical interaction between Earth and Moon in terms of a non-contact force.
That these ideas are pregnant ones in 1600 is beyond question. But did the child
prosper? There is no doubt in my mind but that it did. All of the evidence available to
me at this writing indicates that the *De magnete* exerted strong influence on seventeenth
century and early eighteenth century scientific thought. An investigation of that influence is beyond the scope of this volume, yet in conclusion it would seem worth noting
some of the later evidences of the influence of the *De magnete*. These evidences are
admittedly incomplete and are indicative, not exhaustive.

That Gilbert's book should have been known to early seventeenth-century English
scientific writers is not surprising. Barlowe and Blundeville (pp. 69 and 84) were
familar with his work, probably through personal contact; Nathanial Carpenter wrote
that Gilbert's book was 'a large *Trophie*' to him, that his theory of the Earth as a magnet
'was no sooner broached than it was embraced and wel-commed by many prime wits
as well *English* as *Forraine*. Insomuch that it hath of late taken root and gotten much
ground of our *Vulgar Philosophie*.'[14] I have elsewhere shown[15] that Francis Bacon
knew the *De magnete*. Kenelm Digby cited Gilbert and Harvey as upholders of England's claim for philosophical learning, and wrote that like Gilbert

> any man that hath an ayme to advance much in naturall sciences, must
> endeavour to draw the matter he enquireth of, into some small modell, or
> into some kind of manageable methode; which he may turne and wind as
> he pleaseth.[16]

Robert Boyle, in the first treatise devoted entirely to the subject of electricity, cited
Gilbert.[17] Newton felt it necessary to question the electrical effluvium theory,[18] which
played a prominent role in early eighteenth-century English work in electricity.

[14] Nathaniel Carpenter, *Geography delineated forth in two bookes containing the spherical and topicall
parts thereof*. Oxford, 1625; see Cooke, *loc. cit.* (fn. 10), p. 729.

[15] Duane H. D. Roller, "Did Bacon know Gilbert's De Magnete?" *Isis*, vol. 44 (1953), pp. 10-13.

[16] Kenelm Digby, *Two treatises. In the one of which the nature of bodies; in the other, the nature of
mans sovle; is looked into: in way of discovery, of the immortality of reasonable sovles*, Paris, Gilles
Blaizot, 1647; *Of bodies*, chap. 20, p. 181.

[17] Robert Boyle, *Experiments and notes about the mechanical orgin or production of electricity*, London,
1675, reprinted by R. T. Gunther as *Old Ashmolean Reprints* no. 7, Oxford, 1927.

[18] Isaac Newton, *Opticks or a treatise of the reflections, refractions, inflections & colours of light*, based
on the 4th ed. of 1730, New York, Dover Publications, Inc., 1952, bk. 3, part 1, query 22, p. 353.

Knowledge of the *De magnete* spread abroad rapidly. By 1602 Gilbert was able to refer (p. 69) to foreign opinion of his book, and with reason. Fra. Paolo Sarpi and Galileo were already discussing it in correspondence,[19] and his support of the views of the heretical Gilbert was cited as evidence against Galileo at a later date.[20] For Galileo had, as we have previously noted, found meaningful support for the heliocentric cosmology in Gilbertian magnetism and had discussed it at length in the work that brought about his condemnation. Kepler was aware of the *De magnete* as early as January 1602/03,[21] and later proposed magnetism as the cause of planetary motion in the heliocentric system.

The *De magnete* was known just as early in France. In the period 1602–1604 Guillaume de Nautonier, Sieur de Castlefranc in Languedoc, eagerly adopted Gilbert's ideas on navigation, and his long work on the compass shows strong influence from the *De magnete*, refers to Gilbert by name, and contains 136 pages of the sorts of tables of deviation and dip of which Gilbert urged compilation.[22]

Knowledge of Gilbert's work did not vanish later in the century. Huygens knew of it and mentions Gilbert,[23] as did Mersenne,[24] and there is evidence of a connection between the work of Gilbert and Descartes.[25]

In brief, everywhere that one turns, in seventeenth-century physical science, traces of Gilbert are found. His influences need further investigation.

[19] *Le opere di Galileo Galilei, ed. nazionale*, Florence, G. Bàrbera, 1890–1909, vol. 10, p. 91.

[20] *Ibid.*, vol. 19, p. 353, para. 7.

[21] Max Caspar and Walther von Dyck, *Johannes Kepler in seinen Briefen*, Munich and Berlin, R. Oldenbourg, 1930, vol. 1, p. 183. See also Henry Stevens, *Thomas Hariot the mathematician the philosopher and the scholar developed chiefly from dormant materials with notices of his associates including biographical and bibliographical disquisitions upon the materials of the history of "ould Virginia"*, London, privately printed, 1900, pp. 179-180.

[22] Guillaume de Nautonier, *Mecometrie de leymant cest a dire la maniere de mesvrer les longitudes par le moyen de l'eymant. Par laquelle est enseigné, un trescertain moyen, au paravant inconnu de trouver les longitudes geographiques de tous lieux, – aussi facilement comme la latitude. Davantage, y est monstree la declinaison de la guideymant, pour tous lieux. Oeuvre necessaire aux admiravx, cosmographes, astrologues, geographes, pilotes, geometriens, ingenieux, mestres des mines, architectes, et quadraniers*, Vennès, privately published, 1602–1604.
Nautonier's work was discussed by John P. Edmond in a paper, "On the Mécométre of Natonier," read to the Edinburgh Biographical Society 11th March 1897. I am grateful to Mr. David Wheatland for the opportunity to examine a printed copy of this paper, as well as a copy of the *Mécométre* itself.

[23] *Oeuvres complètes de Christiaan Huygens*, publiées par la Société Hollandaise des Sciences, The Hague, Martin Nijhoff, 1888–1950, *passim*.

[24] *Correspondence du P. Marin Mersenne*, pub. by Paul Tannery, ed. Cornelis de Waard with René Pintard, Paris, Gabriel Beauchesne et ses fils, 1933–1946, *passim*.

[25] Marie Luise Hoppe, *Die Abhängigkeit der Wirbeltheorie des Descartes von William Gilberts Lehre vom Magnetismus*, Halle a.s., C. A. Kaemmercer & Co., 1913.

BIBLIOGRAPHY

I. GENERAL WORKS

Auerbach, F. *Entwicklungsgeschichte der modernen Physik, zugleich eine übersicht ihrer Tatsachen, Gesetze und Theorien,* Berlin, Julius Springer, 1923.

Benjamin, P. *The intellectual rise in electricity,* London, Longmans, Green and Co., 1895.

Bromehead, C. E. N. "Ship's loadstones," *Mineralogical Magazine,* vol. 28 (1948), pp. 429-437.

Brunet, P., and Mieli, A. *Historie des sciences; antiquité,* Paris, Payot, 1935.

Buckley, H. *A short history of physics,* New York, D. Van Nostrand Co., Inc., [   ].

Butterfield, H. *The origins of modern science, 1300-1800,* London, G. Bell and Sons., Ltd., 1950.

Cable, E. J., Getchell, R. W., and Kadesch, W. H. *The Physical Sciences,* New York, Prentice-Hall, 1940.

Cajori, F. *A history of physics in its elementary branches including the evolution of physical laboratories,* revised ed., New York, The Macmillan Co., 1929.

Chase, C. T. *A history of experimental physics,* New York, D. Van Nostrand Co., 1932.

Cohen, I. B. *Benjamin Franklin's experiments,* Cambridge, Harvard University Press, 1941.

Crew, H. *The rise of modern physics,* Baltimore, Williams & Wilkins Co., 1935.

Crombie, A. C. *Augustine to Galileo: the history of science A. D. 400-1650,* Cambridge, Harvard University Press, 1953.

Crombie, A. C. *Robert Grosseteste and the origins of experimental science 1100-1700,* Oxford, Clarendon Press, 1953.

Dampier, W. C. *A history of science and its relations with philosophy & religion,* 3rd ed., Cambridge, University Press, 1942.

Dannemann, F. *Die Naturwissenschaften in ihrer Entwicklung und in ihrem Zusammenhange,* Leipzig, Wilhelm Engelmann, 1920-1923.

Daujat, J. *Origines et formation de la theorié des phénomènes, électriques et magnétiques,* Paris, Herman & Cie., 1945.

Dove, H. W. *Repertorium der Physik, enthaltend eine vollstandige Zusammenstellung der neuern Fortschritte dieser Wissenschaft,* Berlin, Veit & Comp., 1838.

Dreyer, J. L. E. *A history of astronomy from Thales to Kepler,* formerly titled *History of the planetary systems from Thales to Kepler,* 2nd ed., New York, Dover Publications, 1953.

Fischer, J. C. *Geschichte der Physik seit der Wiederherstellung der Künste und Wissenschaften bis auf die neuesten Zeit,* Göttingen, Johann Friedrich Röwer, 1801-08.

Gerland, E. *Geschichte der Physik,* Munich and Berlin, R. Oldenbourg, 1913.

Hart, I. B. *The great physicists,* London, Methuen & Co., Ltd., 1927.

Heller, A. *Geschichte der Physik von Aristotles bis auf die neueste Zeit,* Stuttgart, Ferdinand Enke, 1882-1884.

Hennig, R. 'Die Frühkenntnis der Magnetischen Nordweisung,' *Beiträge zur Geschichte der Technik und Industrie,* vol. 21 (1931-1932), pp. 25-42.

Hewson, J. B. *A history of the practice of Navigation,* Glasgow, Brown, Son & Ferguson, 1951.

Hitchins, H. L., and May, W. E. *From lodestone to gyro-compass,* New York, Philosophical Library, 1953.

Hoppe, E. *Geschichte der Elektricität,* Leipzig, Johann Ambrosius Barth, 1884.

Hoppe, E. *Geschichte der Physik,* Braunschweig, Friedrich Vieweg & Sohn, 1926.

Humboldt, A. von. *Cosmos: a sketch of a physical description of the universe,* tr. E. C. Otte, New York, Harper & Brothers, 1860.

Kistner, A. *Geschichte der Physik: die Physik bis Newton,* Leipzig, G. J. Göschen, 1906.

Mach, E. *Beiträge zur Analyse der Empfindung,* Jena, Verlag von Gustav Fischer, 1886.

Mason, S. F. *A history of the sciences: main currents of scientific thought,* London, Routledge & Kegan Paul Ltd., 1953.

Metzger, H. *Attraction universelle et religion naturelle chez quelque commentateurs anglais de Newton,* Paris, Herman et cie., 1938.

Mottelay, P. F. *Bibliographical history of electricity & magnetism,* London, Charles Griffin & Company Limited, 1922.

Poggendorf, J. C. *Geschichte der Physik: Vorlesungen gehalten an der Universität zu Berlin,* Leipzig, Johann Ambrosius Barth, 1879.

Priestley, J. *The history and present state of electricity, with original experiments,* 2nd ed., London, J. Dodsley, ..., 1769.

Rosenberger, F. *Die Geschichte der Physik in Grundzügen mit synchronistischen Tabellen der Mathematik, der Chemie, und beschreibenden Naturwissenschaften sowie der allgemeinen Geschichte,* Braunschweig, Friedrich Vieweg und Sohn, 1882-1890.

Sarton, G. *A guide to the history of science,* Waltham, Mass., Chronica Botanica Co., 1952.

Sarton, G. "The History of Science versus the History of Medicine," *Isis,* vol. 23 (1935), pp. 313-320.

Sarton, G. *Introduction to the history of science,* Baltimore, Williams and Wilkins, 1927-1948.

Sarton, G. *The study of the history of science,* Cambridge, Harvard University Press, 1936.

Taylor, A. E. *Platonism and its influence,* New York, Longmans, Green and Co., 1927.

Taylor, F. S. *Science past and present,* London, William Heinemann, Ltd., 1947.

Thorndike, L. *A history of magic and experimental science,* New York, Macmillan Co. (vols. 1-2), 1923; New York, Columbia University Press (vols. 3-6), 1934-1941.

Whewell, W. *History of the inductive sciences, from the earliest to the present time,* new ed., revised and continued, London, John W. Parker, 1847.

White, H. E. *Classical and modern physics,* New York, D. Van Nostrand, 1940.

Whittaker, E. *A history of the theories of aether and electricity,* revised ed., London, Thomas Nelson and Sons Ltd., 1951.

Wills, A. P., Barnett, S. J., Ingersoll, L. R., Kunz, J., Quimby, S. L., Terry, E. M., and Williams, S. R. *Theories of magnetism: report of the Committee on Theories of Magnetism of the National Research Council; Bulletin of the National Research Council,* vol. 3, part 3 (1922).

Zinner, E. *Entstehung und Ausbreitung der coppernicanischen Lehre,* Erlangen, Max Mencke, 1943.

II. PRIMARY SOURCES FROM BEFORE THE AGE OF GILBERT

Adelard of Bath. *Questiones naturales.* English translation in Berachya Hanakdan's *Dodi ve-nechdi,* ed. & tr. Hermann Gollanez, London, Humphrey Milford, Oxford University Press, 1920.

Aristotle. *Aristotelis opera omnia Graece et Latine,* Paris, Ambrosio Firmin Didot, 1854.

Aristotle. *The works of Aristotle translated into English,* ed. W. D. Ross, Oxford, Clarendon Press, 1908-1931.

pseudo-Aristotle. *Das Steinbuch des Aristotles,* tr. Julius Ruska, Heidelberg, Carl Winter, 1912.

Augustine. *Sancti Aurelii Augustini episcopi de civitate Dei libri xxii,* ed. B. Dombart, Leipzig, B. G. Teubner, 1877.

Bacon, R. *Fr. Rogeri Bacon opera quaedam hactenus inedita,* ed. J. S. Brewer, London, Longman, Green, Longman, and Roberts, 1859.

Bacon, R. *Epistola Frateris Rogerii Baconis de secretis operibus artis, et Naturae;* Appendix I to *Fr. Rogeri Bacon opera quaedam hactenus inedita,* ed. J. S. Brewer, London, Longman, Green, Longman, and Roberts, 1859.

Bacon, R. *The "Opus Majus" of Roger Bacon,* ed. J. H. Bridges, Oxford, Clarendon Press, 1897-1900.

Bacon, R. *The opus majus of Roger Bacon,* tr. R. B. Burke, Philadelphia, University of Pennsylvania Press, 1928.

Chaucer, G. *The complete works of Geoffrey Chaucer,* ed. W. W. Skeat, London, Oxford University Press, Humphrey Milford, 1929.

Cohen, M. R., and Drabkin, I. E. *A source book in Greek science,* New York, McGraw-Hill Book Co., 1948.

Diels, H. *Die Fragmente der Vorsokratiker,* 5th ed., Berlin, Wiedmannsche Buchhandlung, 1934-1938.

Diogenes Laertius. *Lives of ominent philosophers, with an English translation,* by R. D. Hicks, Loeb Classical Library, London, William Heinemann; New York, G. P. Putnam's Sons, 1925.

Library, London, William Heinemann; New York, G. P. Putnam's Sons, 1925.

Dioscorides. *The Greek herbal of Dioscorides,* englished by John Goodyer (1652-1655), ed. and published by Robert T. Gunther, Oxford, University Press, 1934.

Euripides. *Euripidis opera omnia; ...,* Glasgow, Academic Press, 1821.

Galen. *Galen on the natural faculties,* with an English translation by A. J. Brock, Loeb Classical Library edition, London, William Heinemann; New York, G. P. Putnam's Sons, 1916.

Guiot de Provins. *Les Oeuvres de Guiot de Provins,* ed. John Orr, Manchester, University Press, 1915.

Herodotus. *Herodotus with an English translation* by A. D. Godley, Loeb Classical Library edition, London, William Heinemann; New York, G. P. Putnam's Sons, 1921-1930.

Hippolytus of Portus Romanus. *Philosophumena sive haeresium omnium confutatio opus origeni ad-scriptum e codice Parisino productum recensuit, latine vertit notis variorum suisque instruxit, prolegomenis et indicibus auxit,* ed. Patrice Cruice, Paris, Royal Printer, 1860.

Homer. *The Odyssey, with an English translation* by A. T. Murray, Cambridge, Harvard University Press; London, William Heinemann Ltd., 1946.

Isidore of Seville. *Isidori Hispalensis Episcopi etymologiarvm sive originvm libri xx,* ed. W. M. Lindsay, Oxford, Clarendon Press, 1917.

Jacob of Vitry. *Iacobi de Vitriaco primum acconensis, deinde Tvsevlani espicopi, et S. Eccl. R. cardinalis, se disque Apostolicae in Terra sancta, in Imperio, in Francia olim Legati, libri duo, quorum prior Orientalis, sive Hierosolumitanae: alter Occidentalis historiae nomine inscribitur,* Dovai, Balthazaris Belleri, 1597.

Job of Edessa. *Book of treasures,* ed. and tr. by A. Mingana, Cambridge, W. Heffer and Sons, Ltd., 1935.

John of St. Amand. L. Thorndike, "John of St. Amand on the Magnet", *Isis,* vol. 36 (1946), pp. 156-157.

Brunetto Latini. *Li livres dou tresor,* ed. critique, Francis J. Carmody, Berkeley and Los Angeles, University of California Press, 1948.

Lucretius. *T. Lucreti Cari de rerum natura libri sex,* 4th ed., Cambridge, Deighton Bell and Co., 1886.

Marcellus Empiricus. *Marcelli de medicamentis liber,* ed. Maximilianus Niedermann, Leipzig and Berlin, B. G. Teubner, 1916.

Michel, F. *Lais inedit, des XIIe et XIIIe siecles, publies pour la premiere fois, d'apres les manuscrits de France et Angleterre,* Paris, Joseph Techner; London, W. Pichering, 1836.

Neckam, A. *Alexandri Neckam de naturis rerum libro duo...,* ed. Thomas Wright, London, Longman, Green, Longman, Roberts, and Green, 1861.

Neckam, A. *De utensilibus.* In Thomas Wright's *A volume of vocabularies,* privately printed, 1857.

Peter Peregrinus. *Epistola Petri Peregrini de Maricourt ad Sygerum de Foucaucourt militem de magnete,* reprinted by G. Hellmann, *Rara magnetica,* no. 10 of *Neudrucke von Schriften und Karten über Meteorology und Erdmagnetismus,* Berlin, A. Asher & Co., 1898.

Peter Peregrinus. H. D. Harradon, "Some early contributions to the history of geomagnetism, Part I:

The letter of Peter Peregrinus de Maricourt to Sygerus de Foucaucourt, Soldier, concerning the magnet," *Terrestrial magnetism and Atmospheric Electricity*, vol. 48 (1943), pp. 3-17.

Plato. *Plato with an English translation*, Loeb Classical Library, London, William Heinemann; New York, G. P. Putnam's Sons, 1925.

Pliny. *C. Pliny Secundi naturalis historiae libri xxxvii. Post Ludovici iani obitum recognovit et scripturae discrepantia adiecta*, ed. Charles Mayhoff, Lepzig, B. G. Teubner, 1897.

Pliny. *Pliny's natural history with an English translation*, Loeb Classical Library edition, Cambridge, Harvard University Press; London, William Heinemann, Ltd., 1949-   .

Plutarch. *Platonic questions*, in *Plutarch's Morals*, tr. by several hands, corrected and revised by W. W. Godwin, Boston, Little Brown, and Co., 1870.

Ptolemy. *Geography of Claudius Ptolemy...based upon Greek and Latin manuscripts and important late fifteenth and early sixteenth printed editions, including reproductions of the maps from the Ebner manuscript*, ca. 1460, tr. and ed. by E. L. Stevenson, New York, The New York Public Library, 1932.

Solinus. *C. Iulli Solini Polyhistor ad optimas editiones collatus praemittur notitia literaria accedit index Edito accurata*, Zweibrucken, Typographical Society, 1794.

Theophrastus. *Theophrastus's History of Stones*, Greek and English ed. by "Sir" John Hill, London, 1774.

III. SECONDARY SOURCES FOR BEFORE THE AGE OF GILBERT

Anon. *Al-Biruni commemoration volume*, Calcutta, Iran Society, 1951.

Adams, F. D. *The birth and development of the geological sciences*, Baltimore, Williams and Wilkins Co., 1938.

Ball, S. H. *A Roman book on precious stones, including an English modernization of the 37th booke of the Historie of the world by C. Plinius Secundus*, Gemological Institute of America, 1950.

Brehaut, E. *An encyclopedist of the dark ages: Isidore of Seville*, New York, Columbia University, 1912.

Brunet, P., and Mieli, A. *Histoire des scenices antiquite*, Paris, Payot, 1935.

Burnet, J. *Early Greek Philosophy*, London and Edinburgh, Adams and Charles Black, 1892.

Buttmann, P. "Bemerkungen über die Bennungen einiger Mineralien beiden Alten, vorzüglich des Magnetes und des Basaltes," *Museuum der Alterthumswissenschaft*, vol. 2, pp. 5-8, 102-104.

Davies, O. *Roman mines in Europe*, Oxford, Clarendon Press, 1935.

Eckman, J. *Jerome Cardan*, Baltimore, The Johns Hopkins Press, 1946 (supplement no. 7 to the *Bulletin of the History of Medicine*).

The Encyclopaedia of Islam, Leyden, Late E. J. Brill, Ltd.; London, Luzac & Co., 1913-1938.

Evans, A. *The Palace of Minos, a comparative account of the successive stages of the early Cretan civilization as illustrated by the discoveries at Knossos*, London, MacMillan and Co., 1928.

Fowler, G. B. *Intellectual interests of Englebert of Admont*, New York, Columbia University Press, 1947.

Freeman, K. *The pre-Socratic philosophers; a companion to Diels, Fragmente der Vorsokratiker*, Oxford, Basil Blackwell, 1949.

Ginguene, P. L. *Histoire Littéraire d'Italie*, Paris, Michaud Frères, 1811.

Gomperz, T. *Greek thinkers*, tr. Laurie Magnus, London, John Murray, 1906.

Handbuch der klassischen Altertums-Wissenschaft und Philosophie, Nordlingen, C. H. Beck, 1888.

Haskins, C. H. *Studies in the history of mediaeval science*, Cambridge, Harvard University Press, 1924.

Hellmann, G. "Die Anfänge der Magnetischen Beobachtungen," *Zeitschrift der Gesellschaft für Erdkunde zu Berlin*, vol. 32 (1897), pp. 112-136.

Hirth, F. *The ancient history of China*, New York, Columbia University Press, 1908.

Hooykaas, R. "Die Elementenlehre der Iatrochemiker," *Janus*, vol. 41 (1937), pp. 1-28.

Hoppe, E. "Magnetismus und Elektrizität im Klassischen Altertum," *Archiv fur die Geschichte und der Technik*, vol. 8 (1918), pp. 92-105.

Jaeger, W. *Diocles von Karystos. Die griechische Medizin und die Schule des Aristoteless*, Berlin, W. de Gruyter & Co., 1938.

Jakob, K. G. "Neue Beiträge zum studium des kaspisch-baltischen Handels im Mittelalter; I. Neue studien, den Bernstein im Orient betreffend," *Zeitschrift der Deutschen Morgenländischen Gesellschaft*, vol. 43, pp. 353-387.

Klaproth, M. J. *Lettre à M. le Baron A. de Humboldt, sur l'invention de la boussole*, Paris, Librairie Orientale de Prosper Dondey-Dupré, 1834.

Lasteyrie, F. de. *L'electrum des anciens etait-il l'email?* Paris, Didot Freres, Fils et Ci., 1857.

Li-Shu-hua. "Origine de la boussole," *Isis*, vol. 45 (1954), pp. 78-94, part II in press.

Little, A. G. *Roger Bacon essays*, Oxford, Clarendon Press, 1914.

Longfellow, H. W. *The poets and poetry of Europe*, Boston, Osgood, 1871.

Manly, J. W. "What is the Parlement of Foules?," *Festschrift für Lorenz Morsbach*, Halle a.S., Max Niemeyer, 1913.

Martin, T. H. *La foudre l'électricité et la magnétisme chez les Anciens*, Paris, Didier et Cie., 1866.

Mitchell, A. C. "Chapters in the history of terrestrial magnetism," *Terrestrial Magnetism and Atmospheric Electricity*, vols. 37 (1932), 42 (1937), 44 (1939), 51 (1946).

Mieli, A. *La science Arabe et son rôle dans l'évolution scientifique mondiale*, with several additions by H. P. J. Renaud, M. Meyerhof, and Julius Ruska, Leyden, E. J. Brill, 1938.

Morison, S. E. *Admiral of the ocean sea* (2 vols.), Boston, Little Brown and Co., 1942.

Naiden, J. R. *The Sphera of George Buchanan (1506-1582)*, privately printed, 1952.

Navarro, J. M. de. "Prehistoric routes between Northern Europe and Italy defined by the amber trade," *The Geographical Journal*, vol. 66 (1925), pp. 481-507.

Randall, J. H., Jr. "The Development of scientific Method in the School of Padua," *Journal of the History of Ideas*, vol. 1 (1940), pp. 177-206.

Raven, C. E. *English naturalists from Neckam to Ray*, Cambridge, University Press, 1947.

Robin, L. *La pensée grecque, et les orgines de l'esprit scientifique*, Paris, la Renaissance du Livre, 1928.

Roller, D., and D. H. D. "The prenatal history of electrical science," *American Journal of Physics*, vol. 21 (1953), pp. 343-356.

Sarton, G. *A history of science: ancient science through the golden age of Greece*, Cambridge, Harvard University Press, 1952.

Schleiermacher, F. *Sämmtliche Werke*, part 3, *zur Philosophie*, vol. 2, Berlin, G. Reimer, 1838.

Schuck, A. "Zur Einführung des Kompasses in die nordwesteuropäische Nautik," *Archiv fur die Geschichte und der Technik*, vol. 4 (1913), pp. 40-78.

Semple, E. *The geography of the Mediterranean region: its relation to ancient history*, London, Constable and Co., Ltd., 1932.

Thompson, S. P. "Peter Peregrinus de Marincourt and his epistola de magnete," *Proceedings of the British Academy* (1905-06), pp. 377-408.

Thompson, S. P. "The Rose of the Winds: the origin and development of the compass-card," *Proceedings of the British Academy* (1913-1914), pp. 179-210.

Urbanitsky, A. R. von. *Elektricität und Magnetismus in Alterthume*, Wien, Pest, Leipzig, A. Hartleben's Verlag, 1887.

Whitlock, H. P. *The story of gems; a popular handbook*, New York, Emerson Books, Inc., 1945.

Wiedemann, E. "Beiträge zur Geschichte der chemie bei den Arabern," I and XLII, *Sitzungsberichten der Physikalisch-Medizinischen Sozietät zu Erlangen*, vol. 36 (1934) and vol. 47 (1915).

Wiedemann, E. *Ueber die Naturwissenschaften bei den Arabern*, Hamburg, A. G. Richter, 1890.

Williamson, G. C. *The book of amber*, London, Ernest Benn, Ltd., 1932.

Winter, H. "Die Kenntnis der magnetischen Missweisung im 13 Jahrhundert," *Mitteilungen zur Geschichte der Medizen der Naturwissenschaften und der Technik*, vol. 35 (1936), pp. 16-17.

Winter, H. "Petrus Peregrinus von Maricourt und die magnetische Missweisung," *Forschung und Fortschritte*, vol. 11 (1935), pp. 304-306.

Winter, H. "Seit wann ist die Missweisung bekannt?", *Annalen der Hydrographie und maritimen meterologie*, vol. 63 (1935), pp. 352-363.

Winter, H. "Who invented the compass?", *Mariner's Mirror*, vol. 23 (1937), pp. 95-102.

Wolfson, H. A. *Crescas' critique of Aristotle*, Cambridge, Harvard University Press, 1929.

IV. PRIMARY SOURCES IN THE AGE OF GILBERT

Bacon, F. *The works of Francis Bacon*, ed. James Spedding, Robert Ellis, Douglas Heath, Boston, 1863.

Bacon, F. *Baconiana. Or certain genuine remains of Sr. Francis Bacon, Baron of Verulam and Viscount of St. Albans;...*, ed. Thomas Tenison, London, 1679.

Barlowe, W. *Magnetical advertisements, or diverse pertinent observations and approved experiments, concerning the nature and property of the loadstone: very pleasant for knowledge and most needful in practise, of traveling, or for the framing of instruments fit for travelling both by sea and land*, new ed. with notes by William Sturgeon, London, Sherwood, Gilbert, and Piper, 1843.

Barrow, I. *Opuscula; viz. determinationes, conc. ad clerum, orationes, poemata, etc.*, London, Brabazoni Aylmeri, 1687.

Blundeville, T. *The theoriques of the seven planets, shewing all their diverse motions, and all other accidents, called passions, thereunto belonging. Now more plainly set forth in our mother tongue by M. Blundevile, than ever they have been heretofore in any other tongue whatsoever, and that with such pleasant demonstrative figures, as every man that hath any skill in arithmeticke, may easily understand the same. A booke most necessearie for all gentlemen that are desirous to be skilfull in astronomie, and for all pilots and sea-men, or any others that love to serve the prince on the sea, or by the sea to travel into forraine countries. Whereunto is added by the said Master Blundevile, a breefe Extract by him made, of maginus his theoriques, for the better understanding of the prutenicall tables, to calculate thereby the diverse motions of the seven planets. There is also hereto added, the making, description and use, of two most ingenious and necessarie instruments for sea-men, to find out thereby the latitude of any place upon the sea or land, in the darkest night that is, without the helpe of sunne, moone, or starre first invented by M. Doctor Gilbert, a most excellent philosopher, and one of the ordinairie physicians to her Majestie: and nowhere plainly set downe in our mother tongue by Master Blundevile*, London, Adam Islip, 1602.

B[orough], W. *A discourse of the variation of the compasse, or magneticall needle. Wherein is mathematically shewed, the manner of the observation, effects, and applications thereof, made by W. B. And is to bee annexed to the newe attractive of R.[obert] N.[orman]*, London, Hugh Astley, 1596.

Boyle, R. *Experiments and notes about the origins or production of electricity*, London, 1675; reprinted by R. T. Gunther, as *Old Ashmolean Reprints* no. 7, Oxford, 1927.

Chamberlain, C. *The lettres of John Chamberlain*, vol. 1, ed. N. E. McClure, *Memoirs of the American Philosophical Society*, vol. 12, part 1, Philadelphia, 1939.

Dee, J. *The private diary of Dr. John Dee, and the catalog of his library of manuscripts, from the original manuscripts in the Ashmolean Museum at Oxford, and Trinity College Library, Cambridge*, ed. J. O. Halliwell, London, Camden Society, 1842.

Digby, K. *Two treatises. In the one of which, the natvre of bodies; in theo ther, the natvre of mans sovle; is looked into: in way of discovery, of the immortality of reasonable sovles*, Paris, Gilles Blaizot, 1644.

Dryden, J. *The works of John Dryden*, ed. W. Scott, rev. and corr. by G. Saintsbury, Edinburgh, William Paterson, 1885.

Essayes of natural experiments made in the Accademia del Cimento, tr. R. Waller, London, 1684.

Galileo Galilei. *Dialogue on the great world systems*, tr. Thomas Salusbury, ed. Giorgio de Santillana, Chicago, University of Chicago Press, 1953.

Galileo Galilei. *Le opere di Galileo Galilei*, edizione nazionale, Florence, G. Barbera, 1890-1909.

Gellibrand, H. *A discovrse mathematical on the variation of the magneticall needle. Together with its admirable diminution lately discovered*, London, William Jones, 1635. Reprinted by G. Hellmann, *Neudrucke von Schriften und Karten über Meterologie und Erdmagnetismus*, no. 9, Berlin, A. Asher & Co., 1897.

Gilbert, W. *De magnete*, editions of 1600, 1628, 1633, 1892, 1893, 1900, 1941, 1952, 1956, 1958. See *supra* pp. 323-335.

Gilbert, W. *Gvilielmi Gilberti Colcestrensis, medici regii, de mundo nostro sublunari philosophia nova. Opus posthumum, ab authoris fratre collectum pridum & dispositum, hvnc ex duobus mss. codicibus editum. Ex museio viri perillustris Gvilielmi Boswelli equitis aurati &c. & oratoris apud Foederatos Belgas Angli*, Amsterdam, Elzeviv, 1651.

Gilbert, W. Manuscript will; photostat provided by Somerset House.

Hakluyt, R. *The principial navigations voyages traffiques & discoveries of the English nation made by sea or overland to the remote and farthest distant quarters of the earth at any time within the compass of these 1600 years*, London and Toronto, J. M. Dent and Sons Ltd.; New York, E. P. Dutton & Co., 1927.

Hartmann, G. Letter to the Herzog Albrecht von Preussen, reproduced in facsimile and reprinted by G. Hellmann in *Rara magnetica*, no. 10 of *Neudruke von Schriften und Karten über Meteorologie und Erdmagnetismus*, Berlin, A. Asher & Co., 1898.

"The Honywood evidences, II," *The Topographer and Genealogist*, vol. 2 (1853), pp. 169-185.

Huygens, C. *Oeuvres complètes de Christiaan Huygens*, publiées par la Société Hollandaise des Sciences, The Hague, Martin Nijhoff, 1888-1950.

Kepler, J. *Johannes Kepler in seinen Briefen*, pub. by Max Caspar and Walther von Dyck, Munich and Berlin, R. Oldenbourg, 1930.

Lodge, E. *Illustrations of British History, Biography, and Manners in the reign of Henry VIII, Edward VI, Mary, Elizabeth, and James I, exhibited in a series of original papers, selected from the mss. of the noble families of Howard, Talbot, and Cecil, containing among a variety of interesting pieces, a great part of the correspondence of Elizabeth and her ministers with George, sixth Earl of Shrewsbury, during the fifteen years in which Mary, Queen of Scots, remained in her custody*, 2nd ed., London, John Chidley, 1838.

Mersenne, P. *Correspondence du P. Marin Mersenne*, pub. by Paul Tannery, ed. Cornelis de Waard with Rene Pintard, Paris, Gabriel Beauchesne et ses fils, 1933-1946.

Nautonier, G. de.*Mecometrie de leymant cest a dire la maniere de mesvres les longitudes par le moyen de l'eymant. Par laquelle est enseigné, un trescertain moyen, au paravant inconnu de trouver les longitudes geographiques de tous lieux,—aussi facilement comme la latitude. Davantage, y est monstree la declinaison de la guideymant, pour tous lieuxx. Oeuvre necessaire aux admiravx, cosmographes, astrologues, geographes, pilotes, geometriens, ingenieuxx, mestres des mines, architectes, et quadraniers*, Vennès, privately published, 1602-1604.

Newton, I. *Opticks or a treatise of the reflections, refractions, inflections & colours of light*, based on the 4th ed. of 1710, New York, Dover Publications, Inc., 1952.

Norman, R. *The newe attractive, containying a short discourse of the magnes or lodestone, and amongst other his vertues, of a newe discovered secret and subtill propertie, concerning the declinying of the needle touched therewith under the plaine of the horizon*, London, Richard Ballard, 1581; reprinted by G. Hellmann in *Rara magnetica*, no. 10 of *Neudrucke von Schriften und Karten über Meteorologie und Erdmagnetismus*, Berlin, A. Asher & Co., 1898.

The oath book or red parchment book of Colchester, ed. W. G. Benham, Colchester, "Essex Country Standard" Office, 1907.

Sarpi, P. *Lettere di Fra Paolo Sarpi*, ed. F. L. Polidori, Florence, G. Barbera, 1863.

Stow, J. *A survey of the cities of London and Westminister: containing the original antiquity, increase, modern estate and government of those cities. Written at first in the year MDXCVIII by John Stow, citizen and native of London. Since reprinted and augmented by the author; and afterwards by A. M. H. H. and others. Now lastly, corrected, improved and very much enlarged: and the survey and history brought down from the year (being near fourteen years since it was last printed) to the present time;...*, London, A Churchill, J. Knapton, ..., 1720.

Johannus Stradanus. The "New discoveries" of Stradanus, Norwalk, Conn., Burndy Library, 1953.

V. SECONDARY SOURCES FOR THE AGE OF GILBERT

Anon. "The Gilbert Tercentenary Commemoration," *Journal of the Institution of Electrical Engineers, including original communications on electricity and electrical sciences*, vol. 33 (1903-1904), pp. 68-74.

Anon. "William Gilbert of Colchester," *The Electrical World and Engineer, a weekly review of current progress in electricity and its practical applications*, vol. 42 (2nd half, 1903), p. 480.

Aikin, J., Morgan, T., and Johnston, W., *General biography; or, lives, critical and historical, of the most eminent persons of all ages, countries, conditions, and professions, arranged according to alphabetical order, London*, J. Johnson..., 1803.

Allibone, A. *A critical dictionary of English literature, and British and American authors, living and deceased, from the earliest accounts to the middle of the nineteenth century, containing thirty thousand biographies and literary notices with forty indexes of subjects*, Philadelphia, Childs & Peterson, 1859.

Bayon, H. P. "William Gilbert (1544-1603), Robert Fludd (1574-1637), and William Harvey (1578-1657), as Medical Exponents of Baconian Doctrines," *Proceedings of the Royal Society of Medicine*, vol. 32 (1938), pp. 31-42.

Bayon, H. P. "William Harvey (1578-1657). His application of biological experiment, clinical observation, and comparative anatomy to the problems of generation," *Journal of the History of Medicine and Allied Sciences*, vol. 2 (1947), pp. 51-96.

Benham, C. E. *Colchester worthies, a biographical index of Colchester*, London, Simpkin, Marshall, Hamilton, Kent & Co.; Colchester, T. Forster, [   ].

Benham, C. E. *William Gilbert of Colchester. A sketch of his magnetic philosophy*, Colchester, Benham & Co., 1902.

Benham, W. G. *Guide to Colchester*, 16th ed., Colchester, 1925.

Biographia Britannica: or, the lives of the most eminent persons who have flourished in Great Britain and Ireland from the earliest ages down to the present time:..., London, George Virtue, 1831.

Biographie universelle, ancienne et moderne, ou, histoire, par ordre alphabétique, de la vie publique et privée de tous les hommes qui se sont fait remarquer par leurs ecrits, leurs actions, leurs talents, leurs vertues ou leurs crimes ouvrage entièrement neuf, rédigé par une société de gens du lettres et de savants, Paris, L. G. Michaud, 1816.

Blount, T. P. *Censura celebriorum authorum sive tractatvs in qvo varia vivorvm doctorvm de clarissimis cujusque seculi: scriptoribus Indicia traduntur. Unde facillimo negotio lector dignascere queat quid in singulis quibusque istorum dignascere queat qid in singulis quibusque istorum authorum maxime memorabile sit, & quonam in pretio apud eruditos semper habiti fuerint. Omnia in studiosorum gratiam collegit, et in ordinem digessit secundum serium tempors quo ipsi authores floruerunt*, Geneva, Samuel de Tournes, 1694.

Boas, M. "Bacon and Gilbert," *Journal of the History of Ideas*, vol. 12 (1951), pp. 466-467.

192

Boulting, W. *Giordano Bruno, his life, thought, and martyrdom,* London, Kegan Paul, Trench, Trübner & Co., 1914.

Boyer, B. "William Gilbert on the Rainbow," *American Journal of Physics,* vol. 20 (1952), pp. 416-421.

Caspar, M. *Johannes Kepler,* Stuttgart, W. Kohlhammer, 1948.

Cooke, C. W. "William Gilbert, of Colchester," *Engineering,* vol. 48 (1889), pp. 717-718, 729-730.

Cooper, C. H., and T. *Athenae Cantabrigienses,* Cambridge, Deighton, Bell & Co.; MacMillan Co., 1861.

Daneel, H. "William Gilbert von Colchester," *Zeitschrift für Elektrochemie und angewandte physikalische chemie,* 10th year, no. 1 (1904), pp. 11-12.

Dibner, B. *Dr. William Gilbert,* Norwalk, Conn., Burndy Library, 1927.

Dick, H. G. "Students of Physic and Astrology: A Survey of Astrological Medicine in the Age of Science," *Journal of the History of Medicine and Allied Sciences,* vol. 1 (1946), pp. 300-315, 419-433.

Dictionaire des sciences medicales. Biographie medicale, Paris, C. L. F. Panckoucke, 1821.

The dictionary of national biography, founded in 1882 by George Smith, ed. L. Stephens and S. Lee; from the earliest times to 1900, London, Oxford University Press and Humphrey Milford,   .

Feldhaus, F. M. *Zur Geschichte der Elektrizität. Die Beründung der Lehre von Magnetismus v. Elektrizität durch Dr. William Gilbert (d. 1603). Eine säkularschrift.* Heidelberg, C. Winters, Universitätsbuchhandlung, 1904.

Fuller, T. *The history of the worthies of England,* London, J.G.W.L. and W.G., 1662.

Georgi, T. *Theophili Georgi, Buchhändlers in Leipzig, allgemeines europäisches Bücher-Lexicon, in welchem nach Ordnung des Dictionarii die allermeisten Autores oder Gattungen von Büchern zu finden, welche sowohl von denen Patribus, Theologis derer dreyen Christlichen Haupt-Religionen, und darinnen sich befindlichen Sectirern; Als auch von denen Juris-Consultis, Medicis, Physicis, Philologis, Philosophis, Historicis, Geographis, Criticis, Chymicis, Musicis, Arithmeticis, Mathematicis, Chirurgis, und Autoribus Classicis, &c.&. noch vor dem Anfange des XVI. Seculi bis 1739. inclusive, und also in mehr als zweyhundert Jahren, in dem europäischen Theile der Welt, sonderlich aber in Teutschland, sind geschrieben und gedrucket worden. Bey iedem Buche sind zu finden die unterschiedenen Editiones, die Jahr-Zahl, das Format, der Ort, der Verleger, die Anzahl der Bögen und der Preiss. Anfänglich von dem Autore nur zur Privat-Notitz zusammen getragen, nunmehro aber auf vieler inständiges Verlangen zum Druck befördert, und in vier Theile abgetheilet,* Leipzig, Theophili Georgi, 1742.

Gliozzi, M. "L'elettrologia nel secolo XVII," *Periodicodi matematiche: storia-didatticafilosofia* ser. 4, vol. 13 (1933), pp. 1-14.

Hale-White, W. *Bacon, Gilbert and Harvey being the Harveian oration delivered before the Royal College of Physicians of London, October 18th, 1927,* London, John Bale, Sons and Danielsson, Ltd., 1927.

Hallam, H. *Introduction to the literature of Europe, in the fifteenth, sixteenth, and seventeenth centuries,* London, John Murray, 1939.

Hellmann, G. "Zur Bibliographie von W. Gilbert's 'De magnete,'" *Terrestrial Magnetism and Atmospheric Electricity,* vol. 7 (1902), pp. 63-66.

Hoppe, M. L. *Die Abhängigkeit der Wirbeltheorie des Descartes von William Gilberts Lehre vom Magnetismus,* Halle, a.S., Hofbuchdruckeri von C. A. Kaemmerer & Co., 1913.

Hutchinson, B. *Biographia medica; or, historical and critical memoirs of the lives and writings of the most eminent medical characters who have existed from the earliest ages down to the present time; with a catalogue of their literary productions,* London, J. Johnson, 1799.

Johnson, F. R. *Astronomical thought in Renaissance England: a study of the English scientific writings from 1500 to 1645,* Baltimore, The Johns Hopkins Press, 1937.

Johnson, F. R., and Larkey, S. V. "Robert Recorde's Mathematical Teaching and the Anti-Aristotelian Movement," *The Huntington Library Bulletin,* no. 7 (1935), pp. 59-87.

193

Knight, C. *Biography, or third division of "The English Cyclopaedia,"* London, Bradbury, Evans, and Co., 1868.

Koyré, A. "An experiment in measurement," *Proceedings of the American Philosophical Society*, vol. 97 (1953), pp. 222-237.

Koyré, A. *Etudes Galiléennes*, Paris, Hermann & Cie., 1939.

Krusen, F. H. "William Gilbert, the father of electrotherapy," *Archives of Physical Therapy, X-rays, Radium, with international Abstract*, vol. 1. (1931), pp. 737-743.

Langdon-Brown, W. "William Gilbert: His place in the Medical World," *Nature*, vol. 154 (1944), pp. 136-139.

Langdon,Brown, W. *Some chapters in Cambridge medical history*, Cambridge, University Press; New York, The Macmillan Co., 1946.

LeNoble, R. *Mersenne ou la naissance du mechanisme*, Paris, Librairie Philosophiquqe, J. Vrin, 1943.

Liebig, J. *Rede in der öffentlichen sitzung der K. Akademie der Wissenschaften am 28. März 1863 zur Feier ihres einhundert und vierten Stiftungstages*, Munich, The Royal Academy, 1863.

Lilly, W. *History of his life and times. contained in The lives of those eminent antiquaries Elias Ashmole, Esquire, and Mr. William Lilly, written by themselves, containing, first, William Lilly's history of his life and times, with notes by Mr. Ashmole:...*, London, T. Davies, 1774.

Magrini, S. "Il 'De Magnete' del Gilbert e i primordi della Magnetologia in Italia in rapporto alla Lotta intornio al massini sistemi," *Archivo di Storia della Scienza*, vol. 8 (1927), pp. 17-39.

McColley, G. "William Gilbert and the English Reputation of Giordano Bruno," *Annals of Science*, vol. 2 (1937), pp. 352-353.

Merton, E. S. "Sir Thomas Browne's Scientific Quest," *Journal of the History of Medicine and Allied Science*, vol. 3 (1948), pp. 214-228.

Merton, R. K. *Science, technology and society in seventeenth century England; Osiris*, vol. 2, part 2 (1938).

Metcalfe, W. C. *The visitations of Essex by Hawley, 1552; Hervey, 1558; Cooke, 1570; Raven, 1612, and Owen and Lilly, 1634. To which are added miscellaneous Essex pedigrees from various Harleian manuscripts: and an appendix containing Berry's Essex pedigrees*, London, Harleian Society Publications, vol. 13, 1878.

Morant, P. *The history and antiquities of the most ancient town and borough of Colchester, in the county of Essex*, 2nd ed., London, 1768, reissued, Chelmsford, 1815.

Moriarty, C. A. "The Gilberts of Clare and Colchester," *Miscellanea Genenealogica et Heraldica*, 5th series, vol. 5 (1924), pp. 216-234.

Mottelay, P. F. "Biographical Memoir" of Gilbert, in 1893 edition of Gilbert's *De magnete*.

Mullett, C. F. "Overseas expansion and English medicine to 1800," *Bulletin of the History of Medicine*, vol. 22 (1948), pp. 664-673.

Munk, W. *The roll of the Royal College of Physicians of London; comprising biographical sketches of all the eminent physicians, whose names are recorded in the annuals from the foundation of the college in 1518 to its removal in 1825, from Warwick Lane to Pall Mal East*, 2nd ed., London, published by The College, 1878.

Ornstein, M. *The role of scientific societies in the seventeenth century*, Chicago, University of Chicago Press, 1938.

Pelseneer, J. "Gilbert, Bacon, Galilée, Képler, Harvey et Descartes," *Isis*, vol. 17 (1932), pp. 171-208.

Podolsky, E. "Physician physicists," *Annals of Medical History*, n.s., vol. 3 (1931), pp. 300-307.

Potamin, Brother M. F. O'Reilly. "Gilbert of Colchester," *Popular Science Monthly*, vol. 49 (1901), pp. 337-350.

Potamian, Brother M. F. O'Reilly, and J. J. Walsh, *Makers of electricity*, New York, Fordham University Press, 1909.

Richardson, B. W. *Disciples of Aesculapius*, London, Hutchinson and Co., 1900.

Roller, D. H. D. "Did Bacon Know Gilbert's De Magnete?", *Isis*, vol. 44 (1953), pp. 10-13.

Rosen, E. "Galileo on the Distance between the Earth and the Moon," *Isis*, vol. 43 (1952), pp. 344-348.

Round, J. H. "Dr. Gilberd's birthplace," *Transactions of the Essex Archaeological Society*, n.s., vol. 10 (1909), pp. 307-311.

Singer, C. "Dr. William Gilbert (1544-1603)," *Journal of the Royal Naval Medical Service*, vol. 2 (1916), pp. 495-510.

Singer, D. W. *Giordano Bruno, his life and thought, with annotated translation of his work "On the infinite universe and worlds,"* New York, Henry Schuman, 1950.

Stevens, H. *Thomas Hariot the mathematician the philosopher and the scholar developed chiefly from dormant materials with notices of his associates including biographical and bibliographical disquisitions upon the materials of the history of "ould Virginia"*, London, privately printed, 1900.

Suter, R. "A Biographical Sketch of Dr. William Gilbert of Colchester," *Osiris*, vol. 10 (1952), pp. 368-384.

Suter, R. "Dr. William Gilbert of Colchester," *Scientific Monthly*, vol. 70 (1950), pp. 254-261.

Taylor, E. G. R. *Late Tudor and early Stuart Geography, 1583-1650*, London, Methuen & Co., Ltd., 1934.

Taylor, E. G. R. *Tudor geography, 1485-1583*, London, Methuen & Co., Ltd., 1930.

Taylor, F. S. *Galileo and the freedom of thought*, London, Watts & Co., 1938.

Thompson, J. S., and H. G. *Silvanus Phillips Thompson, D.Sc., LL.D., F.R.S., his life and letters*, New York, E. P. Dutton and Company, 1920.

Thompson, S. P. "The Family and Arms of Gilbert of Colchester," *Transactions of the Essex Archaeological Society*, n.s., vol. 9 (1906), pp. 197-211.

Thompson, S. P. *Gilbert, of Colchester; an elizabethian magnetizer*, London, privately printed, 1891.

Thompson, S. P. *Gilbert, physician: a note prepared for the three-hundredth anniversary of the death of William Gilbert of Colchester, President of the Royal College of Physicians, & physician to Queen Elizabeth*, London, Charles Whittingham and Co., 1903.

Thompson, S. P. *Notes on the de magnete of Dr. William Gilbert*, London, privately printed, 1901.

Thompson, S. P. "Peter Short, Printer, and his Marks," *Transactions of the Bibliographical Society*, vol. 4 (1896-1898), pp. 103-128.

Thompson, S. P. *William Gilbert, and terrestrial magnetism in the time of Queen Elizabeth*, London, Charles Whittingham and Co., 1903.

Townsend, G. F. *The siege of Colchester*, London, Society for Promoting Christian Knowledge, .

Venn, J., and J. A. *Alumni Cantabrigienses, a biographical list of all known students, graduates, and holders of office at the University of Cambridge from the earliest times to 1900*, Cambridge, University Press, 1922.

Venn, J., and J. A. *The book of matriculations and degrees, a catalog of those who have been matriculated or been admitted to any degree in the University of Cambridge from 1544 to 1659*, Cambridge, University Press, 1913.

Watson, E. C. "Portraits of William Gilbert, 1544-1603," *American Journal of Physics*, vol. 12 (1944), pp. 303-304.

Wolf, A. *A history of science, technology, and philosophy in the 16th & 17th centuries*, New York, The MacMillan Co., 1935.

Wood, A. *Athenae Oxonienses. An exact history of all the writers and bishops who have had their educations in the most ancient and famous university of Oxford, from the fifteenth year of King Henry the Seventh, A.D. 1500, to the Author's death in November 1695. To which are added the FASTI, or Annals of the said university*, 2nd ed., London, R. Knaplock, D. Midwinter, and J. Tonson, 1721.

Wright, T. *The history and topography of the county Essex (comprising the) ancient and modern history. A general view of its physical character productions agriculture condition statistics, &c.&c.*, London, George Virtue, 1831.

Zilsel, E. "The origins of William Gilbert's Scientific Method," *Journal of the History of Ideas*, vol. 2 (1941), pp. 1-32.